TAKE CONTROL AND LIVE

This is one of the most remarkable and inspiring stories I have ever read. After being diagnosed with stage 4 ovarian cancer, Gillian Gill's decision to step away from the comparative comfort of the familiarity of conventional treatment and embrace a totally holistic approach was heroic. She knew she was going out on a limb, and her decision would affect not only herself but also all those close to her. Her story is a brilliant example and a vital reminder of how much power as individuals we have to affect the outcome of a cancer prognosis, and the body's incredible ability to heal itself given the right tools: the power of the mind, body and soul when all are working together.

Her courage and determination to stay on the holistic path and face her fear has opened a way through the forest of fear and ignorance for the rest of us.

Gillian was guided and supported by many wonderful people, but the healing 'work' was done by her.

She did it. You can do it too.

Cancer doesn't scare me so much any more.

Hayley Mills
Actress

TAKE CONTROL AND LIVE

Surviving ovarian cancer

An autobiography by
Gillian Gill

Published by Gillian Gill

Published by Gillian Gill
152 Dovers Green Road
Reigate
Surrey
RH2 8BZ

ISBN 978-0-9563121-1-2

Cover design by Cadman Creative
Photograph of the author by Michael Little Photography
Design and layout by Daisy Editorial

DEDICATION

For Joanna, my beloved late younger sister.
Throughout my early childhood, and later still,
you were my best friend.
Always the love for you inspires me to greater things.

DISCLAIMER

This book describes personal experiences of Gillian Gill and her fight against cancer. The book is not intended to provide medical advice or instruction or replace treatment from qualified medical practitioners. It is emphasised that in the event of cancer or any other illness, this should be dealt with through a medical professional.

The publisher and author of the book accept no liability for any actions or decisions resulting from the reading of this book, which is purely autobiographical in nature and in no way seeks or proposes treatment of any kind to any third party in his or her own circumstances.

CONTENTS

FOREWORD

By Dr Rosy Daniel – Integrative Medicine Consultant

Gillian Gill is quite simply one of the most wonderful people I have ever met. It is an enormous privilege to work with her and she is one of my clients from whom I have learned the most in my twenty-five years of holistic cancer care.

I often hear myself describing Gilly as someone who positively 'glows in the dark'. Her energy is so strong and her radiance so bright that all who meet her are instantly uplifted and filled with hope and joy. Gilly's eyes sparkle with life and humour and she is always full of love, kindness and gentle healing for all whom she meets.

Her recovery from stage 4 ovarian cancer through entirely natural means proves definitively to all of us that cancer is a two-way process. It can grow, but it can also shrink and disappear. For those of us who work to encourage and empower people with cancer, Gilly's example is the incontrovertible proof that cancer can be healed. Her return to wellness has been verified both by her own consultant, Professor Hilary Thomas, and by Professor Karol Sikora, who has examined Gilly's medical records and scans.

Gilly's choice to go forward without any medical treatment at all is highly unusual as most people when diagnosed go for the 'best of both worlds', orthodox and complementary. But Gilly told me when we first met, quite simply, 'I would rather die than go through medical treatment.' She supported her sister through conventional cancer treatment and, as an extremely sensitive soul, she vowed that if ever diagnosed the medical path would not be the path for her. But then, Gilly had no fear of death. Her spiritual knowledge gave her the absolute certainty that death is not the end, simply a transition to a more intense and beautiful state of being which she calls 'the return to pure love'. So for Gilly, when faced with a health challenge, it was a question of how to live fully in the present and how to bring herself ever more closely into harmony with life, nature and her spiritual essence and purpose.

As scary as this was for her darling husband and young children, we all witnessed Gilly day after day following her own emotional and spiritual navigational intelligence, making choices on the basis of her highly attuned intuition and guidance. Transpersonal Psychology teacher Barbara Somers once said of the female psyche: 'As women, we zigzag our way straight to the point!' And, my goodness, did Gilly ever do that! She **listened** carefully to herself, to her guidance, to her healers and to exactly what signals her body was giving her. She **focused** herself totally on her healing path with no compromise whatsoever. She **believed** in me, in her therapists and most of all in the power of her own body to heal itself given the right nourishment at all levels of body, mind, spirit and environment. There are some doctors who call a recovery like Gilly's 'spontaneous remission', but this greatly undermines the dedication and hard work that people put into their healing, which in Gilly's case has taken over 13 years.

Of course, the big question is how on earth did Gilly achieve this remarkable healing? What was it that caused first her liver secondaries to shrink and then her pelvis to become almost clear of cancer? Delightfully, since applying myself to this holistic approach to cancer, started wholly on the basis of the feminine intuition of Penny Brohn in 1979 (who founded the Bristol Cancer Help Centre), there has been a steady build-up of scientific evidence for every single aspect of what we now call 'integrative medicine'.

This started first in the mid eighties with the work of Dr Stephen Greer, who proved that survival from breast cancer depended on our coping styles and mental state. He showed that at 14 years post-diagnosis 80 per cent more of those with fighting spirit were still alive, compared with those who were found to be 'helpless and hopeless' in the first week post-diagnosis! This was followed up by Drs Spiegel and Fawzy in the USA, who showed that those attending support groups greatly increased their survival rates. This was the beginning of a whole new science of 'psychoneuroimmunology', which burst into life with the discovery by Dr Candace Pert of receptors in the brain for the natural opiates called endorphins. Soon after this she and other researchers discovered many hundreds of tiny 'informational substances', which she called 'the Molecules of Emotion' in her book of that name. Candace and colleagues showed that, in response to our emotions, showers of these molecules are secreted and affect our tissue functioning profoundly. For example, the haemoglobin of those who are sad and depressed carries much less oxygen than of those who are happy! The main point of this research was to show that, whilst anxiety, depression, emotional repression and grief can subdue our tissue function, happiness, joy, excitement and self-belief can enliven our tissue function, giving us enhanced immunity and more rapid tissue healing.

Next came all the discoveries about the power of vitamins and crucial plant factors known as 'phytochemicals' to stabilize and even repair damaged chromosomes. This theory was resisted by medics who said there is no evidence that changing your diet after getting cancer can make any difference. But recently the 2007 San Diego Study showed that women who adopted a healthy diet and exercised when diagnosed with breast cancer doubled their survival rate nine years later over women who did not. Similar findings of improved survival were found by Professor Leslie Walker of Aberdeen and then Hull after teaching his patients how to visualize their cancer treatments curing them. So, through the nineties it became clear that health is a movable feast, dependent upon our mental attitude, mood, beliefs, nutrition and exercise.

The real icing on the carrot cake has come recently through the stunning 2008 GEMINAL study by Dr Dean Ornish. He tracked the genetic changes in prostate cancer cells in men on his intensive lifestyle programme and after just twelve weeks discovered a highly significant change in the 'up' and 'down' regulation of oncogenes, as well as a lengthening of the telomeres which protect the genes from mutation and unravelling. Dean's programme revolves simply around healthy eating, relaxation, fitness and the development of love and intimacy. Without any controversial 'woo woo', Dean has showed that in this very short time there is protective change, created purely by the individual's own lifestyle habits.

This brand new branch of science is called 'epigenetics' and has at its heart the idea that our genes are not fixed but mutable, depending upon our environment, moods, thoughts and beliefs. The major proponent of this theory has been Bruce Lipton, and his book *The Biology of Belief* shows us in detail how this works and just how finely we can control our biology and therefore destiny.

This subject gets still more fascinating when we start to look at how we are affected by the energy of other people and environments, and this takes us into the territory of energy medicine, spiritual healing and the power of prayer. Even this subject has been well researched. Lead researcher, cardiologist Larry Dossey, confidently shows us in his brilliant books that evidence for spiritual healing is now 'scientifically bulletproof', and he sweetly says that it is no longer medically ethical for him not to pray for his patients!

What shines out most for me about Gilly is how strong her belief was that she would heal and also how high the level of love that she created in and around herself. Way back in the eighties, Caryle Hirschberg wrote a book called *Remarkable Recoveries* in which she reported her mapping of the qualities and therapeutic activities of survivors. What she found was that it all intersected around belief. Belief in doctors, belief in medicines and therapies, belief in self, belief in a higher healing power, and belief-enhancing practices like affirmation, visualization and hypnosis. Recently, when interviewing Gilly about her recovery, she said to me, 'Well, Rosy, you told me at our first consultation that my body knows how to heal cancer. I believed you!'

I do not remember saying that, but thank God I did, because for Gilly that gave her the lifeline along which she could build her own belief and all the strands of her magical healing journey. All doctors and therapists must really take heed on this point and realize the power of the messages we give because, just as we can create positive belief, negative and careless throwaway messages can also kill hope and destroy self-belief!

Another thing Gilly told me was that for twenty minutes every day she went to sit in her 'healing and love chair'. Here she visualized herself completely healed and in shining health first and then after that she 'let go and let God'. She invited all healing love in the Universe to come and heal her in every atom of her being. She **surrendered** to Divine love and in those times allowed herself to become one with the very highest vibration that she could.

I call this filling ourselves with 'lovelight' and I liken it to what happens to the plants all around us in nature when the sun comes. When the plants are lit up with sunlight all the little cells get very excited and photosynthesis is accelerated. The metabolic rate of the cells goes up and they produce lots of oxygen and carbohydrates. Our own cells are just like this. When we are filled with love, happiness, excitement and gratitude, our own cells work optimally, and this happens when we are alight with love and in attunement with the high frequencies of spiritual healing, prayer and our own bliss.

Hmmm… that is easy for those who are excited and happy, you might say; but what about when we are frightened, lost, lonely, desperate and sad? This is when *Emmanuel's Book* written by Pat Rodegast gets it completely right – just make 'The Choice for Love'. How do we do this? We choose to follow our hearts. To love each other. To love our life and love ourselves and to open to the Divine love which is all around us, ensuring that every single decision that we make in our lives takes us deeper into love.

For Gilly's most outstanding example of the return to love I will be eternally grateful.

Thank you and bless you a million times, darling Gilly, for all that you have shown me and taught me.

INTRODUCTION

October 2000

'Well, if I was a betting person, I'd say you have perhaps three months...
you have stage 4 ovarian cancer, with secondary tumours in your liver. It
is quite unique. It is inoperable. You could try a variety of chemotherapies
and radiotherapy and...'

I was stunned. My mind was in a whirl and then, as if regaining
consciousness, I heard, 'It's warm in here. Are you sure you want to keep
that thick overcoat on?'

'Yes, I most certainly do,' I found myself emphatically saying, while
glancing over at Simon, now looking gaunt with this grim prognosis. My
ovarian tumour was almost full-term pregnancy size and I felt so anxious
and vulnerable. We wanted the truth. We got the truth. It was brutal.

I was numb and terrified. My body was in such extreme shock that many
of my normal senses were shut down. I couldn't taste and was freezing cold
from fear. Suddenly the world that I had known became a very different
place.

Yet, prior to being given 'no hope', I had managed without fear or pain,
such was my denial of what was wrong with me. Everything looked the
same outwardly, yet inwardly my world, and my beloved husband's, had
imploded, descending into panic. Confronted with this overwhelming
news, I was helplessly struggling to impose some control over my emotions,
but I was powerless and devastated and unable to comprehend anything.

It's at times like these that we realize how little control we really do have in our lives.

However, I was about to learn all over again, in an entirely new way, just how very important the control of my thought processes would be. It helped to save my life and turn it into something so beautiful I never would have imagined it possible. So I started the process of changing a lifetime's habits. Not for the faint of heart, nor without a 'baptism of fire' along the way; these changes would be something to maintain lifelong.

I was also to learn just how important it would be to tap into powers beyond my physical 'self'. As a child growing up on a farm, seeing ghosts and what I came to learn later on as spirit guides seemed perfectly natural to me. I still believe that these invisible, behind-the-scenes helpers, similar to guardian angels, are sent to us at times of great need, especially when sincerely invited to help through prayer.

You may not share my belief, but I hope you'll join me in my remarkable cancer-surviving journey.

I can sum up my story like this: although different therapies help in different ways, recovery is about trying to give oneself positive healing messages, by natural means and by becoming adept at listening and responding to your body's needs. It's a bit like driving a car and being personally responsible behind the steering wheel. Fundamentally, it's about being empowered to do things for oneself, not about handing it over to others. They can help, yet ultimately it's only you who can do it.

It is now about thirteen years since my diagnosis and I am fortunate enough to be able to share my experience so that others, in similar desperate circumstances, may benefit from the hope and empowerment that I have discovered. At the beginning of this journey of transformation I was diagnosed with a large, rapidly growing ovarian tumour, with secondary tumours in the liver and a prognosis of a few months to live; gradually all the secondary tumours have remarkably disintegrated and disappeared. The ovarian tumour has shrunk to the size of a small hen's egg, with the characteristics of a benign cyst, and my liver function is once again normal.

I achieved this with the unstinting love and support from both those in this world, here on earth, and those beyond, in the world of spirits. The help from all these loved ones boosted my determination to follow my instincts and embrace new ideas, despite all the challenges and setbacks on the way.

During my childhood many strange things happened in the house I grew up in. They were extraordinary and at times terrifying. Things such as the bed lifting up off the floor and floating, pictures being invisibly torn from the walls and flying across the room. All these supernatural occurrences paved the way for my spiritual (Higher, beyond personality) self: the purified, refined alchemy I believe is inherent in us all – some call it God – that would help me many years later as an adult facing a dismal cancer diagnosis. Such a background helped to open up a hitherto unimagined way before me, a whole new way of living that gifted my life back when I was so close to death.

I came to realize that my perception of the simple seasonal images of nature and my responses to them have become my personal form of psychology. I developed a greater bond with nature and noticed how my mood became more powerfully linked to the changing seasons. Darker evenings meant quieter time for reflection and meditation, whereas spring and its new growth inspired similar regenerative responses. I reminded myself that climbing a mountain culminated in a whole new wondrous vista; a surprising expansion of consciousness is born from this elevated viewpoint, and suddenly the mind is aware of new possibilities. Similarly, my heightened sensitivity to the natural world meant I looked at the garden in a new light. I likened changing my belief patterns and leaving behind detrimental habits to pruning the deadwood off a rose to allow room for new growth. And as my outer world became temporarily limited, my inward world expanded and I looked again at the garden and the natural world around me as a source of constant inspiration and hope.

Our dogs also feature strongly in my healing journey. They, with their love, have been my means of escape from cancer, a lifesaver for me and an enormous source of comfort for the whole family each and every day.

You can't constantly focus on the cancer; the dogs were my diversion, my distraction, taking my mind off the constant battle I was waging. Such distractions are welcomed, whether it's a book, a hobby, a creative pursuit or pets.

I know there will always be those who are sceptical in life, but I wish to share my story with those who, like myself, find themselves suffering the chronic shock and disempowering horror of receiving a cancer diagnosis, for those weakened or bedridden and also for all those seeking a 'certain something' missing from their lives.

I won't pretend it's been easy, but it is my desire to share with you as much as I can in my endeavour to talk to you, inspire, give hope and acceptance, whatever the outcome.

My hope is to encourage you to find a reserve of untapped power lying latent within you, as I have found within myself, to help you on your own unique journey, adding 'life to your days' rather than 'days to your life'.

I'd like you to join me in reliving my own incredible journey.

CHAPTER 1

Shock/Horror - Diagnosis

Evoking the Soul
All sorts of things occur to help one that would
otherwise never have occurred. A whole stream of
events issues from the decision, raising in one's favour
all manner of incidents and meetings and material
assistance which no person would have believed would
have come their way. Whatever you think you can do
or believe you can do, begin it. Action has magic, grace
and power in it.
Goethe

Early October 2000

Wake up! But I wasn't asleep. This wasn't a dream. It was a real living nightmare, numbing, chilling to the bone marrow.

I considered myself beyond childbearing age yet I had a large, rounded abdomen, not unlike that of a pregnant woman. Being in hospital and breathing in all the associated smells was bad enough. What was wrong with me? I hadn't a clue. A year or so previously I'd had a check-up. A small golfball-sized lump I found deep in my soft abdominal tissue was thought to be irritable bowel syndrome or a fibroid.

I'd been putting off going to the hospital for some time. Such visits only brought back distressing memories of Joanna, my late younger sister, and my late maternal aunt Joyce. Joanna had cancer, melanoma. The cancer was aggressive, spreading to all parts of her body, and whilst her treatment was equally aggressive, pioneering even, it sadly didn't save her life. My aunt Joyce had breast cancer. She had a mastectomy, chemotherapy and radiotherapy and suffered long-term detrimental side effects due to her treatments. She too fought long and hard, until she lost the final battle. Their journeys had been harrowing, and my emotions were racing at finding myself in this situation.

I was in hospital trying to find out what was causing my swollen abdomen. Perhaps a cyst, I'd vaguely wondered. I heard the doctor saying, 'We'll just take a urine sample to check for the possibility of your being pregnant.' As she handed me a jug for the sample, I thought I couldn't be pregnant, what a crazy idea. Logically I knew this; I was a forty-five-year-old mid-menopausal woman and still taking precautions.

Mindlessly I did what I was told. I'd insisted Simon go to work. He'd tragically lost his first wife shortly after the birth of Clare, our daughter, now eighteen years old. Simon didn't need any more stress and upset.

While the urine sample was being tested I marvelled irrationally at the speed of the NHS procedures. Were my mind functioning correctly it would have seen big red warning lights at this stage.

My friend Lindy had accompanied me to hospital. She was having a check-up at the Well Woman Clinic there and, being concerned, waited with me. We walked our dogs together frequently. She is strong; I like her immensely and admire her feistiness.

What was the lump in my throat? It was my heart bursting. I can't cry here and attract attention to myself, I thought. No, bottle it up. I had always excelled at that. In the household I grew up in we outwardly always appeared confident, rarely letting our guard down. This pattern was ingrained into me along with many other habits. Little did I know then that I would have to unlearn this, and many other damaging habits and belief patterns, and that my life would depend on it.

Mind whirring, I spun back to my childhood where I'd learned to find calm by going out in nature alone and sitting at the foot of an apple tree in the orchard on the farm. As I waited to be called for the next investigation with mounting fear, I desperately tried to recall a piece of that calm.

'You look pale, Gillian. I'm going to stay with you,' said Lindy, looking deep into my glazed eyes. I was fantasizing about the possibility of being pregnant. Trying desperately to convince myself I could be. I was choosing colours to decorate a bedroom. Anything to soothe my tattered nerves and occupy my thoughts positively.

My thoughts were rudely interrupted by someone saying 'Please come this way'. I was guided into a small, darkened room. I felt rising anxiety and stood there shaking, feeling like a lamb being led to the slaughter; such was my dread of hospitals. 'Please lie on the couch.'

I slid uncomfortably onto it, clutching my lightweight regulation hospital gown to me for dignity's sake. Wearing it only heightened my feeling of vulnerability.

Lying there I became aware of a sense of being held by an invisible guiding force, one outside myself. Perhaps the spirit of my late sister, as I'd often sensed her presence around the house. We'd been like twins in spite of the four-year age difference. I suddenly felt I was in a parallel world as time hung suspended, a cushion against the harsh reality of what was going on.

Looking around I noticed a machine with hideous protruding probes. With that a nagging, unpleasant feeling crept over me, the dawning of a realization that all wasn't well. I forced a smile, weak and feeble, and felt utterly powerless.

'We're going to do a scan. Just popping a condom onto this probe...'

What? My mind silently screamed. Why, I wondered, thinking a machine couldn't make me pregnant; such were my unarticulated and jumbled thoughts.

The probe hurt, and I lay there rigid now, almost having a full-blown panic attack. My breathing was quick and shallow. I felt so very alone, vulnerable and unable to reach out to ask for the comforting hand I dearly wished to hold.

'We're ready for the next procedure now,' said the nurse. 'This will feel cold but don't worry,' as she squeezed a tube of jelly onto my abdomen and smeared it in. I clutched my fists tightly. Had I had long fingernails they'd have bitten through my skin.

We all looked silently at the scanning screen and saw a large dark mass; no head, no brain, no arms and legs, and certainly no heartbeat. I felt sick. 'What is that?' I whispered.

'Please get up now and sit outside in the passageway, would you?' the nurse replied. My mind reeling, I staggered out of the door, relieved to spot Lindy still sitting there waiting.

'What's up?' she asked. 'You've aged ten years in there. I know you're quite private but please try and say something.'

'What?' I stammered, feeling exhausted, as though I was in dense fog, yet vaguely aware of her comforting presence. Then I felt a fresh wave of fear as the doctor opened her door and called me in again.

'Come and sit down,' she said indicating a chair. 'We've got your urine test back. We can eliminate your being pregnant. With an abdomen that size what on earth prevented you from coming to see us before now?' My mind spun as panic washed through me; I took a deep breath, focusing on her concerned dark brown eyes.

I stuttered, 'Jack, our beloved rescue dog, just died.' My lips quivered. I bit ferociously back on spilling tears. 'He'd been with us most of our marriage,' I blurted out, uncontrollably now. 'We loved him so much.' With those words I felt warmth flooding through me along with tears. 'He was like a grandfather to the children, protecting them, all of us. We just buried him.'

I thought I was coming out in sympathy with him as he too had a swollen abdomen. Without his presence in our home we felt incomplete. When he'd arrived as a rescue dog he chose to lie on a landing on the stairs, in the heart of the house. Over the years he felt at the heart of our family. No one was missing him more than Lucy, our pining black Labrador.

I remembered how, when Joanna had been ill with cancer, I'd come out in sympathy with her, feeling many similar symptoms. My GP at that time had told me that it was rare, but not unusual, when a strong bond links two people in deep abiding love. He prescribed medication to help me cope with the severe migraines I was experiencing, just one of the side effects I empathised with. I also acquired an angry, irritating rash in my groin, mirroring the site of Joanna's secondary tumour.

'You've been here for hours. Go home and please come back after the weekend, when we'll need to do some further tests,' said the doctor, scribbling an appointment card for me.

I don't remember a thing about Friday night. The weekend passed in a blur. Monday came and Lindy again accompanied me to hospital, taking time out of her own busy life. As we sat waiting, Helen, a friend and mother of a child at the same school as our fourteen-year-old son, David, wandered from her office into the waiting room. The unexpected coincidence was a welcome distraction and lifted my spirits briefly.

'I know you've come in to have a CT scan, Gill. Don't worry about a thing,' she said looking searchingly into my eyes for any tell-tale signs of ill health.

While changing into my hospital gown I noticed a massive blue bruise on the side of my swollen abdomen. Accident-prone again, I thought, remembering having brushed into the back of a kitchen chair. I must learn to be more careful, more alert. And slow down, I thought vaguely.

No sooner had I reappeared than someone was asking me to complete some paperwork, then gave me a litre jug of ghastly tasting liquid to drink. Next, if I recall correctly, I had an injection of iodine to reveal what was going on inside my body. After that I was called into a room where the staff wore masks and gowns. That petrified me. Although I felt like a helpless, frightened child, I went with the flow, lying on the hard mechanical bed. That soon moved into what appeared to me to be a giant polo-mint contraption: the scanning machine. I felt trapped in confined spaces and could feel the beginnings of claustrophobia. A robotic-sounding voice told me to hold my breath and then guided my breathing process to get the best results from the scan.

Becoming aware of the light gown made me feel vulnerable. Suddenly I had the sinking feeling of wetting myself. Apparently this is one of the side effects of the revealing fluid. My mind hadn't been able to process that piece of information when I'd been told earlier as I was in too much shock, convinced the scanner would electrocute me. My mind seized. My emotions plummeted. I instantly spiralled into deep shock and felt sick. Control, where was my control? It had all but deserted me.

'We're all done with you,' someone said.

I'm still alive, I thought, feeling relieved and shakily sitting up.

It became horrifying clear to me that I was to be sent home without knowing what was wrong with me and that I was expected to wait for my results to go through my GP.

My anxiety levels were unsustainable; I had to know what was wrong.

A rapid burst of vast strength, like that of a roaring lion, ripped through my entire being, giving me an assertive voice I scarcely recognized.

What happened next isn't the norm. Pleadingly, I looked into the nurse's eyes: 'I have to know what the matter is. Can you please tell me?' She briefly disappeared through a small door that I hadn't previously noticed, and the next thing I knew a stunned-looking radiologist stepped out and invited me into his room. The darkness of the room was illuminated by a series of scans. He indicated a chair for me to sit down. The expression on his face instantly alarmed me.

'You have cancer,' he said pointing to the various x-rays. It was obvious by the awkwardness of his manner that he was unaccustomed to having to relay such terrible news. Little did I know then that this face, looking at me with such discomfort and gravity, would become one of rare and friendly support in an otherwise impersonal hospital environment.

I felt light-headed, faint. He may well have been speaking double-Dutch for all I could understand.

Taking a deep breath, I surprised myself by asking for Lindy. She appeared, anxious, immediately sitting next to me. She took my hand and squeezed it, almost cutting off the blood supply with her own tension. Another friend, Tissa, an assistant radiologist, came into the room looking for x-rays. He recognized me from the school playground of Clare's first school and walked towards me with a smile on his face that vanished entirely as he looked at the screens. In one step he was beside me and took my free hand. Both hands being tightly squeezed saved me from fainting. Their comforting touches seeped into me, though I felt drained and barely able to breathe. Full-blown terror flooded into me as realization dawned and couldn't be held in check a moment more. I slumped forward in my chair. My head was put between my knees. I was told to breathe deeply.

Lindy took over remembering details. I eventually hobbled out of the room with her arm tight around me. An old riding accident injury recurred out of the blue, shock manifesting in my body. Then, strangely, Helen reappeared, pale and concerned. One of the doctors had spoken to her, sharing the terrible news. She stared into my eyes saying, 'Think carefully how and when you tell Simon...'

I somehow realized the wisdom of Helen's words and some inner strength jolted me from further hysterical thoughts. I'd wanted to phone Simon at work immediately. He was not only my husband but also my best friend. I shared everything with him. He always made time for me, even when overseas on business trips; such is his love for me.

I had cancer! Ovarian cancer: the silent killer.

Thinking of Joanna and my aunt, I knew what a terrible fate could await me. I'd seen the debilitating effects of the disease and its treatments. I wanted to run screaming, but where to?

I stumbled back into the changing rooms, slumped against the wall as I tore off the hospital gown and put my clothes back on. I needed to get home, prepare for what lay ahead.

Lindy drove. She took us first to Vicky's home, a mutual friend. Vicky looked at our ashen faces as we walked through the door. She'd lost her mother at an early age and possessed sound instincts. We sat down in her friendly kitchen with cats wandering through, a dog asleep in its basket, fresh flowers in a vase. We heard horses neighing in the distant paddock through the open window. Remembering what people do when in shock, Vicky put the kettle on saying, 'We'll drink sweet tea. I know that helps.' We proceeded to empty the entire sugar bowl, and none of us takes sugar! The sharing, the friendship and warm sweet tea fortified me to return home and prepare myself for the horrendous task of telling Simon what was actually in my abdomen.

Before Simon returned home I reflected on how, since our return from the west coast of America, where my rock-hard abdomen grew so rapidly, I had dragged him to the shops to buy new clothes. Even hanging the washing outside on the line was a major effort. I got breathless easily. I also thought how I had heartburn and a sore throat. Come to think of it, I'd been noticing my hair was dull and falling out more than was usual, reminding me how trees lose their leaves when suffering in order to survive during prolonged hot spells. I'd also been waking up earlier than was usual for me, with an urgent need to go to the loo. My bowels were playing up.

When Simon returned home, tired as usual from the London office, we greeted each other normally; I was putting on a brave face, acting. Clare was at Newcastle University, David with a school friend. We sat at the kitchen table. Unusually, Lucy the Labrador remained in her bed in the hall. I drew a deep breath, remembering Helen's advice. I opened my mouth, smiling, again masking my true feelings, so the man had no idea of the bombshell I was about to drop. Then I shut it again, letting out a sigh.

'How did you get on today?' he asked innocently.

Breaking into hysterical laughter disguised my unfathomable emotions as I blurted out, 'Well, you'll never guess what I've got wrong with me?'

'No, I won't. So go on, tell me.'

'Cancer!' I said, still putting on a strong exterior face.

'No, do be serious for once, and tell me what they really said.'

'I just did. This bulge', I said pointing to my abdomen, 'is a vast tumour.' With that I noticed his face was now gaunt. The room spun even though I was sitting. He watched the colour drain from my face and moved towards me, holding me tight, while I wept an ocean of tears into his comforting shoulder. Those unleashed tears released some blocked emotions. I felt lighter afterwards, somehow managing to cope.

Neither of us managed to get much sleep that night.

CHAPTER 2
Action Has Magic

There is no light so bright that it does not cast a shadow,
And it is right that this is so.
For without the dark
We would not know the Light
But think that this is how it should be.

As we strive through our shadows towards the Light
We are aware we have a goal to reach,
A safe harbour to anchor,
A warmth for our souls.

But what of the shadows themselves?
Do not the fruits of the earth grow in the dark?
Is not the unborn babe borne in the darkness of the womb?
Do we not rest from our labours in the dark night?

So if your life now seems dark to you,
Look forward to the lighter times to come.
Because, Be assured, They will come.

Since recorded time each dawn has come when the moon rests.
So your Dawn will come,
Softly perhaps, and hard to see.
But the sun will shine again in the heaven of your heart.

Be patient.
Wait in peace and surety.

Recited by Steve Speed, a trance medium, when sitting in a meditation group thinking of Oscar Wilde, and sent to me by a friend.

Over the next few days Simon, in his disbelief and shock, went into automatic mode. He was processing emotions, silently experiencing anger and the unfairness of it all.

I remember begging Simon to allow time for us to come to terms with the news before telling the children. I wanted to reach out and protect them. We'd tell them together. I reasoned that would be best, but dreaded telling them at all. If I didn't, then perhaps I really would wake up and find I was only having a nightmare.

The days passed slowly as we waited agonizingly for a letter of referral to visit a gynaecologist. That day finally arrived. It was a cold, foggy autumn morning. I dressed carefully, exerting all my control as I mentally prepared for the appointment. Wearing Simon's massive navy blue wool and cashmere overcoat felt like the next best thing to cuddling a teddy bear. The child within me was terrified. I'd previously always had robust health, apart from accidents, but I always got over those.

Simon went equipped with questions. He carried his small briefcase, having also dressed smartly for the appointment. Somehow our clothes felt like armour.

I prayed for strength, as taught by my father when I was a child. I'd been praying for courage to do my best, serenity to accept whatever the outcome might be, and wisdom for guidance.

As we walked arms linked into the hospital, the waiting room was busy. Glancing around I recognized the gynaecologist, the father of a child at David's prep school, who was on his way to his office to prepare to see us. Coincidences such as these, at some profound level, offered a measure of reassurance.

Nevertheless, I hugged Simon's coat tightly around me as raw fear left me freezing and my breathing shallow. My stomach was gurgling loudly, filled with dread. I pretended to read a magazine; my mouth felt dry. My mind drifted to a conversation I'd had with a bedridden friend who spent her life researching medical matters connecting mind, body and spirit. That appealed to me. I recalled her saying how a doctor had got testicular cancer as a result of a traumatic experience. While on holiday he'd witnessed his son's shooting, by a crazed gunman, and later was devastated watching him dying. Understanding the power of that experience was the clue to his well-being. He'd made a full recovery after unearthing and processing that trauma.

My mind drifted back as we heard my name being called. I walked on automatic pilot, grateful for Simon's reassuring presence beside me. Much later on I instinctively knew my late sister Joanna's spirit was with me, though I couldn't sense her at the time.

'Please come in and sit down,' the gynaecologist said, indicating two upright chairs on the far side of his large wooden desk.

Again, my mind wandered off as I braced myself, wondering what Joanna had experienced in a similar situation. I recalled how shortly after she died I couldn't sleep. One night she magically appeared to me around midnight, standing in her ghostly form at my side of the bed.

As children growing up on a farm we had both shared frightening experiences of our home being haunted. In the dead of night our beds floated off the floor with us in them. Pictures were torn off the walls and flung across our bedroom.

Joanna's presence reminded me of some of those terrifying experiences. I shut my eyes, willing her away. Then I inhaled her favourite perfume. As though that were not enough to convince me of her presence, opening my eyes in spite of myself I saw a ball, the size of a large football, hovering above the bed. In the centre of that ball of light appeared my late sister's beautiful face. Her thoughts automatically reached mine: 'I'm well; please don't worry about me now. Look at me!' As I did so, she looked better than her old self, younger, vibrant and so healthy. A deep abiding peace flooded through me like warm honey.

Little did I know then that these ghostly visitations during my childhood, and later the gift of feeling Joanna's presence, were the beginnings of a spiritual journey and awakening that would transform more deeply into healing later in life. That acquainted me with spirit guides, as my prayerfulness increased, to help me along my life's journey at pivotal stages, including learning to become a spiritual healer. As a child I'd dressed up as a nurse pretending to make everyone well, including the wild creatures on the farm.

When I looked at the gynaecologist's familiar face across his deep desk I had to adjust to seeing him in his work role, not the friendly face across the school playground. He looked grave. The fact that he looked smart reassured me in some strange way, instilling respect for his opinion. I once more thought of Joanna, what she'd gone through.

Pleasantries over, he came to the point: 'I'm afraid to say it isn't good news. You have ovarian cancer; stage four with secondary tumours in your liver, and possibly elsewhere. It's aggressive and, quite frankly, I've never before seen anything like it.' Icy chills jolted me. I glanced at Simon, sitting rigid, staring alarmingly at him; this was about as bad as it could get. 'We need to run further tests, possibly operate, and then think about chemotherapy.'

I began shaking. Simon took over, briefcase in hand, orderly papers suddenly appearing. He asked questions. 'What is the next step?'

'I'll refer you on to an oncologist. Would you prefer NHS or private?'

Then I remember him saying, 'If I were a betting person, I'd say you have perhaps three months left...' I took a sharp intake of breath. My hearing felt muffled, but through the haze I remembered him talking about putting my will in order. We left his office reeling with the news.

When we got home I stood by the kitchen window wistfully looking down the garden saying, 'I don't want to die'.

'You won't,' came Simon's astonishing response.

Those words once spoken became forgotten, buried, as our shattered lives coped with our daily drama. Though, at the time, I believed him on one level, on another I was terrified, more so than I'd ever been in my entire life. From that moment on I referred to my vast tumour as my 'lump'; that somehow felt less frightening. I was, however, terrified of it, and when I touched it I could feel knobbly branches leading everywhere. I felt I had a monster living inside me. When lying down with wrists resting on my hips my fingers didn't come close to meeting in the middle.

With the shocking diagnosis came pain. I hadn't been aware of extreme pain before, but now it overtook me at times. On one such occasion I desperately tried to find respite by going to bed. I felt comforted as I lay there in my own bed, beneath my own roof, surrounded by ornaments, gifts from the children and happy family photos. Looking at the photos inspired a vision of myself when healthy, and I recorded that image in my mind to revisit regularly. Then I wondered how much longer I'd have the luxury of lying in my own bed. No matter what pain I felt now, could I endure it? What if it escalated? How would I cope in hospital, worse still a hospice – oh such desperate thoughts, I wished they'd stop!

Then there was Simon. He'd only needed to change a nappy to be physically sick from the smell. If I became incontinent as a result of harsh treatments, how on earth would he cope? And so the thoughts went on, unbidden and bleak.

Lucy, our Labrador, what about her? She'd just lost Jack, her canine best friend, and I had little energy to spare to cuddle her as much as she needed these days. She lay inert, dry-nosed in her oversized bed; the one she'd shared with Jack. They had used one another as pillows, for comfort. When he'd been alive she sensed my every mood, often creeping into our bedroom and snuggling down on the floor at my side of the bed. There, she'd nudge my arm and hand until she got a response. For me there was nothing quite like her tender touch. But she didn't come. She lay bereft in her own, now empty, bed. Would Simon, too, soon be like Lucy, a dark part of me wondered?

I'd managed to convince Simon to leave telling the children at least until we had seen the oncologist. That decision weighed heavily on us both, though, in different ways. Simon likes to be honest, so it was hard for him keeping the news from them, but he saw my point of view.

Over the next week, although part of Simon was in denial, in order to cope he went into overdrive instead of despair. He gained strength from my strength and an intervention from a source he couldn't explain. That kept him going. He put all his energy into being constructive and practical. He researched madly, reading about supplements to boost the immune system, so off he set to the chemist's. Whilst looking over the counter laden with pots of supplements, a total stranger bore down on him commenting, 'That's all rubbish. What are you wasting your money on that for?' Simon, a passive man by nature, was stunned. An argument ensued and almost got out of control. The shop assistant was on the verge of calling security.

Simon returned from that trip pale and shaken. After listening to his shocking experience, I thought that unprovoked challenge allowed Simon a natural release of some of his pent-up anger. It gave him back some semblance of equilibrium.

While taking to my bed, overcome by the speed of events, not knowing if I was going to live or die, I wondered why I had got cancer. I racked my brain and prayed for help. Then I had a sudden realization. I had experienced some success as a spiritual healer. I healed out of love; it was a way of life. When Simon met me he was unfamiliar with healing, though he respected my beliefs. He understood and supported my guiding principle that had been taught to me by one of my mentors: how can you put a price on a spiritual gift? Well, I don't, believing that healing is a gift, therefore I pass my gift on to others open to receiving it. Unexpected rewards come along, not least a sense of a deep abiding inner fulfilment.

As a spiritual healer I work with sick people and those with cancer. My work involves death and dying and I have the privilege of helping people confront mortality, though at the time of my diagnosis I'd been overdoing it to the point of exhaustion, running myself into the ground and neglecting my needs. Becoming stressed and weakened I had lost weight, though in my denial prior to the diagnosis I had successfully blocked out these symptoms.

Simon had tried to tell me to slow down, yet I ignored his advice. He worked hard, travelling frequently with his job in agricultural commodities. He thought nothing of returning from a gruelling overseas trip and then automatically switching to the time zone he arrived in.

Somewhere along the line I had lost a certain balance in life. I'd missed Simon when he was travelling, his hugs and presence in our home with the family. Having known it would be like that didn't help the reality. There were some unrealistic expectations. I'd hoped to travel with him, though I found I couldn't leave the children. I loved them to pieces, even though they drove me to distraction at times.

What about all the pesticides I'd inhaled throughout my childhood on the farm, I thought, full of carcinogenic chemicals, especially 30 years ago; perhaps they'd contributed to my cancer?

Then I started planning. If I were going into hospital for surgery I'd take control by preparing for it. Often ahead of myself, I packed a small suitcase, convinced that's how it would be. I packed pretty pyjamas, books I'd bought but never found time to read, imagining myself bed-bound but never realizing I might not feel up to reading.

Over the next few days Simon gently but firmly insisted I tell a close friend the truth, rather than hiding from it. He handed me the telephone and waited for me to dial. Taking a deep breath I phoned Philippa. She listened silently and selflessly. Thinking only of my predicament and the family, she urged me to go on a mind, body, spirit and healing retreat weekend which aimed to find the emotional root cause of illness and awaken key memories, as well as giving me the chance to get away with Simon and give us some space together. Her advice led to us finding and booking the two remaining spaces on a retreat led by Brandon Bays; she had remarkably recovered from a massive tumour herself without surgery, chemotherapy or radiotherapy and is an inspiration to many as she travels the world giving workshops.

In the meantime, I was worried about Simon. What could I do to help him, considering his reluctance to talk to anyone about his feelings? Then I thought of his friend Nick. He was a work colleague. They had travelled together in Africa and had shared many unpleasant experiences, so I phoned his wife, Gita. These two dear Indian friends were wonderful. Before I'd barely started telling Gita what was happening she interrupted me: 'Gillian, say no more. Nick will take Simon out for a drink. Your idea is a good one, it will help relax him and encourage him to talk. To share his feelings is a good thing; let him get it off his chest. You know what a good listener my husband is.'

Some days later, after Simon had seen Nick, I was resting in the afternoon and trying to relax when I heard the phone ringing. Simon had already unplugged three of the four phones we had dotted about the house. They were there out of habit and for ease. He reasoned what precious sleep I could grab shouldn't be disturbed by the phone ringing. He came and found me, peered into my sleepy eyes, saying, 'It's Sara. I just told her our news. She was shocked. She said she and Tony would pray for you, for us all.' I knew how passionately they believed in the power of prayer. Tony was a pillar of strength at the local church. Simon continued, 'Sara's going to get her church to pray for you too.'

On the heels of that phone call our next hospital appointment arrived to go and see the oncologist. We'd opted for private, being fortunate in having Simon's office medical insurance in place to help us.

'Are you ready?' Simon asked as I lingered, pulling a warm scarf tightly around my neck and bracing myself for the appointment. As I stepped outside into the chilly air I shivered. By the time I walked through our solid beautiful wooden front door again there would be no turning back.

The journey to the hospital was spent in virtual silence. I steeled myself each time we drove over a bump in the road. It hurt my fragile abdomen so I clutched it tightly, as I would a baby, to try soothing it. Then I remembered the deep breathing I'd put to good use during childbirth. Remarkably, that helped; it distracted my mind and offered some relief. After a spell, feeling agitated, I glanced out of the car window, noticing the fading autumn-coloured leaves falling from the trees, dying, giving way to decay.

Simon unexpectedly swore.

'What's the matter?' I asked, coming out of my reverie.

'I've lost my bearings.' We were heading for the old site of the Royal Surrey County Hospital, which he remembered from childhood. An uncle of his was a consultant there, but it had moved to a new site in the 1980s.

He had been in such a state of shock when being given directions by the gynaecologist that he hadn't taken them in. 'Don't know what's the matter with me. I've driven to this hospital many times.' He pulled over by the roadside, got a map out and worked out new directions and we turned round and headed off again.

Pointing to a road sign I said, 'There's the Royal Surrey.'

'No, we don't want that one. We want the Nuffield; it's on an estate. Look out for more signs please; we're not far away now.'

'Oh, we're driving up Gill Avenue!' I said, astonished.

'Yes,' stated Simon calmly, 'it's named after my late uncle. He was a consultant at the hospital. Remember, I told you before?'

I didn't remember but was dazed by that coincidence and felt a degree lighter for some reason for hearing it.

'There it is now,' said Simon. 'Look out for a parking spot.' I did. There wasn't one. The car park was jammed full of cars, some blocking others in. Subsequently we were to learn that parking was always a problem.

'What's up?' asked Simon, having parked and watching me move like a snail.

'It's my old riding injury playing up again. My hip's gone weak, making me lame.'

'Come on,' he said striding towards me, 'take my arm and I'll help you.'

We made our way to the hospital entrance. My heart plummeted as fear took hold again. I inhaled deeply, slowly and kept doing so as Simon guided me towards the appointment lounge. My stomach lurched. Looking around I found the sight of other dear souls waiting their turn extremely distressing. In my current predicament I empathised with them. It was obvious many were very ill. Some were losing their hair; others were completely bald due to the harsh chemotherapy treatments. Their skin colour was opaque, rather waxy, a deathly colour. I noticed their eyes had dark shadows beneath them, appearing listless, often tinged with yellow. Their faces were either tormented or devoid of expression altogether. Some were unaccompanied. All, like myself, were understandably fearful. Facing one's own mortality at any time is quite something. How many of us are prepared for that inevitable experience?

My eyes swivelled, turning abruptly to the coffee machine. I had given up coffee some time ago after discovering I suddenly didn't like the taste. I noticed the machine also made hot chocolate; now that was a comforting thought. The surroundings were unfriendly to me, in spite of the careful decorations, and I needed the loo. My anxiety was getting the better of me. I asked the way at the information desk. A pleasant young nurse indicated down the corridor. As I sat there I wondered if the cancer had spread to my bladder. Passing water felt rather like straining jelly through a sieve. It was uncomfortable and such thoughts made me shudder.

Simon glanced up from reading the newspaper and smiled. At that moment an efficient-looking nurse carrying a clipboard called my name.

'Mrs Gillian Gill?'

'Yes,' I replied.

'Please follow me.' The warmth she exuded washed over me, relaxing both of us as we strode arm in arm to the next smaller waiting area. However, I felt a sense of impending doom. Trying to shake it off, I looked at Simon's comforting face instead.

A door adjacent to the waiting room opened and light poured through as a bright, elegantly dressed lady appeared. She wore dark-rimmed glasses and had short dark hair neatly cut framing her face. Her dark brown eyes were alert, earnest. I instantly liked her. This was my oncologist, Professor Hilary Thomas. She indicated her open door, saying 'Please come this way', and led us through to her consultancy room. There was a large desk, neatly stacked with files and papers, in front of a big window; the sunshine streamed in. Two chairs were positioned in front of her desk. Behind them was a curtain with an examination couch and a large square mirror adorned one wall. That's all I remember.

We started talking. Simon did most of it; I was drinking everything in, sensing her. She had my scans on the wall to her right. With the flick of a switch a light came on illuminating them. She started pointing at various internal organs containing large shadows.

'Your blood test results also reveal raised marker levels for your pancreas,' was the last thing I remember hearing. Again, I started feeling remote.

As a child whenever upset, I would make strawberry jam sandwiches with mashed banana, get a bottle of water and find my bike in the chicken shed. I'd blow off the feathers, stow the picnic in my saddlebag, together with an empty jam jar, and head for the dog kennel. There I'd find Cracker, my devoted golden Labrador Alsatian cross. He earned his keep as my father's gun dog during the shooting season. He'd jump up excitedly, sensing an outing, and we'd make our way along the potholed farm road. Eventually we arrived on the edge of woods where a shallow stream ran. I placed my bike against a tree, glancing up, noticing the smell of rotting flesh. Hanging there was what my father called vermin: magpies, crows, rooks and rabbits. Although the sight distressed me, it was normal practice on a farm in those days. I made my way hastily to the stream's edge, taking my socks and shoes off, rolling my trouser legs up ready to step into the water. It was icily cold, numbing my toes. I could feel the small stones mingling with sand at the bottom of the shallow, clear water. I stood silent, still. As I looked into the water a silver fish darted past close to my toes. Inwardly I wriggled with delight. Bending down, jam jar in hand, I waited patiently. My patience was rewarded. Another stickleback slid from beneath a stone right into my jam jar. I scooped it up, water and all, and stood marvelling at the beauty of that small creature. Once satisfied I then released it back into the water and watched it swim downstream with the current. Cracker lay snoozing contentedly on a patch of grass at the water's edge in a cool pool of shade.

Sitting upright in my chair, and coming out of my reverie, I started asking questions about chemotherapy and radiotherapy and their success rates. I needed to know.

Professor Thomas was direct and honest.

'Your tumour is inoperable,' I heard her say. With that she stood up and invited me to lie on her examination couch. The curtains swished shut with Simon sitting on the far side. Professor Thomas gently examined my fragile abdomen, unintentionally making me wince. Then I began to experience a sinking sensation, one of dread. Examination over, we returned to our chairs.

'If we use various treatments and they work then it may be possible to operate later on, of course. However, for now that's not an option. Your tumour is far too big and complex for surgery.'

Light-headedness overtook me. Simon's voice, continuing the dialogue with Professor Thomas, sounded as though in the far distance, as my mind temporarily dislocated from the enormity of what I had just heard. If one form of chemotherapy didn't work, they could try another, then another, and then still another, and if that failed they could try radiotherapy and then more and more still.

My mind hazily refocused as I heard myself ask what percentage of success such treatments had. Professor Thomas listed a stream of statistics. Far from offering reassurance, the thinly veiled starkness of the message was all too clear: these were desperate and drastic measures that at most would buy me some extra time, but not a cure.

Having heard enough, something snapped inside me. I wanted the base line, remembering Joanna's courage, which at the time I didn't feel I possessed, but knowing that if I had all sorts of chemotherapy treatments then my immune system would be compromised.

Memories of how I struggled to come to terms with Joanna's death came back to me. A friend working at a local Marie Curie hospice had suggested I become a volunteer. She thought it might help reconcile my upset, so I started working there as soon as I could. The first time I arrived, just walking through the large double front doors required all my effort. The memories associated with such places overwhelmed me.

As children, Joanna and I chose to share a bedroom for companionship rather than out of necessity. It was many a late summer's night, mid-harvest, that we lay endlessly chatting and giggling. Our loud banter awoke our exhausted father. He would stride into our room and boom reprimands that only served to have the reverse effect on me. It would set me off into peels of louder laughter; my nervous energy often worked like that, much to his annoyance. However, it delighted Joanna and me! We laughed until tears rolled down our cheeks.

'And if I opt for the first chemotherapy treatment you mentioned,' I asked my oncologist, noticing the mirror on the wall adjacent to her desk, 'what will happen to my hair?'

Joanna had sported a proud, thick head of glorious auburn hair that spun like burnished gold in the sunlight, right up to the end of her life, as she'd asked for treatments that allowed her to keep her hair.

'It will drop out!' came the reply, much to my anguish.

'And what about my eyelashes?'

'Oh yes, those too will drop out.'

I got up and walked towards the mirror to look into my eyes.

No, I thought, I'm most definitely not going to view the world without my eyelashes in place. That small gift of vanity gave me the courage to say, 'In that case, I'd like to have some time to think things over before rushing into any decision making.'

Simon sat there looking bewildered. I looked across the void between us pleadingly, urging him to trust my instincts. I knew from the answers we'd heard that my immune system would be compromised. I remembered what I'd observed and read while volunteering at the hospice many years ago, never imagining I'd be confronted with such choices myself.

It's peculiar how interlinked events in our lives are, especially when we sit down and reflect on them, I thought.

The oncologist looked unhappy with my reply but I pleaded with her to at least give me three weeks to think it over. She agreed, making another appointment and asking me to accompany a nurse to have more blood tests done.

Simon, in spite of his phobia of needles, insisted on remaining with me throughout. The nurse, the friendly one that we had seen earlier, didn't mind. Simon held my free hand as she tried to find a vein, chatting and helping to distract me from the procedure.

'I can't find a vein in this arm. Let's try your other,' she said pleasantly. I rolled my sleeve up but the veins there too had all but disappeared. Nevertheless, the nurse tried repeatedly until she succeeded. All the while Simon and I looked in the opposite direction, holding hands, whilst she chatted about her love of circuses. I felt shattered but relieved when it was over and couldn't wait to leave the hospital.

Outside, the world as I'd known it remained the same. Inwardly, however, my life had altered and would never quite be the same again. It was tilting. It felt a bit like when you're trying to go to sleep at night and start relaxing then feel as though you're falling. But of course you're not. What is happening is your perception of reality is changing.

The following letter is from the medical notes taken by my oncologist and sent to my GP after my initial appointment with her.

Thank you for asking me to see this interesting lady who sadly has presented with liver metastases from a probably ovarian primary. I note she has two large necrotic metastases in the liver and a very large mass arising from the right ovary. On reflection Mrs Gill thinks she has noticed abdominal bloating and the mass on the right side of her abdomen for up to one year.

She is very reluctant to have a liver biopsy performed, as she has an idea that this will result in spreading the disease and says that she knows of examples where sticking needles into tumours has made matters worse. I spent some time explaining that this is very unlikely to be the case, and that my professional advice to her was that without a liver biopsy we would not be sure what we were treating. Although on balance this is most likely to be ovarian cancer, it clearly could be stomach, pancreatic or even breast primary, and the likely diagnosis should be narrowed down as much as possible.

On examining her breasts today I could not find any lumps, but she has not had a mammogram. She has symptoms of fullness, but I think these are likely to be due to intra-abdominal mass as there is nothing to suggest a stomach lesion. She certainly has no evidence of pain or visible pancreatic lesion from her CT scan to suggest a pancreatic primary. I have checked her CA19-9 and CA15-3 [tumour markers for pancreatic and breast cancer respectively]. She has decided

31

in her own mind to look at the option of healing first before she embarks on a course of conventional medicine. She herself is a healer, and over the few days before I saw her she has seen a number of her colleagues who are also healers. She maintains that the mass in her abdomen had reduced quite significantly. She points to her xyphisternum as the area where it started, and the fact that is now some 4 or 5 cm below this level. I think that this is clearly very important to her personally, and it is also important given the potential gravity of the situation that she feels she is doing everything possible to prolong her life.

I have therefore agreed with her that she will go off this weekend for her healing course and I will see her again on 18th October to arrange both the conventional tests and, I hope, conventional medicine. She has read widely about chemotherapy and is well versed in the side effects, and I am sure that ultimately she will want to take a dual approach using both conventional and complementary medicine.

I recalled how upon hearing I was a spiritual healer my oncologist had said to me, 'I haven't seen that work. I had a client who was also a healer. She died.'

Simon and I walked out of the hospital, our minds reeling. I noticed as we reached the pavement that I wasn't limping so badly. Leaving the hospital behind, for the time being, was a huge relief.

Once home being practical helped. After a long rest I decided I wouldn't need that little suitcase after all. There'd be no operation. It wasn't an option at this stage. As I opened it up, I ran my hands wistfully over the satin pyjama fabric. Next I replaced the books on the bookshelf, wondering if I'd ever get the chance to read them.

That night I couldn't sleep. I could only find comfort lying on my back as it was too painful to do otherwise. If I made one move in the wrong direction the searing pain made me flinch. I lay there, sweat pouring from me. The odour was a cancerous one that I was familiar with; it horrified me thinking I was producing it and was filled with it from a vast rock-hard lump with what appeared to me in my state of turmoil to be its own heartbeat…

Frightening thoughts reminded me briefly of the horrors I saw as a child on the farm. I'd always had a fascination for the weird things in life. My father had wanted a son and sometimes treated me as one. Latterly, he'd bred turkeys on the farm. I remember one particular day being in the incubator shed with my father. I loved watching those fluffy chicks once hatched, and so did he.

'Look,' he'd said, dangling a two-headed baby chick in front of my eyes. Initially I reeled back onto my heels, repulsed, and then a morbid fascination took hold. I walked forward to take a closer look. Other than the fact it had two heads it looked normal.

'And look at this one too,' he said. 'We've got a lot of freaks today.' I thought I might throw up as I looked at another chick that had four legs and four feet.

Suddenly, I identified with those freakish day-old chicks. I felt like a freak existing in a strange new world. It wasn't like the one I'd known before I was diagnosed with cancer. I couldn't fully comprehend what was happening to me. It felt like I'd woken up in a strange and unfamiliar world and I was grappling to make sense of it all.

The next night, unable to sleep, lying in bed with my heart pounding and mind racing, I listened to the familiar sound of the grandfather clock chiming the hours: midnight, one, two, three. Then I noticed the lavatory's ancient water system dripping incessantly after each flush; I was flushing it frequently. My compromised system combined with over-revving shocking thoughts upset my tummy, to the extent that diarrhoea poured out of me. Embarrassingly so, as the loo's system struggled to cope; often the first flush wasn't always successful, as David discovered soon enough to his disgust. Struggling to sleep, I became sure I could feel something on my neck. It was tickling, unfamiliar. I reached to my neck, felt wiry legs and was horrified to discover it was a large spider! I was terrified of spiders. Even though my heart was pounding I managed to brush it off without a second thought. Previously I would have screamed out for Simon; my dulled senses were overloaded.

Breathe, I ordered myself, willing calm. What was happening now, I wondered, shifting more comfortably onto my back. Suddenly I couldn't smell the fragrance of my lavender pillow that I was trying to inhale to soothe me. Nor, I realized, had I tasted any food I was eating lately, not that much of it was staying in. I found eating little and often and chewing my food fastidiously to be the best policy to help my digestion. My weight loss of the past months showed especially in my face, exaggerating my wrinkles.

I couldn't stand my thoughts and feelings a moment longer, so inched my way agonizingly across the bed to reach out to Simon, fast asleep and curled on his side. I snuggled up to him and that helped ease my panic as my thoughts ran rampant. By staying with them rather than trying to block them out, their intensity curiously lessened. I listened to the haunting hoot of an owl in the garden. A fox on the adjacent farm barked eerily. There in that warm comfort I lightly dozed.

The following morning I vowed I'd make a big effort to help myself. I started by gently taking the sweat-drenched sheets off the bed. I changed them, putting a thick towel on my side of the bed to soak up my night sweats. That would be simpler than washing the entire bedding. I must make the most of the time when the pain subsided, I thought, as it was intermittent.

Throughout the next three weeks Simon and I went backwards and forwards discussing our options, based on the facts we'd heard about various chemotherapy and radiotherapy treatments, to see what if anything they would do. None of them sounded promising.

I asked Simon what he remembered from our meeting with Professor Thomas. 'My interpretation of her comments is that a course of chemotherapy at best would just give you a few extra months.'

The downside of chemotherapy is that it completely weakens the body, which prevents it from being supported in other ways. Neither of us slept well during this time of indecision. I kept feeling shaky, swaying from one mindset to another as uncertainty followed me like a shadow.

Before we knew it the healing retreat weekend arrived. Simon accompanied me, feeling mildly apprehensive, though we found being together strengthening. We both found a dynamic of like-minded spiritual souls who helped us in unexpected ways. Simon was given the opportunity to process some unresolved grief issues. For myself, while sitting in the silence, I suddenly had a flashback to my childhood when I was around nine years old. I remembered my father's nervous breakdown. As a farm manager, he was constantly under pressure to get the best results. In the 1960s he lost his entire herd of cattle due to a severe foot-and-mouth outbreak, which was the final bitter blow. During those dark days my mother coped as best she could as my father spent months in hospital. When he returned home I grew up fast, helping with cooking, washing and keeping the peace when tensions rose; I coped. We all did. Coping under pressure was ingrained in me.

Then I had another flashback of a feisty old lady, a spinster who lived in the adjacent village. She'd been kind to me when my father was ill. She was strong, brave and fiercely independent and lived alone save for her dog, an English Setter named Simon. She also had a regular visitor: a ghost. That ghost disturbed her sleep, playing with her indoor wind chimes. On rare occasions when she came downstairs in the morning she'd find all the furniture rearranged in her sitting room. Even though this defied logical explanation she accepted it, co-existing with the ghost throughout her life.

I reasoned that, if an unfathomable force could do all that, surely I could move my 'lump' in an unorthodox way. With those thoughts, every time I now went to the loo I imagined the 'thing' inside me gradually and gently dissolving, passing through me and down the pan. In spite of the healing work I'd done for other people, I wasn't confident I could heal myself. We both returned from that weekend fortified, feeling somehow better equipped to face whatever lay ahead.

Simon knew the children would both be home at the weekend. Clare would be back from Newcastle. The tension of the past weeks keeping the secret from David, who was living at home, had been a strain for long enough.

'You can't put off telling the children any longer,' he said. 'We'll do it together. And what about telling your parents and sister Jane?'

'No,' I protested loudly, feeling overwhelmed.

'Why not?'

'You know my father has a bad heart and had major heart surgery not so long ago. He's been losing weight and isn't as strong as he once was. And my mother has her hands full taking care of him, along with everything else in her life.' My reasoning sounded good to me. 'And what about Joanna?' I added. 'They don't need to hear their middle daughter has cancer too.'

'No, they don't, I can see that now. But what are you going to do about it?'

'I know, I'll tell them I've got a cyst. I'm already disguising my appearance by wearing your belt through the loops of my favourite red jeans with your baggy rugby shirts.'

'Why not tell Jane?'

'It would put added pressure on her to keep a secret. You know she's divorced, a single mum and has her own struggles.' My natural instinct was to protect her along with my parents. I didn't want to share the bad news with any of them. This was something I struggled with for a long time.

The answer had come easily with that conversation and with it the thought of a cyst remained with me. Though the word 'lump' remained, cyst was friendlier in my confused, irrational mind, better to cope with.

It was hideous lying to my parents and Jane. I felt so deceitful after making those phone calls and had a migraine for days afterwards, accompanied by the usual sickness. I lay in bed feeling dreadful. The bedroom window was ajar, letting in the fresh air, the air I craved. I loved walking and hadn't been able to for a few days. I breathed it in deeply, hungrily and started listening to the birds singing in the garden. It seemed to me they'd never sung more sweetly.

The children were both home. It was the weekend. I was extremely nervous, so was Simon, but somehow we'd tell them together. They'd been home for a while; we couldn't put off the inevitable conversation any longer. We sat in the friendly sitting room. Simon took control saying, 'Mummy and I have got something to tell you.' They sat quietly, expectantly.

'You may have noticed my tummy's got larger lately.'

'Are you pregnant?' asked Clare.

'No, I'm not pregnant,' I replied praying for inspiration. 'I've got cancer.'

David looked stunned and didn't move. That worried me. Clare burst into tears and ran from the room, heading straight for Lucy lying in one of her beds on the stairs. I left Simon to David and followed Clare, praying the right words would come. I never stopped praying at that time.

Clare was sobbing her heart out dejectedly, cuddling Lucy on the stairs. Sitting beside her I reached out, holding her tightly to me.

'It'll be alright, just wait and see,' I offered reassuringly. It didn't help.

Between sobs she replied, 'I've lost one mother. I don't want to lose another.'

That did it, I burst into tears too. We clung to one another sobbing for a while. Then I felt a shift inside me, a force beyond me, giving rise to a new strength that I never knew I possessed. 'You won't lose me.' I don't know where those words came from. I was determined to do the very best I could, if not for my sake then for hers.

Eventually I left her, returning to David. He was obviously anguished; I could see by his taut body. Simon was gently reassuring him. David, being a young teenager, didn't take in the full enormity of it at the time. Suddenly he looked at me saying, 'Well, you healed Jack our dog, now heal yourself.' I had forgotten about that. Those simple words reinforced my fresh determination to do all I could to do just that.

I remembered Jack, our beloved canine grandfather figure, now lying peacefully at the bottom of the garden in our animal graveyard. Jack had lived beyond his years. When he got ill Simon had suggested I give him spiritual healing. I'd been too emotional to think of that myself. When I did place my hands onto his protruding tumour the size of an orange he lay motionless, merely rolling his eyes to meet mine. I felt overwhelming love streaming through me, into my hands, making them hot. Within moments he moved, letting me know he'd had enough. Then he slowly sat up before finally standing, walking to the door and asking to be let outside. He wandered over to the bushes and passed matter from one end or the other, sometimes both. This occurred frequently after healing.

We ceremoniously buried our beloved Jack one evening. Simon had uncharacteristically walked out of a business meeting, returned home and dug a grave. The children and I had got candles out ready for our farewell ceremony. At dusk we followed Simon down the lawn, pushing Jack wrapped in a silk bedspread in the wheelbarrow. As Simon softly placed him in the grave, we stood around forming a circle. I'd encouraged the children to say something about their life with Jack. I started off by thanking him for being our devoted best friend and constant companion. We all cried, finding it devastating. Afterwards I'd found a bunch of flowers left on the doorstep by my friend Lindy. As the moon came up I placed those flowers on top of Jack's freshly covered grave.

With those thoughts, I wondered how I was going to get through the journey ahead. It seemed insurmountable.

CHAPTER 3
Trust

Trust that
All will be well,
Whatever the outcome,
For there is a force at work behind the scenes,
A Divine Force
Far beyond human expectancy
Gillian Gill

Late October 2000

Time as I'd previously known it now appeared to both slow down and accelerate simultaneously. Choices, we had to make choices. 'Your next hospital appointment is due soon. What are you going to tell your oncologist?' said Simon. I could hardly believe where the three weeks since our last appointment had gone to.

I'd been dreading this conversation. In my heart I wanted to listen to my instincts and try to recreate the same effect I'd had on Jack. He'd survived a further five years. With healing prayers I'd been putting my hands on myself several times a day. I'd felt heat and, like Jack, kept passing matter both ends, and that gave me hope, remembering how his tumour had shrunk. I was spending hours resting, listening to my body, and striving to quell the piercing abdominal pain when it came. But what about Simon; how would he react to my decision? I stalled, planning how best to say what

I really felt as I was terrified of taking Joanna's conventional medical route; I couldn't seem to find her courage.

'You know conventional medicine has so much to offer,' Simon continued reasonably. His remarks only deepened my earlier resolve, born from intense talks with healer colleagues about conventional medicine versus the unorthodox method of linking the best of mind, body and spirit together with monitoring progress conventionally. 'You'd be looked after in hospital…' The mere thought of Simon visiting me in hospital with so many unhappy associations made me anxious. He didn't need that. I also thought I didn't want to be in hospital wired up to lines and machines, totally dependent on others for everything. At least at home I had some control, and if I felt terrible I could put myself to bed. My head listened to Simon's endless reasoning about the advantages of conventional medicine, but my heart lay elsewhere. He'd listened patiently, hard though that was for him, to my thoughts about spiritual healing and in a bid for mutual ground surprised me by saying, 'Nutrition, I've been reading more about that. Diet plays a significant part in boosting the immune system.' I remembered how, when I was resting upstairs, he'd been downstairs spending hours on the Internet researching.

That word nutrition suddenly jogged my memory. I remembered how after returning from our holiday in America we'd gone to friends for supper. Not wishing to offend our hosts by refusing their specially prepared meal, I went against my recently adopted vegetarian regime. Increasingly I'd been thinking about what I was eating and I'd gradually been losing my desire for meat and fish. However, I ate the meat casserole to be polite, not wanting to offend our host, who'd spent all day preparing the meal. Though we noticed something unusual over the next few days – especially David, who said, 'Mummy are you sure you're not pregnant? Your tummy is growing bigger by the day.' – I'd laughed it off. Denial; I didn't want to think about it, knowing that our dog Jack was in the throes of dying. In spite of the fact he rallied just before finally passing, I recognized those signs.

This supper was just a few weeks prior to my diagnosis. My changing appetite and diet was linked to my body's intolerance of certain foods due to my unknown illness. I'd wondered about my IBS condition and dismissed it, conveniently burying all thoughts of illness, believing my body would somehow repair itself and return to normal function.

'Darling,' I said pensively to Simon, 'I've made up my mind. If I haven't got long to live, I'd rather choose quality of life over quantity. I can't bear to put myself through the harrowing episodes that I've witnessed others close to me experience who did go down the conventional medical route. I don't want chemotherapy, radiotherapy or operations down the line. I'd rather be at home and tackle this my own way.'

He looked at me stupefied, then finding his voice said, 'We're seeing Professor Thomas tomorrow. Let's talk to her about it.'

'That's what I want to talk to her about.' I took a massive deep breath and inwardly prayed he would back me up. I watched his face rapidly processing his thoughts, my pleading eyes never leaving his.

Standing tall, he stunned me by replying, 'If that's what you've decided then you have my support.'

Suddenly I felt weak, to the point of collapse. It had taken every ounce of energy to say those few words out loud. Once spoken, they shook me to the core as I too heard them for the first time. I felt jittery and remembered how some actors suffer with terrible nerves before going on stage. If I were on the threshold of acting bravely with my oncologist the following day, no wonder I had the jitters, I reasoned. I was hoping to put on the performance of a lifetime to try to save my life.

The following day, time hung heavily before our appointment. Once in the car I thought of the children and remembered one particular glorious sunny day in the garden, the year after marrying Simon. Clare, Simon's daughter by his first marriage, while playing in the sandpit was struggling with my name and called out 'Dillon'. Simon laughed. She'd never been able to pronounce Gillian. Simon had liquid chalk solution in a sprayer, which he used on the greenhouse, and suddenly knelt down on the lawn.

'What you doing Daddy?' said ever-questioning two-year-old Clare.

'Spraying,' he replied.

41

'Why?' she asked.

'You'll see.'

Both Clare and I watched in fascination as the letter M appeared, followed by U, then another M. It wasn't until the second M appeared that my heart caught in my throat and burst. He'd written 'Mummy'. 'Look,' he said to Clare, 'that spells Mummy. Now, try saying that. You might find it easier than Dillon.'

I'll always remember that moment; I had no right to Clare's love. Though I loved her the instant I first saw her, I couldn't demand that it be reciprocated. After all, I'd seen otherwise when working as a volunteer at a children's home in Balham where I'd helped out one evening a week for a few years. Yet when first meeting Clare it was as though we'd always known one another. There was an instant love, which flowed between us and continued to grow and deepen. I felt humbled by this, remembering the stark contrasts I'd witnessed while working at the children's home, where love had not always been returned.

We'd arrived at the hospital. Quite by chance walking along the corridor we bumped into Professor Thomas.

'Hello,' she said surprised. Peering deeply into my eyes she continued, 'You do look well. I'm ahead of myself today. Would you like to come straight through?' With that we followed. I felt relieved we wouldn't have to wait; it's those unexpected small things in life that make the difference.

'How have you been?' Professor Thomas asked, my file open on her desk.

'I've been repeatedly putting my hands on myself, giving myself spiritual healing. I get up at 3 or 4 am when I can't sleep and go and sit quietly in my healing room trying to meditate and pray. When I married Simon I turned one of the rooms in the house into a quiet room. We call it the healing room,' I explained.

'That's interesting,' she replied, making notes in my file. 'I've had other patients who have been healers trying to integrate both conventional and holistic medicine.'

Then she told us about my dismal blood test results. My white blood cells were raised. Simon listened intently as I became detached, my hands unconsciously turning to fists on my lap.

I was pleased she'd advised us to come to these appointments together, explaining how upsetting they can be and how hard it can be to remember everything. 'Let's go and examine you.' I tentatively lay down on the couch behind a curtain and lifted my top as she gently prodded and probed, finding tender spots. 'Yes, your mass is still hard.'

Once we sat down again she asked about our healing weekend. Simon spoke first then she looked expectantly at me. A frisson of fear unfurled in my spine; I willed it away, feeling like a naughty child in front of a teacher, having been brought up not to query people in authority, but I was about to go against that behaviour. Mustering what courage I could I said, 'I've agonized over my decision...' Then stammering and swallowing hard continued, 'I don't think I can face conventional medicine. The thought terrifies me. I've decided I'd like to take the holistic route.'

She looked uncomfortable and continued speaking at some length, reiterating how dangerous this could be, possibly fatal, asking me how I could arrive at such a momentous decision. I told her more about our weekend away, where I'd met an American woman, Brandon Bays, an astounding complementary practitioner who had achieved miraculous results herself in finding another route to healing by getting to the emotional root cause of her cancer. She'd got rid of her football-sized tumour in six weeks! Her way had inspired me to arrive at my own choice. During our weekend, having mulled over the speed of events since last visiting my oncologist, I'd wondered why the pressure to do everything so fast, reasoning I'd had this 'thing' for ages, so surely I could afford a little time. Well, now I'd had my time and made my choice.

We fell into a brief silence as a shadow of fear re-emerged, then I said, 'I can't do this without you. Would you please consider my remaining in your care? I'd like to keep all options open.'

'Of course,' she said, astounding me. 'We'll monitor your blood with regular tests and take scans. I'll want to see you every six weeks.' She broke off briefly before continuing. 'As your case is rather unusual, I'm going to have to think of another way of monitoring you,' she said, reaching for a blank sheet of paper. 'I'll measure your mass with my finger widths and draw a picture of your abdomen, keeping a record of the width and length that way.' Prodding my abdomen during the examination she had said, 'It does in fact seem slightly improved on your last appointment.' My spirits rallied momentarily. But another part of me thought if I was going to die then I'd like her help; I didn't want to suffer more than I could bear.

Being able to talk openly and honestly, and having her support in whatever measure, was reassuring. I had more blood tests before leaving the hospital. Again my veins had disappeared. The nurse laughingly said, 'Oh, now I've found a vein you won't stop bleeding. You are a bleeder!' Curiously, her words made me smile, as I sometimes swear and took her meaning out of context.

On the way home in the car I blurted out, 'I'd like to make my will.'

Simon pulled off the road into a lay-by. He looked deeply into my eyes before replying, 'We'll do them together. I'll rewrite mine.'

Now I'd placed my bet, as it were, recalling the gynaecologist's earlier words: 'If I were a betting person…'

After this appointment, Professor Thomas wrote the following letter to my gynaecologist.

Further to our meeting for the monthly Gynae team today, I saw Gillian with her husband. They spent the weekend in a London hotel seeing Brandon Bays, a well-known healer from the States. Mrs Gill has thought everything through in great detail and has decided that she would like to pursue a path which is most acceptable to her. She does not wish to pursue conventional medicine at the present time, and did not really want to discuss having a liver biopsy as she does not feel this is needed if she is not to have conventional medicine.

I think some of this reaction is due to her recollection of her sister's demise some years ago. She also said that when I mentioned when I saw her last time Taxol would cause loss of her eyelashes, something 'flipped' in her and made the whole idea unacceptable. I did explain that losing eyelashes was not essential, and that in the absence of a biopsy of her tumour it was very difficult to know which chemotherapy agents she would require and what their side effect profile would be. Although I still feel that ovarian cancer is the highest tumour on the list, interestingly her CA19-9, a marker for GI tumours and in particular pancreatic cancer, was also elevated. This was 211, which is not really specific. Her CA15-3 [the breast tumour marker] was in the normal range.

Mrs Gill feels that her tumour continues to shrink. It was four fingers breadth below the ribs on the right at its highest point, which I think may be one or two finger breadths below when I saw her before, but this is very difficult to judge and certainly the tumour may be a little wider than it was before but is hard to assess. At the present time she has normal liver function tests, and I feel that I am unable to ignore her requests or force her down the conventional route.

She has asked for my support and I have given this, but have warned her about the danger of developing abnormal liver or renal function tests and thereby missing the boat for conventional therapy. She has given me her word that if she starts to feel unwell or if she feels that the tumour is getting bigger she would plan to come back and seek my advice. She has my number and will contact me in due course.

I feel that given her social situation and the fact that her husband lost his first wife this is all extremely difficult, both as a health care professional and as someone offering advice, but she has thought this through and is very clear in her own mind. I can see little alternative, as I am sure that if I took a more high-handed approach she would be no more likely to accept this route.

Following the hospital visit, Simon called me to listen to a message from a healer friend on the answer machine. Feeling weary, I sat at the kitchen table to listen.

'You are more than the sum total of your body. You are living spirit encased in your body. From now on, every time you sit on the loo, imagine a ball of white light entering the top of your head. Imagine it cleansing and purifying your entire system as you release your bodily functions.'

By early evening, and feeling as though I'd been hit by a thunderbolt after telling the oncologist my decision, I decided to have a soothing bath and go to bed. I felt about a thousand years old and tried to focus on a healer colleague's life-affirming words: 'Always remember, the will to live is stronger than the will to die.' As I removed the plaster from the blood test I noticed that my arm was not only black and blue but red and itchy too. Could be worse, I thought, absently rubbing the palm of my hand over my abdomen; it wasn't smooth. Under the skin it had what felt like octopus arms or branches leading off in all directions. That frightened me. Leaving the water running in the bathroom, I strolled into the bedroom. I could see out of the window that it was a surprisingly pleasant evening. I opened the window and fresh air streamed in. The garden was filled with fading late blooms; many plants had been gifts from passionate gardening friends. Standing back and glancing down onto the bedroom floor I suddenly noticed something unusual lying on the carpet. Even though bending down was painful I felt compelled. Gingerly stretching my hand out, I grasped a spongy-feeling, raspberry-like object; with that touch my mind reeled. In a nanosecond I knew with vivid clarity, don't ask me how, that it was part of my cancerous tumour. Years previously during my metaphysical studies I'd heard of the phenomenon of physical mediumship whereby physical matter can be moved by spiritual means, but I never thought that I would directly experience it. Standing transfixed, staring into the palm of my hand, repulsion and awe filled me. My mind calmed, cleared and focused: 'I don't want you, I'll get rid of you, and I don't want anyone else to see you.' With those thoughts I raised my hand to throw the object out of the window into the delphinium bed below.

I fell asleep in the bath and awoke shivering in the cold water. Climbing out I burst into tears, wrapped a towel around me, as I was too tired to find a nightshirt, and crawled into bed, uncontrollable tears coursing down my cheeks. Thoughts of Joanna flooded my mind. What had she experienced? How had she coped? I recalled her frantic late-night phone calls crying out for help. Then I'd felt inadequate, being merely a voice on the end of the phone. That pent-up guilt burst out of me as I prayed for her forgiveness that I hadn't done more. I told her I was sorry, and then with a fresh pang I thanked her for being my sister and best friend. As my tears subsided

I thought of my mother; she'd gone to pieces after losing her youngest daughter. Yet she is strong. A born optimist, she keeps a photo of Joanna close by, lovingly tending it, always putting a fresh flower by it, usually from the garden.

I had dozed off when Simon rolled into bed beside me. 'Are you alright?'

'Yes,' I mumbled. He was worn out from managing the school run, working in London and supporting me. As he fell into a deep sleep I lay awake, gripped once more by fear and the uncertainties that lay ahead.

The following day Simon said, 'Don't let anyone tell you how long it takes to improve.' He was referring to a recent phone call where someone had unwittingly upset me. 'We both know this is going to be tough, requiring commitment and hard work.' I hungrily fastened onto his every word as he continued. 'Everyone's an individual. Give your body a chance to heal in its own time.'

His words acted as a balm. 'Last night before you came to bed something strange happened.' I told him about the previous evening.

Fairly new to embracing the world of spiritual healing, this was a step too far for his logical mind, so he said, 'Why don't you go and see your healer friend Irene, down the road? If anyone can explain that, she can.' Once she'd have been known as the wise one in the community, the one to whom all could turn when in need. She was the proprietor and most experienced healer of the Universal Healing Centre.

When I arrived at her home she listened intently and then said, 'Come into the healing room and lie on the couch; we'll see what we can do to help you.' By 'we' she meant her spirit guides, who work invisibly beside her, rather like guardian angels.

As I lay down my abdomen was clutched with a spasm of new, fresh pain. 'Prop your knees up a bit, that will help,' she said, before adding, 'Now you come and see me regularly,' as she looked into my frightened eyes. She then calmly talked me through a guided meditation, telling me to imagine a fine summer's day. 'Just let go of everything, relax, deeply relax. This is a time especially for you. Imagine leisurely walking through a churchyard, admiring the trees and flowers. Now, slowly continue along a winding path to the church door; open it, pause, take a deep breath and walk inside. Let go of that breath. Inhale, now feel the prayerfulness and tranquillity, imbued into the very fabric of the building.'

An hour or so later I heard her softly speaking. 'You did relax nicely, Gill.' More business-like she continued, 'I distinctly heard my late husband, Gerald, tell me that he'd attended a medical meeting in the spirit world. Now he's gone over he's continuing with his spiritual healing. At the meeting he discovered that the strange-looking raspberry object you spoke of is part of your tumour. It had manifested outside your body to explicitly demonstrate the power of spiritual healing in the physical world and your battle against cancer, as well as to reassure you of your choice. He's being told, as you've found the courage to make your decision, you will find forces gathering around to help you. You have work to do yet. Do not scatter your energies, but keep focused on your main goal. Strive to remain calm and carry on. Your spiritual pathway is deepening, your healing gift is expanding.'

I thanked her profusely for her time and wisdom. She was like a surrogate spiritual mother to me, and had been for years. She watched me from the door walking down her garden path towards the gate. My legs involuntarily buckled beneath me and I nearly fell.

'Stop that. Get a grip of your mind. Tell your legs to walk properly.'

I'd always appreciated her directness. Smiling I said, 'I'll do my best.'

'That's the finest answer; it's all anyone can do. Remember, always listen to your intuition; and keep putting hands on yourself with healing intention, as you've been taught. It's simple enough; just invite help from the spirit dear ones, in love and harmony. Oh, and don't let your appearance go.'

My fear was rendering me impotent. Hearing her words reminded me of my inherent healing ability; an ability that I've been taught and believe is inherent in all of us, lying dormant waiting to awaken. With renewed determination I returned home, knowing I would see her again soon. I still felt insecure and knowing that I could count on her help was an immense source of comfort. Looking into the mirror, averting my eyes from my 'lump', I saw my frightened face staring back at me; I hadn't bothered with my hair, or even put a dab of makeup on. That was unheard of for me; I always put a small amount of makeup on, so proceeded to do so with shaky hands.

Increasingly I placed my hands on my abdomen and focused on dissolving my 'lump'. As I did so I felt a twang, like a rubber band. 'What was that?' I wondered disconcerted. The answer came that it was the loosening of the grip of one of those tentacles. Although I was terrified of all the unusual changes taking place in my body, this was another very encouraging sign that I was making some headway down the holistic route.

'You have brightened,' said Simon a day or so later. It was encouraging hearing his words and seeing the relief in his face. The dab of makeup together with washing and brushing my hair helped, although my hair was still falling out slightly more than usual.

'Are you going to try to walk Lucy today? You know how a walk always used to revitalize you and I've read how walking helps some cancers as it oxygenates the blood.'

'That's interesting,' I replied. 'Managing around the house is okay, but it hurts if I walk far.'

'Then walk slowly. Don't look too far ahead. And don't look back. Just keep going gently on…' he replied, ever practical. 'You know how Lucy takes herself off when you walk her. You've always let her spirit run free, as it were, so you can do it your way.'

Yes, I reflected, recounting the number of times Lucy had run off and rummaged through neighbours' dustbins, eating the putrid titbits. Preparing for a walk, I wrapped myself in a friendly old coat with deep pockets.

'Come on, Lucy,' I called, 'let's give it a go.' She nudged my knee in anticipation as we headed for the door. It was a bleak autumnal day, and I inhaled the cold air, recalling that cancer hates oxygen. We live opposite a farm surrounded by fields and woodland and I set off on my favourite circuit, breathing deeply and following in Lucy's wake. In spite of losing Jack she still rallied for walks, though they weren't the fun they'd once been.

Stopping, seized by a twinge, I gasped for air. Urging myself to remain calm, I waited for the pain to pass; it lost its hold and I continued. Every footstep hurt, so I frequently rested against a fence post. 'Don't be too ambitious,' I said to myself, 'start off slowly and build on that.' There was no sign of Lucy now. I'd been distracted and, having taken my eyes off her, she'd disappeared into the nearby woods. Following the scent of a rabbit, forgetting all else, she'd got lost in her own glorious world. No matter how much I called out her name, she didn't return. I'd been too self-absorbed; I chastised myself and then felt panic.

Simon had left for the office in London. In desperation I returned home, climbed into the car and went searching for Lucy. Driving with the window open I spotted her shooting out of the dense woods in front of me. I panicked and hit the accelerator instead of the brakes and was sickened when I felt a bump. Then I heard her yelp in pain and with mounting dread realized I'd run her over. I began hyperventilating as I got out of the car and was relieved to see she was on her feet, though only three of them; the fourth she held raised as it dripped with blood. I bent down and hugged her lightly, saying I was sorry and that I loved her, before struggling to help her into the boot, then made a beeline for the vet's, breathing deeply to steady my frayed nerves.

'Hello, Mrs Gill,' said the receptionist as I walked in. 'Is anything the matter? You look distraught.'

'Yes,' I cried. 'I've just run over Lucy our Labrador.'

'Oh, goodness me. Don't worry, that sort of thing happens all the time. I'll just go and get nurse. You go back to Lucy and stay with her in the car. Nurse will come right out to see you both.'

A familiar face appeared. It was the same nurse who had visited Jack and helped us when we'd faced the agonizing decision to have him put down. Wasting no time, her face concerned, she reached out lovingly to Lucy saying, 'Let's take a look, what happened here?' I told her all about it. She glanced at my tummy, and I told her about that too.

'We wondered if you were coming out in sympathy with Jack just before he died.'

'No,' I said, starting to cry all over again. Whatever was wrong with me, I reprimanded myself, I never cry. My normal behaviour was to bottle everything up. These days I never seemed to stop crying; I hugged Lucy, who was looking mournfully at me.

'Don't worry about Lucy's paw, it's superficial, just a bad graze. I'll soon have it clean and patched up.' She deftly washed Lucy's paw and then stood back pondering. 'I think I'll put a red bandage on her foot, to match her collar.' That made me smile. 'You'll need to keep a plastic cone collar on her so she doesn't try to get the bandage off.'

'I'll try,' I said, thinking that would be challenging, but took it home nevertheless, thanking her for her efforts.

Once home Lucy hobbled to her bed in front of the grandfather clock in the hall, the spot she'd chosen ever since she came into our lives. She didn't like the collar one bit, shook her head and banged it against the clock. Seeing her frustration I bent down saying, 'Don't worry, I'll take that contraption off.' She looked relieved and snuggled down into the depths of her bed for a sleep. Good idea, I thought, feeling tired out, and with that I wound my way upstairs for a lie down, mortified by the day's events. Trying to calm myself I placed my hands on my now painful abdomen and shut my eyes, then I felt a light touch nudging my hands aside. It was Lucy, almost as if she was checking my progress, sniffing my abdomen. Sensing my mood, she then positioned herself at the foot of the bed on the floor and stood there pressing her body against the soles of my feet, immediately making me calmer.

I must have dozed because the next thing I knew I heard Simon saying 'Hello, I'm home'. He'd just collected David from school. 'How was your day?' he called upstairs. As he walked into the bedroom I noticed he looked shattered and there was no sign of Lucy. I got up slowly and came downstairs to prepare supper, after first giving him a kiss.

'Oh no!' I gasped, looking at Lucy in her bed surrounded by the shredded remains of her bandage.

'Whatever's the matter?' asked Simon. 'I ran Lucy over today and had to take her to the vet's as she hurt her paw.'

'Is that all she hurt?' Simon asked disbelievingly.

'Yes,' I assured him. As he bent down to stroke the top of her head, her eyes never left his.

'She's like Harry Houdini', said David, taking in the tattered bandage, 'performing a magic trick like that.' Reassured, both he and Simon watched as Lucy licked her sore paw.

Simon remarked, 'You know how antiseptic a dog's saliva is. Her licking like that will only help heal the wound. She's just following her instincts.'

We sat down to supper, though none of us felt like eating much, and David soon disappeared to get on with his homework.

'I went to pieces today when I ran Lucy over,' I said to Simon.

'I'm not surprised. Is there anything I can do?'

'As a matter of fact there is. I've been having more morbid thoughts most of today.' I could never be anything less than honest with Simon and persevered with difficulty. 'I've been wondering, if I haven't got long left – and let's be candid, neither of us knows for sure – then I'd like to spend as much time with you as possible.'

Simon looked confused. As was often the case, I wasn't saying what I really intended. Communication was so important; I was realizing I had to become clearer. 'What I mean to say is, would it be possible for you to work from home?'

He paused before replying, 'I could always ask my boss, I suppose.' I didn't seem to be able to get enough love or reassurance and felt dreadfully needy and anxious from morning to night. The nightmares, when I did sleep, were getting worse.

Days later the phone rang early one evening. Simon by now was fielding all calls. He'd noticed how easily I became drained after talking on the phone. It was harrowing regaling people with my progress, no matter how well intentioned they were. They couldn't understand why I wasn't taking the conventional route. How could I expect others to understand that? Trying to explain to them only made me agitated. I expended valuable energy reassuring them I knew what I was doing, when in fact I didn't; I was just being true to myself. After those distressing calls I'd wonder if

I'd offended anyone. Then I'd repeatedly question my decision and drive myself demented in the process, the thoughts rudely interrupting my efforts to find calm or upsetting a quiet meditation.

'That was unusual,' said Simon, putting the phone down. 'It was my boss. He never phones people at home in the evening. He's thought over my request to work at home and has agreed to it.' The relief showed on his face and I just sat unable to speak, tears of relief streaming down my cheeks.

Unbeknown to us, Simon's close friend and colleague Nick had also gone into the office and pleaded on Simon's behalf that his job be saved.

Gita, Nick's wife, phoned the following day having spoken to some Indian friends. 'You've got to sleep the other way around in your bed.'

'Why?' I asked bewildered.

'Because we in the East believe the way you wake up facing the sun as it rises has a bearing on your overall well-being. Go on, make the change, it will help,' she urged. Simon and I discussed the idea and recognized that we couldn't physically turn the large bed around in our bedroom. There wasn't space; our bedroom is the other half of what was once a hayloft. We live in a barn and stables conversion, behind an old manor house.

'I'll just make the bed up the other way round,' I told Simon, setting off to do so immediately. Her call felt like another lifeline; I welcomed the Eastern ways. Those first few nights and weeks felt strange lying upside down, as it were, in our beds. However, we persisted in the belief it would somehow do us good.

'I think it's time you thought about visiting your friend Marianne, the nutritionist,' said Simon. 'I'm not an expert and those supplements I bought you may need fine tuning.'

'I could give her a ring,' I said hesitantly.

'When you've fixed up a time with her, I'll drive you.' So I made the call and fixed an appointment. A few days hence, when having a day off from being sick, we set off in the car.

'Hello,' said Marianne, as she welcomed us in her official capacity, indicating that we follow her into a small room at the health clinic. 'Please sit down, Gillian, Simon,' she said pointing to two chairs close to one another. We talked intensely for an hour and she told me about others she helped with cancer and how she thought her work could assist my holistic route. She constantly offered reassurance, yet despite this I was overwhelmed with information and in defence closed my mind to what she was saying.

Feeling daunted by the enormity of the task ahead of me, and all that I'd need to learn, it was too much to absorb, and so I found myself saying, 'Thank you for your time, but I don't think I need your professional help after all.' She sweetly hugged us both saying, 'Should you change your mind, you know where I am.'

After another sleepless night I did just that. 'Phone her,' Simon urged. Feeling embarrassed I dialled her number and she answered the phone almost straight away.

'Oh Gillian, how nice to hear from you. But of course I will see you again. In the meantime I'm going to send you information on nutrition, how to cleanse your system and then boost your immune system. You can read it in your own time. There will only be the cost of the supplements when you visit me. Otherwise there is no charge to come and see me.' I protested. 'I insist,' she said, 'for I am also learning from you.'

I was speechless.

CHAPTER 4
Gathering Forces

Believe a thing and you're half way there…
Believe in yourself… you can do it… only you…
For it's taking one tiny step at a time…
That's all… it's not about the outcome…
It's about each precious moment of each precious day…
Gillian Gill

November 2000

Without thinking I answered the phone and was glad I had. It was Claire, my yoga and acupuncturist friend.

'You know you recently mentioned your sore throat to me?'

'Yes.'

'Is it still sore?'

'Yes.'

'Well, I've been thinking, if you stick your tongue out as far as it will go, then count to seven and repeat the process seven times, this stimulates a natural healing reaction in that area.'

The following day Simon called me to the phone. 'It's Natasha for you. She knows what's happening in our lives. We've had a long chat and she's said that if there's anything from her professional psychotherapy viewpoint she can do to help, we're not to hesitate calling her. That includes Clare and David.'

I knew how she loved our children, sadly not having her own. I took the phone. Hearing her warm voice took me back to our first meeting many years ago when I'd just moved to London from Newmarket. We met quite by chance on a busy London shopping street; she was with Caroline, an old mutual college friend I hadn't seen for years, and a bond was struck almost immediately.

In the 1970s Natasha, sensing something 'different' about me, had introduced me to the late Gee Sumerary. Gee was the founder of a spiritual home circle that I first attended shortly after my arrival in London, when I felt a bit like a lost soul. She acted as a surrogate spiritual mother to many of us, becoming an influential part of our lives. She welcomed us into her home and always had time to support us and listen to our problems. We respected her opinions and guidance, as we didn't always want to burden our families with our day-to-day troubles. It was Gee who introduced me to the late Don Galloway (with whom she worked closely), a medium of the old school and a major influence in my life, whose spiritual and metaphysical course I attended at the Arthur Findlay College, the centre for spiritual and psychic instruction at Stansted Hall in Essex. Between these dear souls I went on to find a missing link in my life – the key to studying spiritual philosophy and learning the art of meditation – while attending Gee's spiritual development group, which led on to developing my healing gift.

'How are you?' Natasha asked.

'I'm managing, though I've virtually retreated from the world and it's all I can do to get through each day. Most of the time I feel I'm being chased, that I'm trying to escape the terror of my cancer and trying to find restored health, improved health even. But I'm striving to remember what we learned when you introduced me to Gee all those years ago.'

As our spiritual development teacher and healer, such were Gee's ways that she made no charge for teaching those of us who found her. We were all seeking a certain something missing from our lives. She instructed us that, by attending her classes, we were making a promise to ourselves involving a level of personal sacrifice through the very act of commitment.

She said, 'With this connection to your inner sanctuary, embracing dark and light, unifying the opposing forces at work within you, you will bring yourself back to the true essence of who you are.' We practised these disciplines in our daily lives. Having made our commitment to attend her classes, we all nevertheless tried to avoid those Monday nights on occasion. But something always made us turn up, unless it was unavoidable not to. I remembered how Gee taught us to discipline our minds for meditation, to focus on an object, whether it is a rose, a candle flame or an orange. We learned to keep bringing our minds back to the object of our main focus. The mind wanders, having its own natural flow, yet with discipline and practice it can be harnessed to relinquish its grip on distractions and to relax, thus becoming nourished and revitalized.

I explained to Natasha that this was what I'd been attempting to do. 'Drawing from those disciplines will help,' she continued. 'By sitting in the silence in love and harmony, as we did before meditating, and quietening your mind, you'll allow for subtle but powerful changes.'

'That's what I'm beginning to feel. But it's so hard.'

'I know, it's unimaginable for me. Just try to draw on the strength from that vast source of boundless energy you tap into when meditating. It'll nourish you spiritually as well. On a more practical level, how are you managing for clothes? Simon tells me your abdomen is huge?'

'I'm wearing jeans mostly, undone but with a belt. They won't do up any longer.'

'Can I buy you any clothes if you're not going out much?'

'Would you?' I asked, my mind fixing on a pair of elasticated trousers.

'What colours would you like?'

'Oh, dark, rich colours, I'll leave that to you,' I replied, trusting her impeccable taste in clothes, and reflecting how I could add bright colours as they lifted my spirits.

Within days a large cardboard box arrived. I'd forgotten all about our conversation and wondered what it was. 'I'll clear a space on the dining room table,' said Simon, 'then you can sit down and open it.' He handed me a sharp knife to cut through the tape and I soon arrived at layers of purple tissue enfolding whatever lay within. Diving in I pulled out a pair of gorgeous burgundy velvet trousers, and a black pair! They had elastic waistbands and still looked fashionable.

'See what else is in there,' urged Simon. Next I felt something soft and tore the tissue apart to discover a faux fur water bottle, and hugged it dreamily thinking how cosy it would be when my back hurt.

'I can smell lavender,' said Simon. I took out the next small tissue-wrapped parcel. Parting the paper, a purple velvet lavender eye mask fell out. That would be just the thing to wear when healing myself in bed. Feeling around the box there was one remaining parcel. This too was soft. Ripping it open, like a child, I gaped at a sumptuous pair of white faux fur fleece-lined slip-on slippers. With my 'lump' it was a struggle to put my existing slippers on. 'There's a card,' said Simon. I tore that open too. 'Please enjoy these gifts…' Her generosity touched me.

Briefly, I thought of my childhood birthday parties. Jim, a neighbouring farmer, doubled up as a magician at the local children's parties, and my father invited him to entertain my friends. My favourite memory was at the end when he pulled a white rabbit out of a black top hat, which always delighted everyone. As a special treat my father filled a large wooden crate with wood shavings and my mother wrapped small gifts and buried them amongst the shavings; that was an exciting way to thank them for coming and making it a special day for us all.

Glancing back at Natasha's enchanting fairy card, I remembered how, when introducing me to Gee, her first words to me were 'You're welcome in my home'. Holding my hand, she had continued, 'You are deeply sensitive; this is ripe for spiritual development.' I read Natasha's words: 'Remember how Gee taught us, and by making a commitment to ourselves and attending her weekly classes, we both learned through meditation to yield and surrender, gently and quietly. To always remain at one within. No matter what insurmountable problems we faced…'

Another week passed. My 'lump' was changing shape I noticed. It was flattening at the top and beginning to lose some of its grip. The nodules and tentacles were changing. In spite of this I still felt terrified most of the time. Upon waking I felt fear flood my entire system. An overseas healer colleague suggested I try hypnotherapy. I phoned Paul, a cranial osteopath friend, who told me that a colleague at the same clinic was a hypnotherapist. Luckily, I got an appointment almost immediately.

Wondering what lay ahead, I waited in the oak-beamed reception of the barn conversion that was the clinic. I was called into a small friendly room. 'My name is David,' announced the therapist. His name alone reassured me, easing most of my apprehension. He spoke softly and invited me to take a seat next to his large desk, and then we chatted whilst he filled in some forms. Once they were completed he asked me to lie down on the couch. 'Do you realize', he explained, 'that we can only use a small part of our brain at any one time? There is a vast potential that lies dormant, untapped.' I listened incredulous. My body became alert, my mind calm. This physical response was something I wished to increase in my life. As he continued talking to relax me, he said, 'Shut your eyes, just relax. No matter how relaxed you become, you're always in control. Now, I'm just going to count...'

Very quickly I deeply relaxed, feeling like a floating cloud in a blue sky on a sunny day. It was lovely. David was still talking when I felt my body involuntarily lurch. In that deeply relaxed state I felt an electric charge, a rush of replenishing energy surge into me. I was astonished; nothing like this had ever happened before. Being guided, I came out of the deeply relaxed state feeling stronger. 'You seem to be able to react to suggestion of relaxation rather well. That being the case, I'm going to give you some notes on technique to take home. Homework, if you like to call it that. You can practise more easily this way. Practise every day, use discipline.' Could I do it alone, I thought, while sensing he was more accustomed to clients wishing to give up smoking than those facing major life-threatening issues.

Over the next few weeks as I read, learned and practised those techniques, they slowly became easier. I could feel myself beginning to get a handle on my fear, telling myself in a deeply relaxed state how close fear feels to excitement. I instilled this in my mind, practising it over and over again. David only requested to see me once more before feeling confident that I could manage at home myself. I was beginning to feel empowered; my four- to five-hour early morning meditations in my healing room improved, though my mind still wandered, as is often the case. Instead of worrying about that and berating myself, I tried to gently bring myself back to my main focus, to breathe in nourishing, nurturing, healing breaths.

I told Simon how I was progressing. Sometimes I worried I wasn't doing very well, fearing failure. 'Just do your best.' Those words sobered me with the realization that I must again try to control my thoughts more and slow them down. I was beginning to understand how thoughts are energy, noticing that when I got wildly agitated and let my mind spiral out of control I felt exhausted afterwards. All my energy had been used up worrying. I remembered how when we'd visited a health clinic in California some years previously a Japanese girl had fastidiously been cleaning the reception area, completely immersed in her task. When I asked about this, she calmly replied, 'It is our belief here to keep the mind focused on what you are doing rather than letting it wander unchecked. By becoming absorbed by minute detail one enters a deeper quality of inner peace. Tranquillity is our inherent birthright, though we can lose sight of it along the way. I keep seeking it out by applying my own disciplines. This is a daily ritual for me. I do it prayerfully, and in this way, no matter what goes on in life, one is able to find peace within it.' I was humbled by her frankness, recalling my own earlier teachings. In my desperation I needed this reinforcing.

The phone was ringing incessantly these days with Simon working at home; it was irritating. Our previously little-used dining room was now taken over as his office. Files lay stacked on the floor all around the edge of the skirting boards. Papers lay strewn across the dining room table, a laptop stood open, ever ready. At times tensions ran high, making everyone in the house edgy. Like sponges we picked up on one another's stresses. In spite of asking Simon to work at home, I was finding it hard to adjust to it; one of the things I increasingly craved was peace and quiet.

'I'll shut the dining room door,' he said reasonably enough when I mentioned the noise, 'then you won't hear the phone when it rings.' The bedroom was quieter as a result. Nevertheless, outside noises such as from passing aircraft were annoyances. I learned to tune their sound out by acknowledging them and then redirecting my focus to sounds in the garden, the bedroom or my own breathing. Then the sounds of the aeroplanes lost their magnitude.

Every day I was resting, especially after lunch, giving myself hands-on healing and trying to keep calm. I also visualized myself doing cartwheels at the bottom of the garden, thus projecting healthy images through my mind to my body. Even though I wasn't very good at them, I had loved doing cartwheels in the garden as a child.

I was finding it increasingly hard to manage household chores and to walk Lucy, as I once had, together with my new disciplines. One day Simon said, 'You can't keep pretending life is the same. It isn't. How about phoning Lindy and asking for some help? I'm sure she'll walk Lucy for you.'

'I can't ask her,' I snapped.

'Why not?' he asked.

'Because she's busy.' The truth of the matter was I'd always considered myself the strong one. The one helping others. One of the hardest things I was confronting was asking for help myself.

However, I took Simon's advice after first mulling it over. As I dialled Lindy's number I felt awkward and stuttered over my words before hearing her say, 'I've been waiting for you to ask, longing to know what I can do to help.' With those words I felt all the tension drain from me. 'I'll be over tomorrow morning,' she said before hanging up. Lucy enjoyed many walks with Lindy's dog Harley, a Golden Labrador, over the next few months. They'd always socialized when Jack was alive and Lucy had been missing out.

Most days, for a short spell, I took Lucy out no matter what the weather; walking in nature acted as my saviour. I'd often lean against a particular fir tree hidden in a copse, cry my eyes out and slowly walk home feeling renewed at my innermost core. That tree became like a best friend.

Days later Simon answered another phone call. It was my brother-in-law Stuart, Joanna's husband and father of their young son, Ben.

Jane, my elder sister, was with Joanna when her breathing started to change. She realized that maybe the moment of her last few breaths had arrived and went to find the caring sister in charge. Jane had left Joanna's side at the very last moment or two, sensing Stuart may prefer privacy to be with his wife, though this action was deeply painful for Jane. Joanna's death occurred in these few moments, with Stuart by her side.

Unlike Jane, I couldn't have been there even in the last few moments of Joanna's life. My last memory of Joanna, as I had the privilege of saying goodbye, is of standing beside her bed. I couldn't tear myself away. Her eyes had fluttered open briefly. 'I love you,' I said.

Staring at me disbelievingly, she replied, 'Are you still here?'

On my way home from that final visit I was filled with admiration for Jane, remembering how as children she'd taught me so much. In spite of our four-year age difference, when disagreeing we expressed it through physical means. We didn't shy away from a fight. Where had that ability gone to now, I wondered years later? Back then, when sensing a fight, I went in prepared and donned a swimming cap. That protected my vulnerable point, my long hair. Jane had good fingernails, hers gouged flesh; I bit mine, but my hands turned into strong little fists. They didn't always reach their target, but I tried. Such spats were quickly interrupted by our horrified mother who, rather than tearing us apart, shouted at us to stop it immediately! Through those spats, I realized, Jane had taught me the gift of having a go, even though it went against my nature. We always made up afterwards, usually over a bag of sweets.

Stuart had remarried since Joanna's death, when Ben was four years old, and his new wife, Emma, had a three-year-old daughter called Holly from a previous marriage. Both Stuart and Emma were now on the end of the phone to see how I was and if we'd had the hospital results back.

'Yes, Gilly's got cancer,' said Simon. She and Stuart were stunned. In Simon's shocked state he hadn't managed to soften his reply, yet they were marvellous. Stuart arranged to come over virtually straight away and take Simon out for a drink to commiserate and offer support. Emma then spoke to me and asked what she could do.

'I'm struggling with cooking,' I replied.

'What do the boys enjoy eating?' came her response.

'Lasagne.'

'I'll make one and bring it over tomorrow.'

The following day, walking through the front door carrying the still-warm lasagne, Emma looked sadly into my eyes and reached out her spare arm to give me a hug. I leant against her. That hug released another layer of inbuilt unconscious tension. We both cried.

'Ben...' she said, 'we haven't told him yet.'

Since Joanna died, Ben had been a regular visitor to our home. He played with David in a similar way to how Joanna and I had once played as tomboys growing up on the farm. I wouldn't be able to have him to stay now, I thought. He felt like another son whenever he came over to our home. Unknown to me then, Emma and Stuart were worried about having to tell Ben that his favourite Aunty had cancer like his mother; they couldn't bear the thought that he might also lose me.

Death and dying still prayed on my mind and I looked out a book on the subject to see how I could best prepare myself for that eventuality. If I was going to die I wanted to die well, I reasoned, staring it in the face. No sooner was that book lying on the bed beside me than a steady flow of other books kept appearing, in the form of gifts through the post. Thoughtful though those gifts were, some contained too much medical information. That overwhelmed me; I didn't look at them again. Medical facts and statistics frightened me too much, especially ones from my oncologist concerning my worrying blood counts. I left those facts to Simon to remember. But there were plenty of books that inspired me, especially tales of cancer survivors. One spoke of fasting for a day, which I duly put to the test; I felt terrible and couldn't stop shaking. It was an experiment I wouldn't repeat. However, a book on self-reflexology that taught pain control, amongst other things, was much more of a success. Poetry and books of quotations uplifted me, both nourishing and nurturing me; they still do, especially before trying to sleep at night. Flowers sent with love brightened our hearts as well as our home. I was deeply moved by these caring gestures.

Cards came streaming through the letterbox as word spread; those cards were a potent tonic. The heartfelt words they contained wrapped themselves around me like hugs. Clare's was the first to arrive; it was a card with a silver star on the front. One was from my mentor Irene, the spiritual healer living down the road. She wrote: 'Gillian, there's a duality of nature in each of us. You have the choice to draw on the one that strengthens rather than weakens you.' Achieving that became a constant battle.

Simon rang Clare to tell her about Lucy's accident and asked her to come home for the weekend. Once home, Clare made a fuss of Lucy. It was time for Simon to update her. She knew something was up and that the test results had come through. She knew I had cancer. It was a painful time in all our lives, one of major readjustment.

Simon told Clare we had made our decision not to have conventional medicine. She felt angry at first, not understanding why I shouldn't have the best of both conventional and holistic medicine. Traumatized, Clare didn't realize that chemotherapy and radiotherapy could compromise the immune system. Why would she know? We hadn't had that conversation. I felt it was a choice only I could make. She struggled coming to terms with my decision and was surprised at the change she noticed in her father; he'd always remained quietly sceptical about holistic medicine. Over the weekend she quickly came to accept the news. She decided it was my body and a brave decision to take a different route. She admired that I was staking my life on what I believed in and was now practising. Simon spoke to her about stress being a factor as we reviewed every aspect of our lifestyle. I was focusing entirely on the family and myself, not others for a change, to preserve my energies and safeguard them, which wasn't easy. Whenever I did otherwise, I paid a high price and felt drained for days afterwards. That had a detrimental effect on the whole family.

Simon and David were the reserved ones in our family, whilst Clare and I shared a passionate and sometimes tempestuous mother–daughter relationship. If something was up we didn't shy away from it and arguments could be fiery before we made up. We both realized such stress levels were now harmful to my recovery, almost toxic. Somehow between us, with restraint on Clare's part as I was too weakened, we changed that aspect of our relationship.

By the end of November, it was time for another visit to see Professor Thomas for a progress check as well as blood tests. We were both prepared for the worst but were individually avoiding influencing the other with negative thoughts.

'You look well,' she commented, glancing down at my open file on her desk. She had been anticipating me looking jaundiced.

'Thank you. You've no idea how the power of your words makes a great difference,' I replied.

'How are you feeling?'

'I have off days. But I get up every day. That's important. I spend hours praying and meditating trying to quell my fear and anxiety.'

'You seem to be making progress,' she said, probing my abdomen and unintentionally causing me to wince at a tender spot. 'You'll be pleased to hear your mass has shrunk down a little more. I can now insert six finger widths from your diaphragm, which I was unable to do at your previous visit.' Returning to her desk she drew another diagram in my file, and before concluding our visit she said, 'I'd like to see you again in another six weeks' time so we can keep monitoring you with examinations and blood tests.'

Walking from her office I braced myself ready for the tumour marker blood tests, with Simon as usual coming in to hold my hand.

Following that appointment she sent the following letter to my gynaecologist:

I was very pleased to see Mrs Gill at the Guildford Nuffield Hospital again today. She is well and on examining her there are now six fingers' breadth between her xiphisternum and the top of her tumour. The tumour may be a little wider, but it is certainly no bigger than when I last saw her.

I have checked her tumour markers again today and will let her know the results. Clearly if these are falling then it would suggest that her healing and other alternative therapies are having some effect. I have explained to her that I want to keep an eye on her liver function tests, because obviously if these deteriorate then I might press a little more firmly on her to consider the conventional medicine option. That would be with the understanding that I would give her chemotherapy which is well tolerated to try to avoid all the side effects about which she is concerned.

Though the news was good, it didn't register. There was a long way to go yet. That thought kept me edgy. I was driven, holding on to my newly adopted daily regimes. They helped me cope better and my breathing was easier.

On nights when I couldn't sleep, so as not to disturb Simon, I wandered downstairs to the sitting room. There I'd lie on the sofa with the soft light of the moon spilling through the windows. On one occasion Clare, home on a visit, heard me and stood in the doorway. 'What are you doing?'

'I can't sleep,' I replied.

'I'll join you in that case,' she said, before returning with a quilt, my late grandmother's. She threw it over us as we chatted for hours, finally separating to find our own beds.

At other times when I was too ill to remain up for long, Clare would cook comforting scrambled eggs on brown toast. She placed the food on a tray, together with a pretty napkin and a small bunch of whatever she found in the garden in a vase. Then she proceeded to put the vase on the bedside table for me to savour; her thoughtful touches knew no bounds. Through my lifestyle changes I saw Clare with new eyes. I saw her strengths, determination and deep caring ways. I felt her love. She managed to continue her course at university and we encouraged that. In the meantime, when she was not at home, we kept in close contact. She had her own life, hopes and dreams. They were important, and life had to go on.

CHAPTER 5
Lifestyle Changes

There are some things in life
Only you can do.
So go ahead,
Do it to the best of your ability.
Don't look too far ahead.
Don't look back either.
Just keep going,
One step at a time,
Constantly refocusing on the positive aspects…
Gillian Gill

December 2000 – February 2001

'What is it?' Simon asked, as I jerked awake.

'Another nightmare.'

'What was it about?' he asked caringly.

'David. I dreamed about his accident when he was five years old.'

We'd been on holiday in Cornwall renting the usual cottage by the sea. It was a sunny day and we'd been shrimping. While boiling them ready for supper, when my back was turned, there'd been a terrible accident. Clare and David were standing on chairs looking into the pan. David, wanting to save the shrimps' lives, grabbed the pan's handle and both children fell off their chairs. Clare was unharmed physically, though she lived with the guilt

67

that it hadn't happened to her; she felt for her brother. David got the full force of the pan of boiling water all down his left side, particularly down his leg through his tracksuit. It could have been worse, he could have been wearing shorts...

Hearing screams, a fellow holidaymaker in the adjoining cottage came running; she was a nurse. 'Fill the bath with cold water. We must put him into it immediately,' she said. I'd instinctively already put the cold tap on in the bath. Looking at Clare she said, 'Go quickly to the chandlery shop and ask whoever's there to call an ambulance.' Clare ran as fast as her little nine-year-old legs could. Simon, returning from an outing to buy rice to make the paella, walked into the cottage shocked.

'The ambulance is here,' he said turning, directing the crew into the bathroom.

After a quick assessment, and seeing the flesh that had fallen from David's leg, they made an emergency call. 'We need the air ambulance immediately. We won't get around these twisting Cornish roads fast enough.'

The tide was coming in. A few moments later and it would have been impossible to land the rescue helicopter on the small beach at St. Anthony. 'You go with him,' Simon urged me, 'I'll follow in the car.'

David's eyes had glazed over, his face was going grey, he was clammy and was in a state of deep shock. The air ambulance crew were a different breed; angels, I thought in my distressed state. As the helicopter lifted perilously close above the dense oak trees, Simon, holding Clare's hand below, thought we were goners.

'You're going to be alright,' I heard one of the crew reassuring David, as he managed to find a vein in his foot to inject a painkiller; all others had disappeared. 'I think you deserve a bravery award,' he said, handing David a teddy bear.

After a couple of weeks, when stable enough, David was transferred closer to home by specialized ambulance from Derriford Hospital in Plymouth to a room in the burns unit at the Queen Victoria Hospital in East Grinstead. After a crucial two-week healing period, the consultants were dumbfounded when the bandages were removed. As David had suffered life-threatening burns, they'd prepared for extensive plastic surgery; but he didn't require any. He'd been receiving distant healing and prayers.

It took three years of daily care once home using pressure bandages and massage, together with regular distant healing prayers and a high-protein diet, before David was signed off by the hospital. This intense care forged a strong bond between us. Years later, against all medical expectations, the severely damaged hair follicles on his thigh regrew. He even went on to play rugby; another miracle in spite of the extensive burns damage to his knee. During his hospital treatment, he'd acquired a high ability to withstand intense pain. The medical team decided to take him off strong painkillers to stimulate his body's natural pain threshold. They knew what they were doing, being experts in pain control. As a mother standing by witnessing his agony, I'd been appalled, inconsolable and blamed myself for what had happened. But I learned to put trust in David's care and this, together with the compassionate nurses and the faith I had in the power of prayer, helped me through those terrible times.

Clare was staying with her best friend throughout this period and she was upset to have only been allowed to visit David once. We deemed the horrific sights on the adult burns unit too much for her; the children's unit was closed due to an outbreak of infection and was being sterilized. I spoke to her frequently on the phone as I remained in hospital sleeping on a mattress on the floor beside David's bed.

It was a fraught time, testing each of us differently. We coped as best we could in our own ways. Sometimes we struggled and didn't feel we did very well, but we never gave up trying. As a result of that horrific accident we became even closer as a family, finding ways to support one another. We all worked hard at pooling our strengths, rather than focusing on our weaknesses. In the process we found deeply hidden reserves of energy that we hadn't previously known we'd possessed.

'David's alright now,' Simon soothed me; my heart wouldn't stop thumping. 'David will cope with your diagnosis, in his own way, as he coped all those years ago. He's stronger than you think; Clare too. They both have a good network of supportive friends. We'll manage. Just try not to judge yourself harshly when you're feeling upset. Try telling yourself whatever you feel is okay; breathe into it. If the feeling becomes unbearable, think of Lucy or the children and their love for you.' I listened intently. 'I've read somewhere that such thought processes can be helpful.'

While striving to pay even greater attention to my thoughts, I made another appointment to see Marianne, my nutritionist. Simon drove me.

'Hello, Gillian and Simon, it's nice to see you again. Please sit down.' She indicated two chairs side by side next to her desk. 'Gillian, I'll just need to take some notes. Would you like a glass of water?'

'Yes, please.'

Handed the full glass I promptly spilled it. 'I'm so sorry, how clumsy,' I spluttered.

Simon reached for his handkerchief to start mopping up.

Marianne merely laughed and grabbed a handful of tissues to lend a hand. 'Have you by chance been doing much of that lately?' she asked knowingly.

'Yes, I have,' I replied, astonished by her question.

'It may interest you to know that when we repeatedly spill liquids it is a sign of an overload to our emotions. So please try not to worry.'

During the consultation I poured out so much to Marianne, sealing a bond of trust.

After we finished talking Marianne muscle-tested me with her kinesiology skills, explaining, 'This is done by pulling and pushing your arm for levels of resistance, to see if your body will co-operate and is receptive to my help… Yes, it is receptive; your body is asking for detoxification. I'll order you some clay and psyllium husk; that's seeds from an Indian plant used in Ayurvedic medicine for colon cleansing as well as to improve blood circulation. It will help cleanse your liver and pave the way for nutrients to be more readily absorbed by your body. It will arrive in the post together with instructions, which includes a specialized diet to accompany the programme. Please phone me if you have any queries.'

We left her mulling over what we were learning.

One evening after school, David saw me lying on the bedroom floor with my top lifted above the 'lump' and asked, 'Mummy, what are you doing?'

'I'm showing Daddy how my tummy seems smaller. There appears to be less bloating and fluid. You did encourage me to try to achieve Jack's results.'

'Yes, I can see it's better than it was,' he said. 'You've got to keep at it. We want to go on a family holiday.'

His words hit home. Keep at it. The book someone had kindly sent me on reflexology was having an impact. I was definitely noticing a decrease in my cancerous abdominal fluids as I constantly went to the loo, though sometimes when working on various pressure points on my feet I over-zealously bruised myself in the process. The pressure point that helps alleviate overloaded emotions, frequently felt in the solar plexus and diaphragm region, is found at the base of the middle finger. By firmly holding this tender point with the thumb and middle finger of the opposite hand while inhaling and holding the breath for a count of three, then releasing for three, relief follows. Repeating this several times helps, and I used this practice regularly.

One morning the postman delivered a large parcel. It contained the pots of clay and psyllium husk that Marianne had ordered. Such parcels were to become a regular feature in our lives. I struggled with the gloopy texture of the husk when mixed with water, and thought it peculiar to be drinking a glass of water mixed with clay, but the directions were simple enough to follow.

Simon rang Clare for a chat, telling her our good news, and then put her on to me.

'How is your course going?'

'Good, thanks, and you'll be interested to know there's a module on Shamanism covering the ancient art of healing coming up later. I'm enjoying the English course too.'

Before we knew it Christmas was fast approaching. I had difficulty with ideas for Christmas gifts but wrote all the cards.

I'd also tried to remember, with the aid of a birthday book, to send birthday cards to family and friends. Writing those made me feel normal for brief interludes.

We all joined in dressing the house festively. Usually I loved nothing more than dressing the house for Christmas by myself, even though it required effort; it never failed to thrill me.

David went to the attic to bring the decorations down. I tied the familiar silver-sprayed beech branches onto the hallway banisters. Clare helped me string white fairy lights on them, and then we hung small gold decorations. One morning I noticed a spider had spun a perfect web between the beech branches. The web enveloped an ornamental glass angel and on seeing that I unconsciously found tears trickling down my cheeks. Previously I'd have dusted that cobweb away; now it struck me as the most beautiful Christmas decoration I'd ever seen.

However, by the morning of Christmas Eve I could hardly breathe. What was happening to me, I wondered? Simon walked into the bedroom, took one look at me and said, 'I'm calling the doctor.'

'Please don't,' I whispered; I couldn't bear making a fuss, worrying what the children might think if they saw a doctor coming into the house.

'I insist. You look absolutely terrible.'

As he phoned for the doctor I tried to find a comfortable position in bed but couldn't. My body was riddled with excruciating pain, particularly all down my right side, the site of my ovarian lump. Lying there I kept repeating to myself, 'I breathe out pain. I breathe in relief.'

My GP walked into our bedroom, her small black doctor's bag in her hand. 'Hello, Gillian. I hear you're not feeling very well. Let's take a look at you. Stick your tongue out, will you?' She peered down my throat. 'Let's see your eyes. Would you look away?' she said, shining a blinding little torch into my eyes. 'I'll just take your blood pressure... Hmm, that's low, but not abnormal.'

'Can you give me some painkillers?' I whimpered.

'I'm sorry to say there is nothing in my little bag that will alleviate the level of pain you're in.' Looking grave, she walked out of the room and closed the door while speaking to Simon in hushed tones.

In desperation I reached for a teddy bear, a gift. Hugging it tightly and closing my eyes, I prayed with all my might, inviting help for pain relief and control. I heard the bedroom door open, squinting one half-eye open, and saw no one there. Perplexed, I felt a sharp prick in my left arm, as though a needle pierced my vein. It hurt, and I flinched at the sting before sensing a benign presence fill the room. Suddenly I felt drowsy, as though I'd been given an anaesthetic; I was floating.

The next thing I knew I was waking up. Opening my eyes I saw a large puff of blue light, which vanished in an instant. Looking at Simon's bedside clock I noticed I had slept solidly for five hours, the most sleep I'd had in one stretch for months. When fully awake I realized the pain had mysteriously vanished, and I felt deeply relaxed. Then I said a prayer of gratitude.

With the children home for the festive season, I couldn't help but think back to past Christmases. They'd involved hard work and been characterised by mounting excitement, and often tension when undercurrents burst through from visiting relatives. This Christmas had its different tensions but was strangely peaceful at times with just the four of us, five counting Lucy. With a heavy heart I again had to recognize my limitations; to do otherwise would be over-tiring and unwise with my fragile health, as well as making me short-tempered, which was unpleasant for everyone. Clare and David helped; together with Simon they'd done most of the Christmas shopping.

On Christmas morning we spoke to family and friends on the telephone instead of seeing them. Then we worked closely together, preparing and cooking a traditional Christmas meal. I ignored the mess, realizing I couldn't clear up as I went along as was customary as things were different now. While lunch was cooking in the kitchen we wandered through to sit, as we always did, in front of a blazing log fire, where Lucy lay curled up fast asleep. Simon, according to tradition, handed gifts around. Looking at everyone, I suddenly remembered something that David's nursery teacher had taught the children. She told them, 'The best gifts in life are invariably the ones you can't wrap up.'

There were sad moments that Christmas, not least because Jack wasn't lying by the hearth with Lucy. Then David handed me a present. Looking at the label my heart did a somersault. It read, 'All my love from Jack.' I felt my eyes sting as I re-read David's handwriting. A knowing smile passed between him, Clare and Simon. I felt my heart swell as we all remembered the love we'd felt for Jack. We'd always given one another gifts signed from the dogs, as well as giving gifts to the dogs themselves.

The juicing machine that Simon had investigated and bought, in the belief the raw juices would help me, proved invaluable. The whole family enjoyed fresh juices. I was by this time accustomed to juicing an entire pineapple for breakfast; my body hungered for it. The children couldn't believe the precision required in keeping the machine clean. Taking it apart and meticulously washing it became a routine, sometimes twice a day. It was time-consuming, but that was by now part of my daily pattern. It was becoming one of the disciplines that helped focus my attention away from my emotions.

'It looks funny', said David, 'watching the fibre from the pineapple coiling like a sausage out of that end.' He pointed at the fibre falling into a bowl beneath one end of the machine. Lucy learned to enjoy eating some of that fibre; the rest went into the compost. Interestingly I noticed the children didn't get the usual colds that winter.

On Boxing Day Natasha and her husband Lawrence dropped in briefly on their way past. Natasha and I went and sat in the kitchen to have a heart-to-heart, while Lawrence joined the rest of the family in the sitting room, where a fire burned in the hearth. The smoke from the fire mingled with the scent of pine from the Christmas tree.

In the kitchen I didn't hold back: 'I have such demons rearing up at times, over my decision, the long-term outcome and the effects of my choice on the family.'

'It's no wonder, with your nature and level of anxiety. But by staring your demons in the face you're absorbing them; this is how you are managing.

With your newly adopted lifestyle and regime it keeps you focused, otherwise you couldn't cope, and you do look incredibly well.'

'That's all the lifestyle changes and the water I'm drinking,' I replied.

'Your hair looks glossy,' she said. It was also dropping out far less, I'd noticed.

Speaking to Natasha about my fears and insecurities, paranoia and hopes helped me offload. She simply reassured me, no matter what I was feeling or thinking. She understood, rather than trying to fix or judge, and was a constant source of comfort in the early days, believing in all I was doing. Our listening skills and support of one another had always been the basis of our friendship, before and after her professional training.

After our friends left Clare said, 'I couldn't sleep last night.'

'Why not?' I asked.

'I kept hearing strange sounds.'

'Are you sure it wasn't the water pipes?'

'No, it was coming from the computer area in the adjacent room,' she said, looking mystified.

Simon checked the computer area and couldn't see anything wrong. I quietly wondered if it weren't her mother's spirit trying to send her a comforting sign, remembering how when Clare was about three years old I'd often heard her having conversations and laughing in the wee hours. On those occasions I'd tiptoe downstairs to her room, which was below ours, and peek around the door. No one was ever there. Yet she'd appeared animated, kneeling on top of the end of her bed as though she was talking to someone. Many young children have sharper senses; they have the ability to see and hear things which most adults don't.

For the next few nights Clare continued being awoken by a strange rustling sound and stole out of bed trying to get closer to the source. She located it in the computer printer. Not wanting to disturb us, she waited until the following morning. Lucy was sleeping on Clare's bed at this time, sometimes almost pushing Clare out as she snuggled down into the duvet alongside Clare for maximum comfort.

'Daddy, I think I've found the source of the noise,' she said.

Simon went to investigate. On opening the machine up he exclaimed, 'It's a mouse, and one with a taste for chocolate! You know those Christmas chocolates you were given? Well the mouse has eaten several, come and look.' Peering inside we saw that the printer was filled with colourful chocolate wrappers.

In the following weeks, Simon's research knew no bounds. He'd read about an American Indian herbal medicine called Essiac, which is reputed to help with certain cancers. He learned that a fresh brew was necessary to get the best out of the herbs, and overnight he became a herbal pharmacist. Or rather a dawn one, as he arose before the working day began and then turned the kitchen into a laboratory. That was challenging, as the kitchen had previously been my sole domain. Brown bottles now lined the worktops, stainless steel pans and sieves took over the stove. Glass jugs stood at the ready next to a funnel and yet more small brown bottles waited to receive the elixir.

'Are you sure this is good for you?' I grimaced at the first disgusting taste.

'Yes,' replied Simon before proceeding to tell me all he knew about it.

When I next saw Irene for a routine visit and healing she took another photo of my ever-changing abdomen when I was lying down, having suggested it would be a good idea to keep a photographic record.

'You've got to keep at it, learning to tame the tiger, that's what I call this,' she said pointing at my abdomen.

Soon it was late January and I was due for another appointment to see Professor Thomas. She wrote the following letter to my gynaecologist:

I saw Mrs Gill again recently at the Guildford Nuffield Hospital. She looks extremely well and I had a very long and detailed talk about all the different techniques which she is using to deal with her disease.

I have to let the facts speak for themselves and she showed me a series of photographs dating back to when I first saw her. These clearly show a progressive reduction in the size of her abdominal mass. In October I could sneak four fingers between her ribs and the top of the mass. This had increased to six fingers by

22nd November, and today I could actually insert nine fingers in the space. There was some firmness in the epigastrium medially, and I wondered whether this was her liver metastasis. I explained this to Mrs Gill and she felt that this was useful information, as it would help her to 'work on' the area.

In essence I have a patient who is known to have advanced cancer (although we do not have a biopsy) who is using a whole range of different methods herself to deal with her tumour. I have not closed the door to chemotherapy, and have also explained that it may well be possible for us to give a form of chemotherapy that would be well tolerated and lacking in the side effects which she dreads, such as alopecia and sickness. She admits that she is always sensitive to drugs, no matter what their type, but I have reassured her that this does not always follow when it comes to chemotherapy.

Mrs Gill's liver function tests are essentially normal. I have not yet seen her tumour markers. Although these had risen before, she is happy to be guided by me. I have said that if her liver function were to deteriorate at any stage I may well advise her to think about conventional treatment, at least as an adjunct to the other methods she is using. I think she still has an open mind to this and I look forward to seeing her again for our regular six-weekly appointment.

During the usual blood tests, I asked the nurse if she had a smaller needle that would more easily pierce a deeply hidden vein.

'I'll use the butterfly needle,' she replied.

Clare knew the butterfly acted as a talisman and symbol of transformation for me, as the chrysalis's metamorphosis gradually turned it into a butterfly. She occasionally sent me pretty cards of them, to encourage me to keep going. So I replied, 'Yes, please,' to the nurse and hardly felt a thing as she successfully drew enough blood to fill several small bottles for testing.

Simon drove us home, mulling over what we'd heard. It was good. But I still worried; was it good enough?

'It is good news,' Simon reassured me. Though it was hard to process, and in spite of the evidence, somehow I couldn't manage to accept that it was a positive change.

'I think it's time to see someone else. An expert in the field of holistic medicine,' said Simon. 'Do you remember you mentioned Dr Rosy Daniel ages ago?' She is the former medical director of what was previously known as the Bristol Cancer Help Centre, now the Penny Brohn Cancer Centre.

'Yes, but I'm not sure.'

'You've been reluctant for a while now. I really think the time has come to make your mind up.' Taking a deep breath I replied, 'You're right. We should try and see her. Can you remember anything else about her? I seem to have forgotten.'

Simon explained, 'Dr Daniel has the knowledge and expertise of both conventional and holistic medicine. That embraces all spiritual aspects.'

'Then I'd like definitely like to see her,' I continued. 'I have an insatiable, insecure appetite gnawing away at me. No matter what I do, I feel I should be doing more.'

'It's understandable. You want to get well. We'll make an appointment.' We fell into companionable silence as I drifted off into my own world.

The following morning I awoke, stood up and felt dizzy, almost fainting, and sat back on the bed.

'What's the matter?' asked Simon concerned.

'I feel faint for no reason at all.'

'Do you remember the doctor told you your blood pressure is low?'

'Did she?' I asked bemused.

'Yes, you're just one of those people, so why not sit there for a moment and give your body a chance to adjust from lying down to sitting up before standing?' I breathed deeply and gradually began to feel better. It wasn't anything sinister I realized, relieved.

From then on I reintroduced a ten-minute gentle yoga practice after early morning meditation. I stood in front of the bedroom window overlooking the garden while practising deep breathing, gently rolling my shoulders and then stretching my arms. Next, I'd roll my eyeballs around in their sockets, before sticking my tongue out as far as it would go. I repeated all these actions seven times, while focusing on my breathing. Then I sat or lay down for five minutes for the movement to assimilate, while imagining myself somewhere peaceful.

A dear Nigerian friend, Eli, a doctor and healer, had reminded me of the value of such disciplines to focus and harmonize the body and mind. Years previously when working in London I'd regularly attended a yoga class; somewhere along the line I'd let it slip.

Both Simon and I were filled with mixed feelings as we boarded a train for London. We had an appointment to see Dr Rosy Daniel. I'd prepared myself as best I could for the day ahead by focusing all my energies into sustaining me for the trip. When we finally arrived at her practice, having first got confused and lost, we waited in the comfortable waiting room. Next, we were led to her consulting room, where as soon as we walked in we were hit by her positive energy and sense of purpose and felt reassured in our decision to come. Radiance shone out of her sparkling dark brown eyes and she smiled widely as she greeted us, hugging us each in turn. I noticed her lustrous, curly auburn hair.

'Please take a seat, Gillian, Simon,' she said indicating two seats opposite her large wooden desk. I'd already noticed a curtain concealing an examination couch.

'Gillian, please tell me your history,' she quietly asked before sitting back in her chair.

I told her, 'I'm meditating between five and six hours at the start of the day, as I'm not sleeping very well.'

'That's an exceptional level of meditation,' she replied surprised.

'I've never done it to this extent before, but it's the only thing that helps me. I'm also taking Essiac.'

'Yes, I know of those herbs,' she replied, and then I just couldn't stop talking. Looking into her compassionate eyes drew out so much that I went way beyond recounting the events of the past six months; I spoke of the ups and downs in our marriage throughout the years, my childhood and more. She had a unique ability to not only listen but also to restore confidence and make me feel put back together again.

Dr Daniel discussed simplifying lifestyle, nutrition and diet. 'There's a link between diet and lifestyle. It's proven that sugar, certain refined and processed foods and an unhealthy lifestyle are detrimental to people suffering with cancer, as is stress. Research and statistics in this field back this up. Caffeine should be avoided along with all sugary drinks.'

My heart sank at the thought of all the dietary changes I would have to make. I'd miss my cups of tea. Strangely enough, though, every time I made a cup of coffee lately, for some reason it never reached my lips. By repeatedly spilling the cups of coffee, I sensed my body was trying to tell me something and I had given up drinking it. 'I am currently seeing a nutritionist,' I said.

'Good. Tell me about what you're doing.'

'Marianne, my nutritionist, put me on a detoxifying programme to purify and cleanse my system, which includes excluding salt from my diet. The detoxifying process has been tiring and has laid me low at times.'

'What about vomiting?'

'Yes, I'm regularly sick.'

'That will be the build-up of toxicity. You may find sipping freshly grated ginger in hot water helps against nausea.'

'Thank you,' I said before adding, 'I've read that garlic acts as a first line of defence against disease.'

'It's good to eat plenty of garlic in your cooking,' she encouraged. I remembered how unpleasant the odour from that was for Simon, especially as I was eating it in greater quantity.

'You need to eat sufficient protein,' she added.

Simon took everything in, remembering the minute details. Dr Daniel continued, 'As far as relationships with others are concerned, seek out loving ones; rage and anger only cause toxicity. Love is the finest medicine of all.'

'There's one more thing,' I said. 'I'm having nightmares. A residue of them remains in the day by way of my feeling I'm being chased by an inescapable monster.'

She said gently, 'In effect, you are.'

With startling clarity I recalled how as a child aged around seven I'd walked into my parents' bedroom, expecting them to be up, only to find them both still in bed. They were feverish with a nasty gastric bug. My mother asked me to go and tell one of the farm workers to phone for the doctor.

I thought they were going to die, they looked so listless and ill. In that moment I was paralysed by my fear of losing them, but found my legs carrying me automatically down the stairs, remembering my mother's urgent words. I ran down them two at a time, rushed out of the house and up the farmyard, and in doing so found a courage that hadn't been there. With hindsight I realize there's always been a part of me that feels like a twin sister, stepping in when I've most needed it. This part is non-thinking, purely reactive.

We listened to Dr Daniel before she invited, 'May I examine you now?'

'Yes,' I replied, as she guided me towards the examination couch.

When we reappeared to join Simon, she said, 'What incredible progress you're making. Let me get a sheet of paper and draw a diagram detailing all of the methods linking mind, body and spirit that I suggest.' With that she proceeded to draw a pie chart.

'You are already doing so much for yourself, but there is one thing I'd like to draw your attention to and it's visualization. Simply put, that's mind energy that can be directed to the body.'

'Can you please explain?' I asked.

'By all means. I have a client also using conventional medicine who for years has imagined she's lying on a sandy beach on a sunny day. Then she imagines her tumour like an iceberg melting. Over the years her tumour has shrunk dramatically and she still enjoys a good quality of life.' I nodded earnestly as she continued speaking. 'Instruct your brain to replace your outgoing diseased, dead blood cells with healthy, vibrant new ones and see this happening.'

'Thank you, I'll try that.'

'You said you have discomfort and swelling beneath your armpits?'

'Yes.'

'That's quite possibly your lymph glands filled with toxicity. You have lymph glands sited around your body.' She told us their function:

elimination of toxins from the body. 'Try to imagine the excess toxicity being gently siphoned off.'

Before she finished speaking I had a clear mental picture. I remembered one of the biology classes at school when I was around seven years old. I'd been fascinated by those classes. A teacher had shown me how to suck one end of a small rubber hose, with the other being immersed in the unclean fish tank, which contained pond life. I'd sucked too hard once and choked on dirty pond water; what I should have done was suck just enough to draw the dirty water and then let it syphon into a waste bucket held at the correct level. From that mistake I'd been sick during the night, but my body knew best how to rebalance itself; all I had to do was follow its rhythm.

Dr Daniel concluded, 'When you get home, continue with your disciplines, adding visualization. Remember, your body knows how to heal itself.'

She then looked at Simon, saying, 'Simon what are you doing to support yourself as Gillian's carer? That role is so important, and needs nurturing too.'

'I'm not doing anything in particular. What do you suggest?' he asked surprised.

They discussed various options, then Dr Daniel said, 'Exercise is a great stress buster.'

'I enjoy walking and cycling,' Simon responded.

'More than that, listening to your history, there is a therapy called the Bowen technique. It's a physical, gentle and non-invasive method that releases trauma and stress.'

'That sounds appropriate,' Simon said pensively.

'The technique allows the body to process emotions at many levels through physical light rolling touches. It's a bit like spring cleaning, clearing out debris to make way for the new. It can bring in fresh vitality, be invigorating. Remember, it is a process and will require time. That goes for both of you,' she concluded.

We stood up to leave. She reached out, hugging us both warmly. Her touch, the human element, made such a difference to us.

We left her office feeling uplifted. Dr Daniel has an amazing way of restoring people, infusing them with her infectious charisma. We both felt better for being in her company and I felt surer of what I was doing. Her approach varied from most of the medical professionals that I had experienced, though I've come to understand it must be difficult for many doctors and consultants to have a caring bedside manner, whether due to heavy workloads, time constraints or, in some cases, as a form of defence to prevent getting too close to a patient with limited chances. However, this can have a strong effect on the outcome. Being listened to and supported deepens belief, giving rise to hope and increased determination, and has major health benefits. But by the nature of their jobs they know not everyone will survive. If doctors became overly involved with patients, how would they feel at the end of the day? How would they go home to their own lives, or relax?

During the train journey home I drifted off, my head lolling on Simon's shoulder. I had a curiously vivid dream of the legendary figure King Arthur. He was standing in his shining armour, holding a magnificent sword. He extended it to me. I felt a surge of positive energy and heard the words 'This is for you, it is the sword of courage'. From then on before going to sleep at night I'd conjure up that image, inviting protection in the hope it would help during the nightmares. I reflected on the power of the unconscious mind.

At Dr Daniel's suggestion, over the next few days Simon, through a contact of ours at a local health clinic, found a Bowen technique practitioner also working there. Making an appointment he set off with an open mind. When he returned I asked, 'How did you get on?'

'It was very interesting, gentle and I did wonder if anything happened, as my therapist kept leaving the room in between treating me by pressing certain areas of my body. She told me this technique sends healing to where the body most needs it.' That night Simon was extremely sick.

'I feel as though I've let go of something. It's indefinable but I know I've had a positive reaction to the treatment,' he told me the following morning.

When booking another appointment, he asked about his reaction and was reassured it was a good sign and perfectly normal. Another couple of visits later and he got a high temperature. That was another positive release.

'You do look better,' I said, noticing how he seemed to be coping well in spite of everything.

My old back injury was constantly resurfacing; it was painful and at times making it difficult to walk. Mentioning it to Simon he said, 'Why not make an appointment to see your old cranial osteopath? That always used to help when your hip and back were playing up. I'll drive you.'

Years previously, in my late teens, I'd worked in Newmarket for the racehorse trainer Luca Cumani. I worked in the office and also helped exercise the racehorses on the early morning gallops, as I loved riding. On one occasion I had a bad fall, resulting in a nasty neck fracture and damaging my lower back. Luckily, with time I'd recovered, but still got the occasional persistent reminder.

Morag, my cranial osteopath, listened sympathetically, and told me that her brother-in-law, with newborn twins, was currently undergoing chemotherapy for his cancer. She was interested and listened carefully to my own approach to the illness before inviting me to lie on the couch.

'Your back is out of alignment and will be affecting your digestion, as the nerves feeding your stomach are compromised.' With that she gently placed her hands beneath my spine, encouraging my body to readjust itself. To relax me, she talked about her grandmother's parrot going bald and how it flew around the living room of her home in Scotland, or perched on the back of one of the upright chairs, when not in its aviary.

Afterwards she advised, 'Please come and see me next week, so I can check how you're getting on. Thereafter, visit when you need to, and I'll do my best to support your body with that large mass which is responsible for pulling your body out of alignment.' I thanked her and, feeling tired, went home to rest.

Many things were changing in our lives due to the force of circumstances. Simon and David's relationship deepened, developing a passion for the outdoors. They discovered how off-road cycling, in the heart of nature, helped provide an outlet for their intense emotions. They often looked pale and drained before setting off on their bikes, and always returned looking replenished, though sometimes tired.

Having forged a codependent bond with David after his accident, I felt left out at times, but knew this was my issue to deal with. I was ashamed of my jealous feelings, but at the same time was happy to see the love they shared for one another deepening, along with their passion for the outdoors when exercising, and realized my feelings stemmed from the sibling rivalry I experienced throughout my childhood. Though I recognized I could alter my behaviour, behavioural responses are only one aspect of the whole person. I was learning ways of confronting such issues when they surfaced; by feeling them and accepting them, they lost their intensity.

At times it was draining, but with my lifestyle changes I was increasingly spending time alone and learning to cope anew. How had I previously managed when I hadn't put so much effort into thinking so intensely about my actions? I'd done the best I could with how I was at that time.

With the elimination of so much from my old lifestyle, I welcomed the new support and human contact with those helping me. The caring, human touch made such a difference, as did their expansive listening skills.

My taste suddenly returned with greater sensitivity; I tasted saltiness in vegetables that I hadn't previously noticed. My mind was more alert too, my body less sluggish; the new diet was benefiting me.

We were struggling to adapt to the new daily regimes and juggling everything in our lives when our friends Susi and Ed, whom we had met through Clare's nursery school, unexpectedly offered their help.

'We'd like to do the morning school run,' they insisted. Not to be deterred, even though their children were beyond school age, Susi arrived promptly each morning at 7.30 to collect David. He was shy to start with but Susi, naturally outgoing, chatted throughout the entire car journey, putting him at ease.

Simon still collected David most evenings, but one evening they were late home. I was resting on the sofa with Lucy lying asleep beside me on the floor, keeping one hand on her shoulder and feeling her warmth. Her tail kept twitching and her paws were running. She was dreaming. It was getting darker and, feeling particularly low and tired, I hadn't bothered to put the lights on or draw the curtains. 'Where were the boys?' I mused, beginning to worry.

I must have drifted off as the next thing I knew Simon was in the house saying, 'Something peculiar is going on. Why are our chainsaw and garden strimmer lying beneath a hedge, halfway up the drive?'

Groggily I replied, 'I've no idea.'

'Dad,' panted David, running into the room and glancing at me before continuing, 'I've got the curry takeaway for supper so Mum doesn't have to cook. I noticed there's a strange large white van with the engine running parked halfway up the drive.'

'I'll go and see what's going on,' said Simon unwaveringly.

'I'm coming too,' said David, putting the curry down and hastening after him.

Simon was the first to notice a movement in the dense undergrowth. 'What are you doing?' he asked a youth hiding there, as David caught up with him, standing shoulder to shoulder.

'Got lost,' he stammered, hastily stowing what looked like a hammer into his inside coat pocket.

'Where are you trying to go to?' Simon asked.

'Don't worry,' the boy said, sprinting off up the drive and heading towards the white van.

I heard the doorbell ring.

'We've just had our shed broken into,' said an angry neighbour, 'and some of our garden equipment's gone. The car's also been broken into and the radio has been stolen.'

Simon ran outside to see the lock of our shed had been jemmied open. He ran up the drive, relieved to find that at least his prized chainsaw was still lying where it had been.

'I'll phone the police,' said Simon when he returned.

A policeman arrived to take a statement, accompanied by a younger colleague. After completing the statement, he looked up saying, 'It's always wise not to incite situations like this, Sir.'

I asked, 'What is the best form of deterrent?'

'A dog, preferably one that barks.'

'Lucy doesn't bark,' I replied.

'You want another dog; one with big ears that picks up the least noise such as a leaf falling.'

After they left we all felt shaken.

'It's just as well you didn't hear anything unusual, or you'd have gone out to investigate,' said Simon.

'In your state, that wouldn't have done you any good, Mum,' added David.

That incident made us more alert. Simon went shopping and bought stronger padlocks and chains to secure the outside shed. He felt we couldn't consider the idea of another dog with so many uncertainties in our lives. We were barely managing as it was. I was still being sick much of the time and felt weakened as a result. Following that incident, Simon brought his and David's bicycles into the house, finding a space in the computer room, formerly a stable. The bikes were the boys' pride and joy, their means of escape. The outdoors beckoned us all in different ways. For Clare and me it was dog walking.

Another visit to my nutritionist was due. Marianne was pleased with my detoxifying progress and introduced some new mineral supplements to support my body. She also told me that when suffering chronic pain as a result of trapped wind either drinking peppermint tea or taking peppermint oil capsules would help disperse it.

It was May and spring was unfolding. I often awoke to the joyous sound of geese honking as they flew overhead. In the evening, ducks flew low over the garden calling to one another, searching for a place to sleep.

My birthday was due following our next appointment to see my oncologist. To ease the time before I was due at the hospital, I sat on the closed loo seat lid. Armed with a tube of liquid cement and a palette knife,

I repaired the loose loo roll holder that had been annoying me for months. That way the morning just went by unnoticed.

The following is the letter my oncologist, Professor Thomas, sent my gynaecologist after that appointment:

I saw Mrs Gill at the Guildford Nuffield Hospital on 9th May. She remains very well and her weight is going up. I was due to see her a couple of months ago, but she cancelled the appointment due to another engagement. On examining her today there are now nine fingers' breadth between her epigastrium and the large pelvic mass, but there has been no real change since January. I have checked her bloods again today and will contact her as soon as the results are through. We do have a pattern of rising markers, but in the presence of a very well patient with disease which is likely to be suitable for palliative therapy, I feel it is not appropriate for me to put pressure on her to have chemotherapy at this stage. I do hope, however, that over time I will win her confidence and persuade her that chemotherapy which does not cause severe side effects would be reasonable.

My relief at seeing Dr Daniel again the following week for my next appointment redoubled. This time we went straight to the correct address. During the train journey I reflected on my birthday. It had been celebrated quietly at home with the whole family. Clare had come home specially. At dusk we went for a walk up the driveway with Lucy. Her paw was completely healed now from when I'd run her over. The fresh green leaves on the trees danced in a breeze and we heard woodpeckers tapping on the branches.

'Look,' said Clare and David together, pointing. Ahead, up the drive, three baby owls perched on three consecutive fence posts. Joanna, I thought, she'd have loved that, and she had had a particularly soft spot for Clare. Joanna had told me she loved those sights, as she increasingly stayed with us towards the end of her life. That thought stirred something in me, believing the three owls were her way of wishing me a Happy Birthday.

'Hello,' said Dr Daniel. 'Before I go any further, I'd like you both to call me Rosy. How are you, Gillian?' she asked sweetly, giving me a hug.

'I don't feel as though I'm struggling as much as I was. You're helping me come to terms with all I'm endeavouring to do. I can feel a glimmer of control returning in my life by using visualization techniques.'

Smiling, she turned to Simon, asking 'What about you?'

He told her about his progress with the Bowen technique. Then I mentioned my recent results from Professor Thomas. She listened intently before Simon asked, 'Is there anything else you can tell us about that may help Gillian?'

She mentioned one or two things then my ears pricked up as she said, 'There is an Ayurvedic herbal medicine called Carctol. A wonderful lady living here, called Yashu Amlani, brought it to my attention. Her fellow countryman Dr Tiwari impressed her very much when she visited him in India. I too have visited him, accompanied by Yashu. I learned how a large number of cancer patients who hadn't responded well to conventional medicine, and had all but given up hope of getting well, consulted him. He prescribed Carctol. The percentage of people where health then improved was significantly high. The worst-case scenario was that there was no change for the worse in those who didn't respond.'

That resonated with me. So many people who had previously found their way to me as a healer often arrived as a last resort having tried all else.

'How many people are you prescribing Carctol to at present?' I asked.

'Five or six,' came her answer. I listened, flinched at the low numbers, remembering how Joanna too had been a guinea pig with conventional medicine. Then I felt a quickening response; in spite of my logical apprehension, something else in me was calling out to be heard, my intuition.

'Please tell me more about Carctol.'

'If you decide on Carctol you must first come off Essiac, otherwise you will have contra-reactions. They're incompatible. There's one pre-requisite that accompanies taking Carctol and it's this: you need to adhere to a strict alkaline, vegetarian diet, as well as drinking two to three litres of water a day. The principle of this regime is that the diet is entirely alkaline, and cancer doesn't thrive in this environment. As yet there aren't millions of pounds for research in this country, but let me assure you, from the tests we know of, not one mouse has died in trials with Carctol.' It would appear that the tests hadn't reported a negative effect.

This was important to me because what Rosy didn't know was that as a child I'd had a pet mouse, an albino called Whiskers. Whiskers was the love of my life. I'd been fascinated by her pink eyes and long twitching whiskers when she washed. We spent many happy hours together in the garden shed on the farm. She lived there in a cage with a wheel to play on and a cosy nest to sleep in. My father didn't want her living under our roof; what he didn't know was when it got very cold in the winter I brought her cage into the house and put her in a little-used back room, next to the cellar where newts and salamanders roamed in the spooky, dark dampness.

Suddenly, I found myself saying, 'Yes, I'd like to give Carctol a try.'

No sooner were the words out of my mouth than I remembered Whiskers had cancer herself. She'd had a large purple lump on her right side. I was sad when she died, and I buried her in one of my favourite spots in the garden beneath a willow tree at the edge of the pond, formerly a disused brick pit.

I heard Rosy saying, 'The diet also excludes all dairy products.'

Bother! I thought, as I enjoyed cheese, especially on toast with tomato sauce. This was a childhood favourite, one we'd often had for a light supper on Sunday evening after a full roast for lunch.

'And, of course, no meat, fish or fowl.' That was something I'd been adjusting to with difficulty already. She repeated the exclusion of cakes, chips, crisps, no processed sugars or carbohydrates, so that ruled out another favourite: fresh white bread with homemade jam. No condiments or preserves were permitted and no salt. Even the bitter, dark type of chocolate that's supposed to be good for you was included under the banned chocolate heading.

Never mind, I thought, feelings plummeting, if my life depended on it, it was worth a try. I would just have to accept it and learn how to cook tasty, interesting dishes from the things I was allowed. I'm one of those people who live to eat. I was taught to cook by my mother at an early age and have had a passion for it ever since, though this new list of limited ingredients would certainly present a challenge.

'Alcohol is also forbidden.' That didn't bother me too much as I'd never been able to drink. Even a small amount made me giggly or sleepy. However, Simon, following in his father's footsteps, is something of a wine connoisseur, and I did enjoy the occasional small glass of some of his choices. But that would have to go.

Rosy continued, 'Smoking is not to be recommended.' No problem there; I'd managed to give that up after marrying, remembering how I'd had a terrible chest pain when I did smoke. I'd only taken it up to keep up with others and to calm my nerves. The banned list seemed endless.

'Tomatoes are acidic and should also be avoided. Most fruits need to be avoided.' My heart sank. Although my body was weary, my mind was strong, focusing on new goals as I paid attention. That particular year we had many tomato plants growing in the greenhouse. They were a summer seasonal favourite. The mere smell of leaves crushed when tending the plants sent me into raptures. Tomatoes are a wonderful base for many cooked dishes. I thought I'd share them with the neighbours; the peaches too, as the tree was already showing a promising harvest. I'd have to skip jam making this year.

I had a fresh sinking feeling, daunted by the realization that I was now responsible for putting a more challenging degree of effort into improving my health and well-being. We thanked Rosy for all her support and information and left her office with a prescription for Carctol.

'I'm glad Rosy is helping you,' said Simon. 'She's like a conductor of an orchestra, coordinating your holistic medicine and monitoring your progress, ensuring you're on a safe path.'

Crossing the road I overhead someone say, 'Everything's possible, you know…'

Simon and I chatted for a while on the return train journey and then fell into silence. By the time we arrived home I was tired. I sat by the window looking out into the garden, sipping a glass of water, lost in thought. Clouds had darkened, bursting as rain fell heavily, and the smell of fresh earth drifted in through the open window. I could smell, I realized! My sense of smell, which I had lost when first diagnosed, had returned.

As the rainfall lightened, I spotted a pigeon sitting on a flowerpot containing a bedraggled plant. First, it lifted one wing horizontally, preened it, then leaned over and readjusted its position. What was it doing, I wondered. It wobbled, then lifted the other wing, leaned over sideways and preened beneath that wing. The rain was like a welcome shower to wash with! With that it flew happily off. Raucous screeching ensued from beneath the skirt of an ancient yew tree at the bottom of the garden. I stared in disbelief as two magpies were attacking a hawk on the ground, or so I thought. As I watched I realized they were all pecking at something together. The hawk was holding a superior position atop its prey, a sickly collared dove that I'd noticed the previous day. I was witnessing nature in all its grizzly glory. Silently I wished the collared dove's spirit a peaceful onward journey to a loving, non-predatory place. I tracked down a comforting chocolate biscuit and ate it without thinking, forgetting it was now forbidden. I resolved not to be despondent but to try harder.

We ended that day encouraged by our visit to see Rosy, where we'd been given hope for new life with Carctol. Yes, it felt like a big undertaking. The diet was prohibitive and there was fear, too, over the unknown herbs, but it was worth giving it a try. After all, we'd been seeking something new.

CHAPTER 6
Nourishing Invisible Guiding Forces

Love yourself
Forgive yourself
Gently be with yourself
Accept all aspects of yourself
Your life is a gift
Don't let anyone spoil it
You are a gift most precious
May your life lead you on to lush new pastures
Gillian Gill

March - December 2001

'How will I cope with so many dietary changes?' I said to Simon.

'You will.'

I'd been ill for a week and was feeling worse than ever, having not parted company from the loo after drinking a raw green juice too quickly. It had weakened rather than strengthened my immune system. I couldn't blame anyone else for it; I'd done it to myself with the best of intentions, not realizing that I should have drunk it slowly. Remembering that there were many far worse off helped level me and I set about the new dietary changes as soon as I felt stronger. I phoned nutritional supply companies, asking what was alkaline and what wasn't, and started making lists. It was mentioned that globe artichokes are a good natural liver tonic and I made plans to grow them in the garden.

Meanwhile, I pored over nutritional books trying to discover new sources of protein. Wheatgrass powder contains a certain amount and also acts in a similar way to a blood transfusion in the body, as a natural, boosting healing agent. I found it helped Clare's sore gum when I made a paste of it by mixing half a teaspoonful of the powder with a little water in an eggcup, then scooping it into a handkerchief, twisting it to form a small ball shape as a poultice to place against the gum. Wheatgrass is frequently referred to as 'nature's finest medicine' and I wondered at reading case after case of people with cancer who had benefited enormously from taking it.

The taste was disconcerting to begin with but I persevered, and for a spell I grew my own to freshly juice. I sent away for the seeds and began the business of soaking then refreshing the grain in a sieve ready to sprout before growing in soil. It was time-consuming but fascinating to watch the tiny shoots sprouting from the seed.

Then one day, after a particularly bad bout of sickness and diarrhoea, I could no longer tolerate drinking it fresh without almost being sick. I had a rest from it altogether and then resumed taking dried wheatgrass powder mixed with a little water. My overall physical sense of well-being began improving. A few years later I was to reintroduce fresh wheatgrass into my diet.

Emptying out one of the kitchen cupboards, I replaced it with food I could eat. Often things fell out when opening the cupboards, which annoyed Simon. Permissible foods included: pulses, which are good sources of protein, such as chickpeas, cannellini and aduki beans, quinoa, different lentils, brown rice, spices, and herbs both dried and fresh from the garden for flavouring to replace salt. Parsley is good and helps with bloating, being a natural diuretic. To the list I added oat bakes, nuts and seeds in a greater variety. The four alkaline fruits I could now eat were bananas, melon, figs and papaya. Rosy had told me beetroot is good for the blood. I juiced it raw with carrots, which were delicious, as well as eating it cooked. When going to the loo I noticed how the beetroot often turned waste an alarming red! As I was going along I was learning and discovering what suited my body and what didn't.

I wondered about which water to drink, with so many choices, and settled on bottled spring water after Simon had looked into the chemicals that can appear in tap water. Due to omitting salt from my diet Simon researched sodium levels contained in the various brands of water and we selected low sodium water.

I experimented with the choice of non-dairy milks and opted for soya, which led to a mild panic when Clare read the label closely and spotted that 'added apple juice gives sweetness'. Previously I hadn't noticed that, or that there was a choice between sweetened and non-sweetened, which I now opted for. There was so much I didn't know, and the more I learned the more I became aware of my ignorance and the gaps in my knowledge. That overwhelmed me at times so I simply learned to focus on what I needed to know and to accept my limitations, reminding myself there were others to whom I could turn for help.

I felt bombarded with the daily challenges of adapting to my new diet; I grieved for my loss of choice and I craved for the simple foods that were now classed as acidic. Abstaining from these foods made them seem even more desirable. It was my choice to take this alkaline diet, to support the Carctol that I wanted to add to my regime. At times I felt like a sailing boat caught in turbulent waters, then I thought of Simon's late father, a keen sailor whose passion was his cruising yacht. I wished for him to 'fill my sails' with a good strong wind, to help keep me steering my course, and at times for respite, to drop anchor and be steadied. Simon's father would have wanted to help; he'd have been upset especially for Simon, as he himself had tragically lost his first wife, Shelia, to cancer, leaving three small girls behind.

My night sweats persisted. With my renewed sense of smell I once more became aware of the unpleasant, cancerous odour my body gave off as it eliminated the toxins. After one such night I awoke feeling totally despondent and got up, but I couldn't face the day so returned to bed unsettled. I got an idea to phone my friend Philippa. She'd repeatedly told me if I needed her help in any way not to hesitate to phone her, so I walked to the kitchen to dial her number.

'Hello,' I said quietly.

'Are you alright? You don't sound it.'

'No. Can you come over?' I asked hesitantly.

'Yes, you've caught me on a day when I'm working at home, so it's not a problem.' When she arrived she took one look at me and said, 'Go and lie down. You look worn out.'

'I feel it,' I mumbled. 'I feel desolate.'

She just sat on the edge of the bed quietly, patiently, holding my hand. Lying back on the pillows, I shut my eyes as tears tumbled quietly down my cheeks. This was the first time I managed to reach out in this way. It helped more than any words could have conveyed in that instant; for me that was an enormous breakthrough in my behaviour. I had so many needs, mostly unspoken ones that I couldn't put words to. They all revolved around love, trust and breaking down the old defensive walls of self-protection that I'd unconsciously built around me. By the time she left I felt imbued by her love, contained and safe. This help from Philippa gave me the strength to manage similar recurrences alone. Suffering is a part of being alive and, like all things, it passes.

I was making radical changes to my diet. With hindsight, I should have done things differently, gently and gradually. Such was my mindset that I was quite honestly beyond reasoning at times, which was hard for Simon. Some of the side effects that I suffered, due to giving up certain foods immediately instead of gradually, were increased migraines and shaking. On rare occasions I needed the psychological lift from a chocolate biscuit. A healer friend told me, having researched natural sleeping methods on the Internet, that a ginger biscuit, if eaten half an hour before bedtime, together with drinking a small mug of warm soya milk, aided sleep. It certainly helped me and was soothing. This was my kind of medicine, though only adopted on exceptional occasions, as biscuits are on the forbidden food list.

One morning a welcome letter fell through the front door. A healer friend wrote about the value of giving the mind freedom of creative expression, stating the many benefits to someone in my situation. The idea appealed to me, remembering my mother's painting, which helped her so much when my father was unwell. This suggestion was for another creative outlet, writing. My friend elaborated, knowing my predicament well, and mentioned finding a good correspondence course on writing. That way I could dictate when I wrote, without the added physical strain of attending a class. I researched the idea and was all but ready to give up when I spotted an advertisement in a magazine. Through a writing agency, I fell into the hands of a published writer who acted as my tutor on a tailored course. I had no idea what I was letting myself in for. It was hard work, requiring discipline again, and I struggled to comprehend some of the work. Having left school after 'O' levels, I hadn't done brilliantly, and had to relearn the English language. When chatting to Simon about it he came up with an idea: 'Why not ask David's old history teacher from his prep school? His love was the English language, and you always got on well. I'm sure he'll help you if you ask him.' I mulled that idea over. When I phoned him, the teacher was delighted to accept Simon's proposition as he passed our driveway after school on his way home from work and had some spare time. It seemed to suit us both.

I studied and wrote almost every day, no matter how little. I had always had a passion for writing letters, something a special friend had commented on, saying she enjoyed reading mine. This new skill slotted well into my daily pattern.

Before we knew it the parcel containing the Carctol had arrived. I'd been adhering to an alkaline diet since discussing it with Rosy in preparation for beginning the course. I opened it up hesitantly. 'Look at the vivid turquoise colour,' I said to Simon, somewhat alarmed.

It reminded me of the exotic birds my father kept throughout much of my childhood as a hobby after his nervous breakdown. He discovered being with the birds soothed him. He imagined where they'd come from and did his best to recreate their natural habitat. He built vast aviaries and put branches with leaves in them for the birds to enjoy. When stronger after his breakdown he turned from cattle and pigs to turkey farming and went on to become a reputable turkey farmer, building large naturally lit barns for them to wander freely in. He wanted them to enjoy what life they had and considered how best the birds should meet their end before they arrived at market. He became recognized by buyers at Smithfield, the London meat market, for producing good-quality turkeys. He not only had a gift for growing crops on difficult soil but also managed to produce good harvests, due in part to his natural ability to judge the weather. He could tell what it would be like just by looking at the sky and smelling the air.

'Read the instructions first,' reminded Simon, as I tentatively held two capsules in the palm of my hand wondering whether to take them.

'Remember Rosy mentioned setting yourself achievable goals.' I'd set some of seeing the children graduate and marry, but that was far off. Looking at the opened pot I took out the instructions. The first words I read were 'New life…'. I liked that. Now, set yourself an achievable goal, I thought. Take the next breath and continue reading. The directions said either take two capsules whole or empty the contents into a teaspoon then swallow the herbal concoction. That's what I decided to do, but not immediately.

It took several hours before I mustered the courage. Recalling Joanna and how she'd been a guinea pig with her own treatments, my mind had become muddled and couldn't at first separate her experience from my own, then my emotions got the better of me. After finally reading the directions twice I tried to swallow the powder; it got stuck on my teeth, so I fidgeted it off, swallowing it down with a gulp of water. Next I swallowed the enzyme digesters my nutritionist, Marianne, had suggested to accompany the Carctol. I recalled Marianne's angelic voice. She'd asked about Carctol and what the herbs did. I told her it was my understanding that they help break up tumours ready to be eliminated, and Rosy had endorsed her enzyme advice during a telephone consultation. The enzymes help aid digestion, and mine was compromised by my condition.

'What do you think will happen to me now?' I asked Simon nervously.

'Nothing, you'll be fine,' he reassured, but I still sent up a silent prayer and then felt my breathing calm and deepen.

Looking into the parcel that had contained the Carctol, I noticed a personal handwritten message. The words touched me deeply; they flowed through me like nectar. Those thoughtful, encouraging words were written with love by the lady Rosy had spoken of to me, Yashu Amlani. Her husband was the pharmacist dispatching the prescriptions; they worked closely together as a team.

Over the following weeks I struggled to come to terms with the alkaline diet; I berated myself for finding it so difficult, and then remembered that anger wasn't the answer. It sapped my energy, draining me. I had to find a more peaceful way. In her note Yashu wrote, 'Please phone, if I can help in any way.' I tentatively dialled her telephone number. When she answered I explained who I was and that I'd recently received a Carctol delivery, for which I thanked her.

'What good timing, Gillian, I have just finished my prayer practice for the day and was in the kitchen preparing food.' Listening to her relaxed me; imagining being in the kitchen was always a soothing thought for me. We got on right away. She elaborated on her prayerful start to the day: 'I start by lighting candles, offering the light in prayer to light a more peaceful way in the world, offering it to others around the globe stumbling in darkness. I also offer prayerful thanks for my abundance, for my many blessings and for my night's sleep, and especially for those I love.'

'That sounds beautiful,' I said.

'How are you, Gillian?'

'Well, I'm having problems with the strict alkaline diet,' and then mentioned what I'd been eating, which had included yoghurts every day. 'When I take Carctol with water I get a burning sensation in my tummy.'

'Gillian, it is obvious to me your diet has inhibited your response. Try drinking soya milk instead of water when taking Carctol, which may suit your body better. But above all else, please try not to worry.' Already I felt calmer as we continued to talk. 'You need an alkaline tummy to achieve optimum results,' she cheerfully and confidently told me. I felt her strong, warm voice wrap its vibrations around me. 'Try to relax around food when preparing it, and especially when cooking it.'

'I always used to be relaxed when preparing food,' I said.

'Now things are different, everything has changed, so try to honour yourself by looking after yourself well.' I'd always taken for granted what I could eat; I'd never previously put this amount of effort into my diet.

'People don't generally understand how the disciplines of an alkaline diet have an ongoing effect that requires time for the body to process. It isn't instant; energy flows alter with dietary and holistic practices, and need embracing and attending to. Just altering one thing can make all the difference. Keep going and remember I am always here for you. Namaste.'

Having spoken to Yashu I marvelled at our empathy and became more confident when preparing food and cooking. She had also stressed the importance of an added magical ingredient: love.

I'd always enjoyed cooking but wondered if I had consciously included that ingredient previously? From then on I did so, to all food that I served, including the nuts and seeds that I fed the birds in the garden. Lately I'd been noticing differences in the birds visiting our bird table. One, a crow, had a white wing and a robin had a club foot. Henceforth, Lucy's dog food was also prepared with love.

Reflecting on my chat with Yashu I felt relieved and uplifted. By taking Carctol and not adhering to the diet correctly I had set opposing forces at work in my body, and this explained the increase in fatigue which had made me feel so low-spirited. Remembering to be patient with myself was hard, but a must while my body adjusted. Then I remembered that before saying goodbye Yashu had added, 'I always bless everything throughout the day, especially the food I eat, and the liquids I drink. I express my abiding gratitude for each small act and deed I achieve each day.'

Once I'd got the diet established I soon started noticing subtle changes in well-being. My skin's lustre improved, my hair thickened and grew faster, as did my nails. Mentally, too, I started to feel calmer; it was as though my mind were supported in a splint as a broken bone would be.

Prior to taking Carctol, breakfast was challenging and my stomach reacted disconcertingly to much of what I ate. I discussed this with Simon.

'Do you remember Rosy suggested porridge with nuts? Porridge is a slow-release energy food and source of many nutrients, including being a source of protein, and it's a good gut-cleansing agent.' As soon as I tried that my stomach reacted favourably and settled down. By this time our entire dietary regime was changing; gone were the Sunday roasts. I hadn't realized how much David and Simon missed them until two years into my regime when I resumed cooking them. But up until that point, my heart had gone out of preparing them. They seemed impossible. I had tried and the meat had been tough, the Yorkshire puddings flat and the gravy lumpy; they never used to be like that.

I was still having difficulty retaining as much food as I'd have liked and was concerned, thinking I wouldn't get completely well unless this changed. Rosy had told me how orange and red-coloured foods, like carrots, peppers and pumpkins, are high in antioxidants. 'They're good for someone with cancer,' she'd said.

One day I was standing in the kitchen, despairing about how food constantly kept passing through me, and began praying. Suddenly, my mind calmed and then filled with new ideas for recipes. Reaching for a notebook and pen I started writing down ingredients. As I wrote I felt a beautiful presence beside me.

When I cooked the resulting recipes, they tasted delicious to me. I experimented with Simon and David. David tentatively took the first mouthful of my latest creation, spicy carrot, sweet potato, red onion, ginger and garlic with spinach and coconut milk soup. I'd flavoured it with generous quantities of cumin and turmeric as I discovered that they are anti-carcinogenic and have beneficial effects. David's lips curled into a smile as he declared, 'Mmm, this is delicious!'

'I agree,' chimed Simon, also smiling. From then on they, and Clare when she was home, became my dietary guinea pigs, always giving their honest opinions, which I valued no matter what. Simon doesn't like garlic as much as I do, so I added extra to my food for health reasons.

One night I simply couldn't settle or sleep. Climbing wearily out of bed, I trudged downstairs in my dressing gown. Lucy roused in her bed, looked up and joined me as I opened the front door. 'I don't feel good,' I said to her. In response she nudged my leg with her nose. Walking out of the front door and down the step into the gravel driveway, I drank in the cool night air. There was a full moon in the inky dark sky. I sat down on one of the large hand-carved wooden mushrooms that sit either side of the front door. Glancing around I caught sight of the ornamental fairies sitting in the deep window ledges, next to lanterns. The candles had been extinguished long ago. Would I be like those candles, I wondered? Lucy nudged me again and then settled down, resting her head in my lap. My bare feet pulsed on the gravel as I became aware of the earth's power beneath them. I must have bare feet outside more often, I thought, noticing the powerful, energizing earth connection streaming into me.

'There you are,' said Simon joining us. 'What are you two girls doing?'

'Enjoying the night air, couldn't sleep.' Simon sat on the other mushroom.

'What's that sound?' I asked, knowing it couldn't be the chickens from the adjacent farm. Dawn was some way off yet.

'It's the natterjack toads crooning,' Simon replied. I thought of the neighbour's beautiful pond. 'They're the only species with legs, apart from man, that sing in a chorus.'

'How beautiful they sound. Of course, it's late spring, so it must be their mating ritual.'

We sat there looking up at the stars, enjoying the cool refreshing breezes and the sounds. 'Look,' said Simon pointing to a corner in the sky, 'a shooting star! You must remember what we've been told, that the body needs time to process and assimilate everything you're doing.'

'How did you know I was worrying?'

'I know you…'

The following day I was feeling slightly better so got up and dressed. It was a warm breezy day so I decided to wash the sheets. Hanging the washing out on the line had been a trial but now I was finding it less so, my breathing was easier. I enjoyed watching the sheets flapping in the breeze and inhaled their sweet fragrance once dry. Typically I'd leave them at the bottom of the stairs, waiting to be carried up. At such times, the dogs used them as pillows, and on occasion they got covered in mud and needed rewashing.

Walking back inside Simon handed me the phone. 'It's Marianne.'

'Hello,' I said.

'It's good to hear you, Gillian. I was just wondering how you are? It's your nutritional appointment today.'

'Oh, I'm so sorry. I forgot!' I felt bewildered and upset.

'Don't worry, we'll make another one.'

Simon saw my face and asked, 'What was that about?'

'I think Marianne might have made a mistake. She said she was expecting me for an appointment today.'

'Look at your diary,' Simon suggested.

'Oh, she was right. It's written here on the wall calendar.'

'Don't worry, it's easy to make mistakes.'

It took me several hours to shake off my sense of unease over that confusion. I worried about what was happening to my memory.

The Carctol diet was strict and, on one particularly difficult day, I felt stuck with what to cook.

'But you know about food,' said Simon, 'you're a trained cook.'

My father had sent both my sisters and myself to college for a year; there I'd learned secretarial skills, cooking and flower arranging. I was keen to start working and got my dream job with a racehorse trainer immediately after I left college, having first passed my driving test, which the job required. Little did I know then how invaluable all those skills would be later in life; the secretarial skills equipped me for writing, flower arranging for giving demonstrations to day care patients at a hospice and for pleasure, and cooking inspired me to new creative, healthier levels.

As I was unable to go out shopping, Simon and David opted to food shop online. 'Just tell me what you want this week and David and I will place our usual order to be delivered.' I made a long list (these days I was making several lists to help myself) of fresh ingredients, brown bread for the family

(I'd been advised to avoid bread altogether, which I did for two years), brown rice, carrots, sweet potatoes, red peppers, onions, leeks, celeriac, garlic, ginger, almonds, porridge, soya milk, bananas, melon, chickpeas, lettuce, parsley, spinach, broccoli, avocados, beetroot, cucumber, globe artichokes, celery to nibble on, olive oil to cook with and eggs. I added fish, chicken and meat as protein for Simon and David, and treats for them such as chocolate, biscuits, cakes and crisps.

I mentally ran through my banned food list to make sure I hadn't made a mistake: white bread, white pasta, potatoes, all dairy except for the boys, no jams or marmalades, pickles or chutney and nothing with caffeine. Though everyone else in the family still ate them, they did so more sparingly to support me.

For juicing I needed cucumber, celery, ginger, carrots, beetroot and mint. I usually juiced five carrots, one beetroot, three sticks of celery, half an inch of ginger and half a cucumber with a few mint leaves to make a drink. Sometimes I just juiced carrots. I said to Simon, 'At last the food I'm eating seems to have calmed my digestive system. Having a structured routine, including juicing at the same time each day, is becoming enjoyable, though some days are easier than others.'

'That's good. I've noticed, though, that you haven't been listening to music nearly so much.'

'I get so many headaches I haven't felt like it.'

'Do you remember Irene taught you that music is food for the soul?'

'I'd forgotten that.'

'Perhaps we should invest in a new sound system? The old one hasn't worked properly for years.'

'I don't want you spending money unnecessarily,' I said.

'Don't think about it like that. Remember my mother. When I last visited her in the nursing home, in spite of her dementia and fragility, she still wanted to give us her full support. She was listening to music – she won't be without it; it's one of the few things that give her pleasure.'

I thought of Simon's cantankerous mother, of the love–hate relationship we had and her kind support now. She'd unknowingly taught me so much throughout our marriage, not least how to protect myself emotionally and not take on board unintentional messages. To illustrate this, I remember one particular summer holiday in Greece, sitting at a table near to the sea and watching a very large wasp, wondering how painful a sting from such a creature would be. I sat motionless, watching the wasp as it came closer to my hand. I thought of the comparison of being fascinated by people with stings in the form of sharp tongues. Such people can be true teachers of many invaluable lessons, and deserve respect for the part they play. In their own way they help us to discover ourselves and our individual pathways and how to deal with our reactions. It's ultimately our choice as to how we interpret another's comments and behaviour and discriminate whether or not the hurt was intended. So often it isn't. When below par or ill one can feel over-sensitive, and this is something I had to learn to protect myself from so that I didn't take on board imaginary insults.

To return to the wasp, when it landed on my hand I became oblivious to everything else by focusing all my attention on it and infusing it with love rather than fear. It didn't sting but just vibrated its body. That experience helped me change my attitude by admiring it as a creature rather than focusing on its sting. The wasp responded to my letting go of fear and felt the love filling its place.

The days were flying by, and in no time at all Simon was saying, 'It's time for me to take you to see Marianne for your next nutrition appointment.'

'I'm sure I can manage to drive myself,' I replied.

'Not this time. Drive yourself next time.'

'Gillian,' said Marianne as I walked through the door, 'how lovely to see you.' She hugged me. 'We'll just start by seeing if you are drinking enough water… As I thought, you are dehydrated. Here you are,' she said handing me a glass of mineral water. 'So often we feel hungry when in fact we are thirsty. It's all about retraining the brain and the body, then listening to the body to see what it's trying to tell you.'

'I feel awful much of the time, get bloated, and I've suddenly got spots,' I commented.

'Don't worry. Often that happens as a sign you're getting better. It's the body's way of cleansing impurities. You're getting something right, as you're so well overall,' she said cheerfully. 'Come and lie on the couch and we'll test you since your detox and see what new supplements may support you at this stage.' I lay quietly as she worked, testing my body with her kinesiology. 'I always ask the body for permission first. I don't want to intrude!' she laughed.

'Now, this is good,' she said towards the end. 'You are ready for more minerals and vitamins. The prescribed dosage of Carctol and enzyme forte is correct and agreeing with your body nicely.'

'I'm struggling some days taking so many pills: sixty odd, including the following. I'm taking 8 Carctol, 16 enzyme digesters, 6 buffered vitamin C capsules, 3 vitamin B capsules, 3 potassium capsules. You know my body's fluctuating need for them, and I can't remember all the names of the mineral supplements which I brought along to be checked. Increasingly, before visiting you, I have noticed a dip in my well-being, having omitted them prior to you muscle-testing my body. After re-evaluating the vitamin and mineral dosages, within half an hour of going home and eating a little something then taking them, I notice improving energy levels, especially in my throat, as my voice becomes husky without the vitamin C supplements.'

'Don't worry. Pace yourself, take them throughout the day. Also, silently thanking them for their benefits is a nice thing to do.'

'Thank you, I'll try that.'

Looking at Simon she said, 'How are you?'

'I'm managing. I'm doing more off-road cycling with David, our son; we find it's a good outlet for stress, increases our fitness and we enjoy it. We keep in close touch with Clare. She's doing well at university in spite of everything.'

'That's good. Please let me know if there's anything I can do to help you, as I'd love to see if you need any nutritional support at this stressful time.'

Looking at me, she said, 'Gillian you might like to try body brushing. It's very simple. You use a bristle brush to brush the skin of your body, always moving towards the heart. Just do it for a few moments at the start of the day. Skin is the largest organ for elimination, and showering afterwards will complete the process.'

We both thanked her and hugged her farewell, as she reassured us the supplements she'd ordered would arrive in the post shortly. During the journey home I reflected on how the breast pain and feared breast cancer that followed my dismal diagnosis had disappeared. I hadn't had breast cancer, but fear cast a shadow of doubt; doubt manifested in pain. Yet, by constantly imagining my breast region clearing of cancer, relief followed.

When we got home and tried to get into the house Simon looked perplexed. 'That's odd,' he said as he unlocked the front door.

'What's the matter?' I asked wearily. The effort of seeing Marianne had used all my reserves of energy and I needed a rest. As the front door swung open we both heard classical music filling the sitting room.

'I've disconnected the sound system as it's broken. What's going on?' Simon asked.

We looked at one another quizzically. Opening the sitting room door, the music filled the room to the vaulted ceiling. 'It's your father,' I said, suddenly smelling his distinctive cigar smoke.

'What do you mean?' asked Simon bemused.

'You know how he loved classical music. Especially after he retired, when he loved nothing more after lunch than sitting and listening to his favourite music composed by Alfred Brendel, together with smoking a fine cigar.'

'So he did,' said Simon wistfully. I was thinking how busy Simon's late father, Frank, had been trying to connect to us both by giving us evidence of his spiritual presence, filling the house with music together with his tell-tale cigar smoke smell.

'Do you remember how shortly after he died you couldn't find your silver cufflinks? Your late grandfather's that your mother gave you after he died?' They'd mysteriously found their way from their usual spot on our bedroom windowsill, in the conch shell, a gift from two divers we befriended while on our honeymoon in St. Lucia, to the downstairs windowsill at the foot of the stairs, where Simon looked each time he came down. We knew then that the missing cufflinks had been the work of his father as a sign to let us know that he was still close to us, closer than we imagined. Now he was trying to reach out to help us again. We found great comfort in this, remembering how in life he'd always done all he could to help not only us, but also many others.

'He obviously wants me to buy a new sound system,' grinned Simon.

Throughout the following days, as was to become my usual practice after that incident, I'd lie stretched out on the sofa listening to the new sound system that we had bought. The pain ebbed and flowed through me and, with Lucy beside me on the floor, listening to either a guided relaxation or glorious music seemed to help me in different ways. The music moved me profoundly. While lying there, I mentally thanked my body for the one thousand things that it did for me each day. Previously I'd always taken it for granted. I was overcome by the many functions my body performed without my even having to think about it, and lay humbled, filled with gratitude.

'I'm glad to see you're making the most of the new sound system and enjoying the music,' said Simon. 'Why not come and watch television this evening.'

'I find I can't watch it any longer.'

'Why not?' he asked puzzled.

'I don't seem to be able to stop myself getting emotionally overly involved with what's on the screen, and with all the distressing news stories and harrowing plots of TV dramas, I feel depleted and drained.' By the end of most days I was so tired I went to bed early to lie in a darkened room to rebalance myself by deeply relaxing, or to contemplate my day and then read a spiritually uplifting book. Sometimes I'd lose myself listening to beautiful music in the hope of encouraging sleep.

Five weeks into taking Carctol I received a phone call from Yashu to check on my progress.

'How are you?' she asked. We talked animatedly. 'You feel like a soul sister to me,' she continued.

'I feel the same,' I replied.

'Namaste greetings to you. Do you know what that means?'

'No.'

'Literally translated it means I bow to you within; to me it means may the highest and purest in me reach out to the highest and purest in you.'

I warmed, listening to her words, feeling empathically infused with love, and repeated 'Namaste' back to her.

'Yashu?'

'Yes, what is troubling you?'

'I've been remembering...'

'Tell me,' she coaxed.

'It might sound strange.'

'Don't worry. Say it anyway.'

'Many years ago, when I visited Clare in London, my shoe slipped off and fell on the track as I was getting off the train.'

'What did you do?'

'I asked a porter for his help. He found something with a hook and retrieved it for me. We laughed at the time.'

'Some people are very kind and resourceful.'

'Yes, they are. I've been thinking, I feel as though I've lost certain aspects of myself, certain qualities. I'm not sure who I am any longer.'

'That's not uncommon. When we're low and below par, particularly with long-term illness, our vital energy reserves, our life force, becomes sapped. We need to find ways of inner nourishment. I find it through prayer and meditation, by stilling my mind, disciplining my thoughts and through the constant support and love of family and friendships.'

I contemplated her ways. Wrestling with thoughts I termed as 'junk' and casting them out as soon as they came in became an occupation. I called those times 'junk in', then immediately noticing those unwanted thoughts said to myself 'junk out'. So many old memories were coming to the surface to be revisited. I'd learned from one of my healing colleagues to stay with them, no matter how disturbing or painful, no matter if the person with whom I'd had an altercation were alive or dead, and to offer forgiveness through prayerfulness, either to myself or the other person. Such behavioural upsets are only one part of the person, often not intended. I reflected on Yashu focusing on the higher, purer self of each person at such times, and sought to follow her example. If I struggled when inwardly focusing on forgiveness issues, I'd imagine Yashu being present as a peacekeeper, overseeing events with myself and whoever else. Chatting to Yashu helped enormously.

Later, when reflecting on our conversation, I remembered a fellow pupil, David, at Gee's spiritual development group. We'd had an intense discussion about the same themes, upsets with others and actions versus reactions.

'Good intentions', started Gee, 'are one's own personal responsibility. How another reciprocates is entirely a different matter.' I learned so much in those groups, some of which I forgot at times and had to re-learn all over again. We realized we all wore social masks that we hid behind, though we let them down during our classes. We looked at ourselves, at our behaviour, as though viewed through a magnifying glass. Gee continued, saying something along the following lines: 'Focusing on our own behaviour can be uncomfortable; we usually avoid it. It can seem easier to attempt to force change on others, no matter how frustrating and futile this is. Yet, if we work to establish behaviour that expresses our true values, and take responsibility for our own actions by interrupting our automatic responses, it can have a knock-on effect of improving our relationships with others. To make these improvements we need to observe ourselves clearly, know our boundaries and select our responses. From this position we can notice our words and actions and the influence we have on other's reactions. Action causes reaction, we often tend to react rather than act. So it's preferable to monitor our actions if we want a more satisfactory reaction. Only we can choose how we exert our free will.'

David, the New Zealander pupil, added, 'I've learned that emotions are but mere tools. We can apply them to the mind to use as a key, to unlock the door to a better way of living. We do this by engaging the mind to use thoughts more wisely to help govern our jangled emotions, and by nurturing ourselves with gentle, loving words, directed by our mind, to soothe and calm ourselves.'

Gee answered, 'Thank you, David. All new things require time, commitment, patience, respect and perseverance. By its essence the law of attraction is such that if you live increasingly in harmony with nature, your inherent self will be honoured by conscious awareness. You'll find the desire to live more simply in the world, then your spiritual side and Divine nature will become more apparent. Revere Mother Nature. Work with her by observing the seasons closely, notice your bodily rhythms and strive to listen to them. Act in ever-increasing harmony with your highest nature. You are a precious gift to the planet; nurture and love yourself.'

With those thoughts I remembered our neighbour Tony, who inspires me. He made a complete recovery from throat cancer using conventional medicine. He'd lost his voice box through surgery, but had found, quite by chance, that by channelling his anger when he was carved up while driving, he'd regained the power of speech; it was his sheer determination that improved his speech over time. I thought of him when experimenting in the kitchen and had cooked too much soup one day. It was another recipe that came to me as different ingredients popped into my mind. Tony would enjoy some of the soup, I thought, as he loves cooking, and I strolled over to see him, with Lucy at my heels. He greeted me warmly and then Lucy, breaking off from cutting the hedge. It was a glorious, sunny day.

'Hello, Gillian, what have you got there?' he said looking up.

'It's a new recipe I'm trying out to boost my immune system and heal myself.' Putting down the hedge cutter, he came over and sniffed the open pot.

'Smells nice, I'll enjoy that. A tasty meal offers great comfort, I find. I'd like that recipe please.' He strolled off into the kitchen through his open stable door, which reminded me of my late grandmother's house. Lucy followed. She returned chewing a treat he'd given her and wandered off outside.

'I'll be happy to give you it,' I smiled. Calling Lucy, who was by now sniffing the scent of rabbits in his dense woodland, we walked home. The leaves on the trees had never looked greener.

That same evening Tony phoned. 'Gill, whatever ingredients you put in that soup did me the power of good. I didn't need to take my usual pills after eating. I felt warm and soothed, but on the inside.'

The weeks flew by as I continued my many practices, including on good days experimenting in the kitchen and writing down all the new recipes in a little notebook that had been an inspired gift from Clare. On the bad days, resting and practising visualizations helped. When Clare was home I ventured out to try food shopping with her. Unable to find figs, I despaired and burst into tears in front of the empty space where they had been. 'It's alright, Ma,' I heard Clare say, as she hugged me tightly. Thereafter, on occasions when I went food shopping the staff were extraordinarily helpful, especially when I almost fainted after a trolley veered out of control and into my painful abdomen. They thought I was pregnant; it was hard explaining to strangers that I wasn't and what my predicament was. However, it meant they always kept a lookout for me when I was in the shop and offered their help if needed. Their kindness and support encouraged and helped beyond measure while I was regaining confidence in something I'd once taken for granted. When home, Clare and David helped; Clare did some of the cooking, while David mowed the lawn.

Help came in many other forms. Marianne had passed on a new idea to add to the body-brushing regime. When taking a shower or bath, she suggested I imagine toxicity being gently washed from my body and disappearing down the plughole. Then imagine it as garden fertilizer, spreading out goodness in its wake.

At other times, I imagined my blood cells healthy and well, especially my white ones, healing my whole body, as Rosy had mentioned.

A friend had discovered that a doctor working in the field of mind, body and spirit was visiting the UK to attend a holistic cancer conference in London. She passed on the details to me and I felt compelled to try to speak to him. Luckily when I rang the hotel and conference centre I was immediately put through to his room. He was taking a ten-minute break.

'Hello?' I heard his German accent.

'Have you a moment?' I asked

'Yes, please continue,' he replied amiably. Wasting no time, I told him about my predicament. 'What emotional imbalances have you had recently?' he asked.

'The loss of our old rescue dog,' I responded.

'I sense you're storing much grief, more than for the dog. That, though, is at the forefront. The remedy for that grief is to try to find another dog of exactly the same type and nature, and similar in every way as far as possible.' I was speechless. He added, 'If you can do this, it will be an added factor to your health and well-being. It will be a tremendous aid to your recovery.'

I thanked him profusely, though it was worrying to think about telling Simon that we should get another dog as he was already carrying such a load. But I did so with difficulty and he quietly mulled the idea over.

August had disappeared. I hadn't harvested the usual blackberries for jam making but remembered how Lucy had always assisted me in the past with Jack, our old rescue dog. She'd nibble the juicy, ripe blackberries hanging low in the hedgerow while I filled a basket.

By now it was September 1st. 'Are you ready to leave?' asked Simon as we prepared to go to Chalice Well, a renowned retreat centre in Glastonbury founded by Tudor Wellesley Pole in 1959. During the Second World War he'd persuaded Churchill and the King to introduce the 'Silent Minute', by which at 9 pm each evening the whole country entered into silence for a moment, sending out thoughts of peace.

'Yes, I'm ready. Are you sure you'll be alright walking while I attend the retreat that Donald and Steven are holding?'

'I'm looking forward to it, and have my maps with me ready to explore.'

'Do you think David will be alright staying with his friend for the weekend?'

'Yes,' Simon assured me. 'They're going off-road cycling. It'll do me good to have a break from it, to be honest. It gets quite tough at times trying to keep up with David.'

By now I kept noticing how every time Simon experienced challenges in his world outwardly, I experienced challenges in my world inwardly. It was like a mirror image. I admired his ability for self-expression, feeling myself at times inarticulate.

Unsure of myself because of the prospect of being away from my familiar surroundings at home and all that felt safe in the world, I remembered what I had taught and passed on to those I had worked with in a healing capacity: to only accept and do what felt right. Inspired to use gardening as a metaphor, I used to say that, rather like sifting soil, sift through everything you hear before making your own mind up on what to do. For me, the retreat felt right.

The car was loaded. I'd packed my supplements, milk, bananas, nuts and oat bakes for snacking if I needed them. I'd known Steven for years. We'd sat in Gee's class together. I had also grown to like and trust his partner, Donald.

'Why don't you shut your eyes? You had a restless night,' said Simon. Doing so, I saw two angels side by side with wings down to the ground, and wondered at their significance.

'We've arrived; you slept the entire journey. It's doing you good having a break,' said Simon, turning off the ignition.

I looked at the pretty building in the sunlight and, turning, noticed an archway. 'Let's walk this way,' I said turning to Simon.

'Good idea. I'll just lock the car first.' As we walked side by side it felt as though we were entering another world. Tall plants either side of the path covered an arbour and seemed to enfold us. Everything else just fell away.

'St. Michael's, the retreat house, is this way,' said someone pointing helpfully. 'Hello, darlin',' said Steven in his whimsical Irish accent, and we hugged. 'Your room's downstairs, with an adjoining bathroom. Come on, I'll show you.'

We followed, drinking in the peaceful atmosphere. Standing in the doorway, I took a deep breath. It was a twin-bedded room. At the bedheads were two full-length pictures of angels, with golden wings to the ground as I'd seen during the car journey.

'Supper's in the kitchen, and there's a fridge if you want to use it. I'll show you.' Steven led the way; my feet barely touched the ground, soaking up the peaceful atmosphere.

'I think that I'll go off and explore. When is supper?' asked Simon, pecking me on the cheek ready to go.

'It's 7 pm. I'll go for a lie down while you're out as I need to absorb my new surroundings.'

Prior to supper Donald called everyone into the retreat centre, a spacious room with two richly coloured, almost identical patterned rugs, though one was light and one dark.

'I'd like you all to form a circle please. When you're sitting comfortably, before we start tomorrow, I'd just like to go round inviting everyone to introduce themselves and then say a little about yourself. Whatever you're relaxed with; remember we sit without judgement.'

That, I thought alarmingly, was something I did all the time: judge. My stomach did a somersault as I thought of being in the spotlight when my turn came, wanting to run and hide. A young girl said her name then added, 'I start the day with hope in my heart. I try to do the best I can throughout the day. At night I'm filled with gratitude, no matter what.'

Finally my turn came. I introduced myself, with Donald and Steven beaming their radiance at me. 'I have cancer and I am taking a holistic route.' I crimsoned, feeling my inferiority complex rising to the surface. Everyone merely remained steadfastly in an atmosphere of serenity. My voice stopped, I was overcome by a wave of loving support, for the group dynamic was of one mind, unity.

As residents we were permitted access to the glorious gardens before they opened to the public. Shortly after dawn, I strolled barefoot around the many different areas of the garden wearing a full-length navy blue kaftan, an old Christmas gift from my mother. The grass was springy underfoot. A small waterfall cascaded down a piece of a modern artwork known as the Flow Form. I entered an area of the garden surrounded by a low box hedge, with a manicured lawn divided by a narrow straight path. It led to water running out of a lion's mouth from a well where a glass sat invitingly.

While drinking I thought how many revere this water as an elixir. The water was cool and ran easily down my throat, sending a tingle down my spine. Then I turned and walked towards an ancient yew tree overhanging the shallow healing pool. Stepping into the icy water, I shuddered, stepped out, then meandered towards the sacred well mouth and sat beside it, enjoying the early morning bird song and sheep bleating in the adjacent fields. Bees were buzzing on the flowers, feasting on nectar. As I walked back to find Simon, glancing up I noticed where the garden rose towards an apple tree. It looked like a haven. Pausing, feeling drawn, I decided to give myself reflexology outside for a few moments, in quiet seclusion beneath the apple tree. Rubbing my fingers over the soles of my feet I felt crunchy releases.

We ate breakfast in silence, encouraged to saviour every mouthful. I noticed I chewed mainly on one side and started deliberately chewing on the other. At the allotted time we all assembled in the retreat room. Donald guided and led us throughout the day. During a guided meditation, I faced inner conflicts with my demons and then felt pains releasing their grip in my stomach.

By evening I was tired from the inner work that we had done.

'Hello,' said Simon appearing in our room as I prepared for supper. 'I got stuck in a bog today, had difficulty getting out, but walked miles.' He was glowing in spite of the challenges of the day. Again I marvelled at our parallel worlds, his viewed outwardly pulling himself out of bogs and mine inwardly pulling myself out of destructive behaviours and thought patterns. We slowly walked around the garden perimeter together enjoying the soft air. I noticed a man and two women working reverently in an apple orchard. Drawn to them, I ambled over to the wooden fence.

'Hello,' I called out, with Simon beside me.

'Hello,' called the man, walking towards us with the two women. I was wearing a cloak Steven had lent me to keep the chill air out.

'Are you here for the retreat?' he asked.

'Yes,' I said. We all introduced ourselves.

'I'm Buster. This is my wife Jani and our daughter Hannah, otherwise known as Blue Sky.' She was beautiful, ethereal-looking and twenty-one years old. 'She's an artist, sketches nature and fairies, and is also my apprentice. I'm healing the trees in the apple orchard, as I like to do what I can for the planet.' Fascinated, I instantly warmed to them all. Simon too looked on with interest.

'My work here is almost done,' said Buster, carrying an unusual copper spade. 'We came up in our old camper van from Braintree in Essex.'

'Goodness,' I said, 'one of my relatives, Henry Crittall, created a model village there for the employees of the family metal window frame business.'

'I worked for him!' grinned Buster. 'He was known as The Governor. I was his gardener. He travelled the world over on business, especially China, and created an Oriental garden, full of cherry trees. You should see the blossom in springtime. Silver End was the last model village created by an industrialist, and the first garden village in Essex.'

As I listened I noticed how Buster looked like a tree. His craggy face looked as though it had weathered many a storm and his eyes were filled with wisdom.

'I was once in the Royal Marines. It wasn't for me so I quit to become a gardener and never looked back. People talked about the Governor, how he sat relaxing in the evening, drifting off with a cigar and whisky, lost in thought. That's when ideas came to him of a different way of living. He employed many disabled ex-servicemen, and formed a Welsh choir. He was self-effacing, called himself the bottom dog as opposed to the top dog.' It was fascinating to listen, discovering more about my family background than I'd previously known.

With his arms leaning on the fence, Buster continued in a faraway voice: 'People said the Governor was fixed on the idea of his creation. Couldn't be shifted, even though it meant years of toil and anxiety; he was happy seeing it evolving. His vision of creating that model garden village was his answer to increasing unemployment and housing shortages.'

Later on I researched Henry Crittall and ordered a book about his life, discovering how his family motto is 'Why Not?', and I remembered having the same thought on hearing about Carctol. Silently, I thanked all my ancestors for their inspiration. When stronger I went to the National Portrait Gallery to see a painting of Henry by Augustus John. It was delightful seeing him hanging next to Beatrix Potter, whose books I've enjoyed.

Simon and I exchanged addresses with Buster, promising to keep in touch, and I reflected on my conversation about missing links with Yashu.

After a surprisingly good night's sleep and breakfast Simon asked, 'Would you like to go for a walk and see Glastonbury Tor, next to the garden? It's not far.'

'Yes, I've been looking up at the top of it from a corner of the garden.'

'Come on then, I know you'll need to be back here soon.'

'Oh, this is too steep,' I said sadly, panting and out of breath, unable to make the climb up the steps leading the way up the hillside.

'Don't worry, we'll try another route. Look, there's another path that should be easier. Come on.' Following in his footsteps I noticed the hedgerows smelled of wild honeysuckle.

'Just go slowly. Remember to take one small step at a time,' Simon urged. 'Just look at where you're walking and concentrate on where you are putting your feet.'

My heart was pounding, blood pumping as I continued walking, and then I noticed the discomfort I'd felt in my abdomen was receding. Suddenly the top was in sight and as I reached the summit my heart exploded with a sense of triumph. Breathlessly I looked around at the 360-degree view, as Simon told me, 'Years ago all the surrounding land that you can see was water…' Others were also silently enjoying the view.

Looking around me and marvelling, I drew in a deep breath, remembering how I'd been taught to silently say, 'I wish to renew and rebalance my link with the source of all life.' Usually I'd done that sitting quietly at home.

I heard Simon saying, 'Come down steadily as the path is uneven.' And before we knew it we were back at the base.

'I didn't think I could do that,' I said. 'Thank you.'

'It's amazing what can be done when we try. I'll see you later as I'm off now for my day's walking. Enjoy your day.' Reaching up I kissed him goodbye before turning to go and change my shoes ready for the day ahead.

During the morning meditation I relaxed deeply, felt blissful and strangely tasted butter; but I hadn't eaten butter in months. Sharing our experiences afterwards, Donald reassured me that 'sometimes our senses, when in a blissful state, can experience an exquisite enrichment in one form or another'.

We gathered for lunch in the dining room. I mainly ate salad, as we were encouraged to eat frugally to enhance our experiences. Late in the afternoon Donald and Steven led us into the garden, with the instruction to wander around until we found a plant or insect that attracted us and to then put our entire focus on just that. I wandered off up the garden path before finding a profusion of purple pansies, and sat on the grass cross-legged, staring and marvelling at them and then at the vastness of the universe, suddenly feeling poetic. I saw a butterfly flutter down into the warm embrace of a pansy and drink its fill. Then I had a flash of understanding of nature's cycle, of the flower's connection to the vastness through its roots below and offering up its sweet replenishing nectar above ground. Like the plants we too, when rooted and grounded, offer up our own unique nectar to those who flutter into our lives.

Immersed in a deep abiding peace, I declined the opportunity to explore the town. All desire for shopping and crowds had fallen away. How could they compare to the rare inner peace I was experiencing in the garden, I wondered, wanting to lock myself away in it.

We gathered together in the retreat room before departing at the end of the weekend. Each took a turn to speak briefly. At the end I was humbled when a round of applause rang out in support of what I was doing. I didn't want to leave the group, or the garden, but with a wrench we drove off. I experienced difficulty adjusting at first when we returned home. All those intense, warm feelings were lost; but were they, I mused? They'd been absorbed and were part of my fabric now, and I could sit quietly and revisit them whenever I chose.

By mid-September it was time for another visit to Professor Thomas. That prospect made me nervous, but instead of ignoring my nerves, I breathed into them, telling myself to breathe out tension, breathe in calm. It's about being sensitive to one's nature, not going against it, I remembered.

'Hello,' she said, inviting us into her office. 'You do look a healthy colour. Have you been on holiday?'

'No, we haven't,' I said, looking at my tanned palms in my lap. 'I don't understand why I've turned this colour,' I said hesitantly.

'What are you currently eating more of?'

'I'm drinking more carrot juice.'

'Ah, that's the cause. I had a former patient who turned completely orange she drank so much. Just ease off it and your normal colour will return,' she reassured. I was so relieved, as I'd secretly been looking in the mirror to see the colour of my eyeballs, wondering at the state of my liver.

'Tell me, Gillian, how do you heal yourself?' asked Professor Thomas.

'Simply put, I sit or lie quietly, mentally shutting out the outside world, aware that I'm drawing into the silence. Then, as taught, I imagine a light switch being turned on and a current of Divine energy surging into me, healing me. When I've finished I imagine the switch turning off.'

'Thank you for explaining it to me. I think it would be a good idea for you to have another scan, so we can take a look at what's going on.' I looked at Simon, who nodded in agreement, as Professor Thomas made notes.

'You'll receive your appointment in the post,' she said. Later she examined me on the couch and then I had the usual blood tests, with a nurse discovering that my blood vessels were more easily accessible this time. I'd been visualizing them closer to the skin's surface when blood samples were required.

After my visit, Professor Thomas wrote the following letter to my GP:

I saw Mrs Gill again yesterday for the first time in about four months. Her abdomen is clearly still distended but she does look extremely well in herself. She has been taking a number of herbal remedies, including something called Carctol which she received from Dr Rosy Daniel, who used to work at the Bristol Cancer Centre. She says she has now plucked up the courage to have a further CT scan so I have asked the radiologist to arrange this for her.

A couple of months later, when I next saw Marianne, she looked deeply into my eyes and said, 'Your eyes are looking clearer. Those small dark spots that used to be there are all but vanished!' I credited this in no small part to my dietary and lifestyle changes.

After these two visits, something strange happened to distract me in an altogether different way. Repeatedly, when I took Lucy for a walk, I'd glimpse three runaway dogs, panting heavily, skirting the adjoining tree-lined boundary of the farm. One dog was black but otherwise looked like a fox. I couldn't get it out of my mind; it haunted me. I was also dreaming of a dog that resembled a fox. I asked Simon, 'What do you think it means?'

'Not sure.' Then I reminded him of my conversation with the visiting German doctor.

'I don't know how we're going to manage another dog. However, Lucy is still listless, pining for Jack. Maybe we should consider it?'

'Please think about it,' I urged; like a dog with a bone I wouldn't give up trying to persuade him. He had to overcome his uncertainties about the future and my long-term health prospects.

It didn't take long before Simon came round to the idea and we started to visit the local animal rescue centres.

'I like the Bull Mastiff called Lily,' said David, ever hopeful as we strolled around one of the centres.

'Think of the drool on the parquet floor!' I replied, remembering how it had taken me six months at the start of our marriage to lovingly restore it by hand. It was an unusual Canadian wood mixture and had been hidden beneath an old carpet. We trailed around several rescue centres but no one dog stood out from the rest. Then I had a flash, remembering where we'd found Jack. Finding the telephone number for the local animal rescue mission, my heart was somersaulting as the phone rang.

'Hello,' a lady answered with a gravelly smoker's voice. I recognized her in an instant.

'We found and fell in love with a rescue dog you had many years ago. He was a Collie Labrador cross with a distinctive white flash on his chest. Sadly he died a year ago.'

'Oh, I remember him. He kept being returned to us, before you gave him a home, due to children with allergies to his fur.'

Taking a deep breath I said, 'You might think I'm slightly unusual, but lately I keep dreaming about a fox-like dog.' Holding my breath I waited for her response.

'Curiously enough, I'm also a little unusual. After the life I've lived, witnessing what some humans do to animals, I rather prefer animals.' That fortified me. 'It just so happens we do have a dog who looks like a fox. He keeps being returned. You'd better hurry along and take a look. How soon can you visit?'

'Nine o'clock tomorrow morning is the earliest I can get the whole family together.'

'Do you have any other dogs?' she asked. 'Yes, Lucy, a black Labrador; I forgot to mention her.'

'Then you'd better bring her along. We'll let her do the deciding. My husband, Peter, will meet you and take you into a paddock. You'll all stand back and let Lucy meet Charlie, as if they're meeting in a park for the first time. This is very important and the consequences will tell us all we need to know.' I was awed by the sequence of events conspiring to help us.

I trusted the woman's instincts implicitly. When we arrived at the rescue centre Clare was excited, having come home from university. 'Oh look, Mum,' she said pointing. At the end of a long concrete path in the stable a dog was jumping almost to the stable roof.

'He's a bit lively,' said Peter, noticing our faces.

'I'll just go in and put him on a lead. Please go ahead and wait in the paddock with Lucy.'

What a peculiar dog, I thought. He didn't look like Jack. 'Clare,' I said, realization dawning, 'that's the very stable we found Jack in! You probably won't remember, as you were only five years old. David was only a few months old.' The memory stirred me.

'Look at Daddy's face,' Clare said amused. It was a puzzle as he stared disbelievingly at Charlie's boisterous antics.

'Now,' said Peter, 'who is going to walk Lucy around the paddock?'

Simon looked at me expectantly. 'I will,' I replied.

'Just walk her over to that gorse bush,' Peter said pointing. He kept firm control of Charlie, now walking, or I should say prancing, beside him on the lead. His movement was exquisite, like a wild dog. Lucy looked the other way, disinterested. We all stood riveted watching the two dogs, staring from one to the other.

'He is the result of generations of cross-breeding; that's why he moves like a wild dog,' said Peter, noticing my widening eyes.

Then both dogs met, their leads now off. Their noses touched. They erupted into a game, running round in circles and sniffing every tuft of grass in the paddock. It was as though they'd known one another forever. Lucy was smitten. Her entire body relaxed, as relief washed through her at finding another canine friend.

'I'm coming over now', said Peter, 'to put Charlie back on the lead and introduce him to you all.' Charlie greeted the children and me warmly. Sensing Simon's reluctance, Charlie slowly strolled over, sat at his feet and looked adoringly into his eyes. That did it.

'I think he's the one, don't you?' Simon said emotionally. No one could replace Jack, but I believe Jack had helped lead us to find Charlie. It was by this time a year and a month since my diagnosis and a bit longer since Jack's demise. All Lucy's listlessness disappeared in an instant.

'We'd like him,' said Simon to Peter. 'Can you tell us his history?'

'It's sad,' came the reply. 'His previous mistress has cancer. She's been in and out of the Royal Marsden Hospital. Charlie's been like a surrogate child to her and her husband. She's in there at the moment, and they can't cope with him.' Simon and I exchanged a look. 'Follow me into the office. My wife takes care of the paperwork.'

'What an exceptional dog,' she said looking at Lucy placidly sitting in the corner by the door. I was so proud of her.

'We've come to do the necessary, as we'd like Charlie,' said Simon.

'I can see he's at last found his true home. Lucy will look after him well.'

As Clare and I walked both dogs out of the office on their leads, Simon and David sprang into action preparing the car. Simon unlocked it and

David opened the boot. Wondering what to do, Lucy did what she always does, leaping into the open boot, and Charlie simply followed, to Peter's surprise.

Approaching home at the top of our drive David said, 'If you stop the car, Dad, Clare and I will walk the dogs home.'

'Good idea.'

Once out of the car Simon drove slowly as we watched Charlie being walked down the drive with his tail high; all seemed well. Inside the house Charlie sniffed about, familiarizing himself.

'Look,' said Clare pointing, 'he's going into the sitting room. Oh no! Mum will be pleased,' she giggled, seeing Charlie lift his leg on the same pink armchair Jack had christened when he first came into the house.

'Mop and bucket with plenty of soapy water will fix that,' said Simon looking at me.

'I know my place,' I replied happily.

'I'll put this bag of toys in the hall,' said David, tipping out the dog toys that came with Charlie.

'He was loved,' said Clare, looking at the smart ceramic water and feeding bowls and leather-studded collar and lead, together with the many toys.

The first night went well enough. 'Let him find his own spot to settle,' advised Simon, as the rest of us fussed around. He opted for a landing on the stairs, at the heart of the house, as Jack had. The following morning, we discovered how busy Lucy had been in the night.

'She's shredded all his toys!' said Simon.

'I wonder how he'll manage without his familiar comforts,' I replied and thought how alike we were. With my dietary regime and different lifestyle we were both adapting to new ways.

'He'll be alright,' reassured Simon. 'Remember how the lady said that Lucy will look after him.'

That first night, the night before Bonfire night, with Charlie safely beneath our roof, as I drifted off to sleep I remembered why I'd become a vegetarian. It was born of my desire to become a purer channel for healing. Then I remembered a conversation I'd had around that time with someone

I highly respect, who said, 'It's more important what comes out of your mouth than what you put into it.'

Later on I asked Simon, 'What's your interpretation of this?'

He replied, 'I would think in order to have healthy relationships and a healthy diet, one needs to apply some control over both.'

The next morning, in spite of the bitter cold autumn weather, I wrapped up with the fresh incentive to walk both dogs.

'Take the leads with you,' said Simon. 'Remember Charlie's not familiar with his surroundings yet.'

'Good idea.' With that I turned my coat collar up and put my gloves on. The freezing air whipped colour into my cheeks. I felt invigorated.

'Come on you two,' I said looking at Lucy and Charlie. As we walked up the drive Lucy made for a rabbit burrow. Charlie watched, unsure. He saw her having fun and wanted to join in as that, understandably, had been missing from his life lately.

'I'll take your lead off, shall I?' I said. His tail went up and ears pricked, he quivered with excitement as he burrowed alongside Lucy, learning the ways of the countryside. That joy is his rightful inheritance to claim, I thought. Watching them I realized happiness is everyone's rightful inheritance, and thought how much more accessible it became by decluttering life and living more simply.

Charlie didn't need to go back on the lead. He followed Lucy, as she had previously done with Jack, and he kept looking behind to make sure I was there. When we got home and I looked at their faces closely, I noticed Charlie had a small white feather stuck to the end of his nose. My heart stirred, conjuring thoughts of him being a gift from the angels.

By evening the sound of fireworks drifted in. Charlie ran into the room quaking, seeking us out, terrified by the loud bangs. Lucy followed and calmly settled down, while Charlie stayed close needing lots of reassurance.

While I stroked Charlie, Simon put the television on. 'So much has changed in such a relatively short time, I can hardly believe it,' I said.

It was soon mid-November and I was due for another hospital appointment. Simon and I set off and had the usual trouble finding a parking spot at the hospital. While waiting to see Professor Thomas, I imagined myself on a warm, sunny day in a glorious garden, to quell my anxiety and to try and prevent myself from dwelling too heavily on my latest CT scan results, which we were about to hear.

'You look well,' she said, as she invited us into her consulting room. 'How have you been?'

'Well, some of the time I keep being sick and have diarrhoea; other times that stops and I feel stronger. Before CT scans I get anxious and use hypnotherapy techniques to try to control my phobia of confined spaces. Going into the machine I repeat to myself "I breathe in calm, I breathe out anxiety" to try to help minimize that.'

She took notes and I mentioned that Rosy and my nutritionist advised me to take buffered vitamin C to help eliminate the high levels of radioactivity after the scan.

When we finished talking she examined me. 'Not much change,' she said. Then she put my latest CT scans on the wall for us to look at and pointed at the small amount of change. My heart sank. I reflected on all the natural healing methods I was applying. Was I mistaken with all I was doing, I wondered? But I feel so well most of the time, I thought.

Walking towards the front door after the appointment, we heard barking. Charlie was singing us a heartening welcome home. Immediately the door opened he jumped up, like a jack-in-the-box, and continued to do so until he'd smothered us both with affection. Lucy looked bemused, but then barked too, wagging her tail furiously. Simon and I looked at one another and he said, 'Well, who'd have believed it. We now have two dogs that bark.'

Going to lie down to process the news from my latest hospital appointment, I was surprised by the sound of paws coming up the stairs. Charlie nudged the bedroom door open and came alongside the bed, nuzzling my hand, and I felt the tension beginning to drain out of me.

Professor Thomas sent the following letter to my GP after that appointment:

I saw Gillian at the Guildford Nuffield on 14th November. Her recent scan shows very little change from last year but still shows a large pelvic mass and large metastases in the liver.

Mrs Gill is extremely well in herself with no real change in the clinical findings. I suggest that I continue with the low-profile approach and that we keep our fingers and toes firmly crossed. I am due to see her again in the New Year.

CHAPTER 7
Whispering Angels

At certain times in our lives we're called forth
To be true to ourselves;
It's about self-preserving,
And self-learning;
And merely at times just being you.
Rather than struggling and striving,
Trust, yield and surrender.
Gillian Gill

January – September 2002

'You're doing better than you think,' I groaned, and rolling over in bed heard an owl hoot then slept again. 'Many things are done in the belief of free flow, and flow away quite naturally.'

Even though I was dreaming I was aware of a radiant man standing over me, dressed entirely in blue, and a voice saying calmly, 'Matter is dissolving, liquid is evaporating, momentum is gathering and occurring without effort.' I became aware of being in a race and was within a hair's breadth of others, of the distant finishing line. I was on the right track, leading to 'the home straight', even though there was some way to go.

Later that day Simon said, 'Charlie and Lucy seem to be bonding well. They love it when you rub their ears; look at them both.'

'They do,' I replied, 'and you know what? As I rub their ears, I feel them slump and let go and then I feel more relaxed too.' Lately I'd also noticed that Lucy was increasingly coming to find me when I was healing myself. Then she'd gently nudge my lump with her nose and sniff, as if to see how I was progressing. At these times I felt infused with her love.

Simon continued, 'They do help us all relax in different ways. Charlie greets David from school like a hero, jumping up and singing. When Clare comes home, he licks her face and sings to her in ecstasy. She's intrigued by how he waits until Lucy's finished her food before starting his, as he watches her every move. I like the way he's adopted the habit of lying right next to me when I'm working; from time to time he takes deep sighs. When are you taking him to the vet for his check-up?'

'Tomorrow.'

'See how old the vet thinks he is as it's hard to tell.'

Setting off to the vet, I suddenly had a blank as I couldn't remember the way, and I began panicking. I took a deep breath, slowed the car down and noticed my hands were tightly clutching the steering wheel. Deliberately relaxing my grip, I took another slow, deep breath and another. My mind cleared and the road became recognizable again, as did the rest of the familiar route to the vet. Such blanks occurred from time to time as I strove to remain calm while regaining lost confidence in everyday skills.

Charlie, on the lead, walked beside me into the surgery without hesitation. He sat, interested in his surroundings, while we waited our turn. A young red-haired boy had a cat in his backpack as a convenient way of carrying it. The cat's head popped out from the opened top, curiosity getting the better of it. I smiled at the boy.

'Makes him feel secure, this way,' he told me.

'Mrs Gill, please come through.' It was the same nurse who'd seen Lucy after I ran her over. 'Who have we got here?' she asked.

'Charlie, our new rescue dog.'

'How long have you had him?'

'A few weeks.'

'That's unbelievable. He looks so relaxed, as though he's been with you forever.'

'We do seem to have an affinity. He's lifted Lucy's spirits too.'

'He will. She needed a new friend. Let's see your teeth, shall we Charlie? Good boy. Now let's look at the rest of you. He's very good natured. Oh, this is a nasty rash, an allergy I'd say.'

'He was on a bed of straw in a stable,' I told her.

'That's probably the cause. Just bathe him with a mild salt water solution and sponge.'

Next I asked, 'How old do you think he is?'

'I'd say about ten months. He looks just like a Dingo doesn't he? That's the result of the cross-breeding. These kinds of dogs are strong and know how to use their instincts.'

On my return Simon asked, 'How did you get on at the vet?'

'Very well,' I replied, repeating everything that had happened.

'As he's settling in so well, and as it's our wedding anniversary next week, I'd like to take you out for a meal?'

The idea thrilled me. Although I was stronger I was still laid low at times with healing crises; they manifested in the form of old injuries and conditions coming to the surface. At these times I felt new layers of pain rising to be released from deeper levels; on occasions emotional issues accompanied the pain, which I released and supported as best I could by merely acknowledging them and usually crying. Visualizing myself being well on the night of our wedding anniversary was another goal to attain.

'It will be such a treat to go out for a meal,' I said.

Our anniversary arrived. 'Let's confine Lucy and Charlie in the kitchen. I'll put their big bed next to the radiator and switch the radio on. That should keep them happy while we're out celebrating,' said Simon.

The local restaurant was lovely, but I felt slightly apprehensive.

'Here you are, Madam,' said a friendly waiter handing us menus, after first seating us at a table.

We chatted for a few moments, enjoying the sense of occasion; then I glanced at the menu. Simon asked, 'What's the matter?'

'There doesn't appear to be anything I can eat.' My heart sank.

'Ask to see the chef and have a chat with him.'

Feeling embarrassed, and swallowing hard, I did just that. Chef came out of the kitchen wearing a stripy apron. After listening to my plight, which I stumbled over, he surprised me by saying, 'Tell me what you can eat and I'll go and create something special in the kitchen.' I was amazed.

'There you are,' said Simon, 'that wasn't so bad was it?'

'No, I suppose not,' I said, coming to terms with another milestone.

When the food arrived at the table it looked so beautifully arranged on the plate. I hesitated, admiring it before eating.

'It's a little salty,' I said concerned.

'I'm sure just this once your body will cope,' replied Simon. It did and I enjoyed every mouthful. We returned home in good spirits and headed straight for the kitchen to see the dogs.

'What a mess!' said Simon perplexed.

'What's that smell?' I asked.

Looking shocked Simon replied, 'Someone's been at your stash of supplements.'

'Oh, it's Charlie. He's been at my Carctol. Look, his face has empty capsules stuck all around his muzzle together with a fine powder!' I was so worried. The instructions said to strictly adhere to the prescribed dosage, a maximum of eight capsules a day. Charlie had eaten almost an entire pot.

'I'll open the back door', said Simon rushing to unlock it, 'and take the dogs around the garden.' They appeared fine, Lucy looking deliberately demur as though she'd played no part in the affair.

While Simon was in the garden, I looked around at the vegetable rack in which I'd left my entire vitamin supply. How would Charlie react to the herbs, I worried? Then, while sweeping up the mess, all thoughts of my new outfit and happy evening gone, I noticed another pot of supplements open, my antioxidants; out of the fifty or so pots why were these the only two touched? As I started feeling guilty, what I was learning came back to me; stopping myself, I realized I could alter my attitude and see the situation differently. Rather than feeling guilty and negligent, and scolding myself about leaving the supplements unwittingly, I paused. Refocusing, I acknowledged the slip and redirected my thoughts. After all, Charlie appeared fine. Let's just get through the night, as you can't phone the vet, I thought. I was also sure that they would never have heard of the pills Charlie had taken.

All night, every hour or so, I kept a vigil, peering over the banisters to look at Charlie in his bed fast asleep. By morning, though weary, I accompanied Simon on the dogs' first walk of the day.

'Look at him go,' said Simon proudly watching Charlie. Far from collapsing, Charlie launched himself rocket-like around what we call the 'flying field', a meadow used by a local model aeroplane club. Lucy, in her own world, carried on steadily, while Charlie tore round in circles, his entire body rippling in a state of euphoria.

'Maggie will be here soon. We'd better go home,' said Simon looking at his watch.

'What a godsend Maggie is in our lives right now, coming over for a couple of hours to help with the house,' I replied.

'Yes, we have dear Irene to thank for introducing us to her. What would we have done without her love and support early on?'

I didn't know. All I did know was I hadn't been able to bend down to wash the kitchen floor tiles, or polish my pride and joy, the parquet floor. Previously, I'd found housework absorbing and rewarding, and I was frustrated by the situation. Maggie was a strong, able-bodied sixty-something who cycled the mile or so over to our home every week, and her help was invaluable. She'd had a tough life. I enjoyed our chats at the kitchen table, covering many subjects, including her having seen ghosts, once or twice, like me. She also sensed her late husband and late cat around her at times, especially when she felt low, and always welcomed their love.

'When we get home I'm going to phone Marianne and see what she has to say about Charlie's escapade,' I said.

'That's a good idea.'

'Why are you laughing so much, Marianne?' I asked mystified when I phoned her.

She replied, 'Dogs are remarkable, and unlike human beings they haven't lost their natural ability to find from nature what herbs they need to heal them. He obviously had an imbalance and knew how to correct it. Charlie has, by the sound of things, rather overdone the dosage, but with no harmful side effects. Just keep an eye on him and see what happens. Give him lots of water to flush his kidneys through, with all the physical processing that he will naturally be undergoing. By the way, have you tried dandelion coffee? It's caffeine free and most health food shops sell it. I think you'd enjoy it.'

I thanked her for that unexpected information, and then marvelled at what a clever dog we'd found, although in truth he'd found us. He instinctively knew which of my supplements to select. He also knows precisely when I'm going to give myself healing after lunch. He pads upstairs, paws the door asking to come in, then waits for a signal at the foot of the bed. When I raise my left hand he leaps up beside me where I have his blanket ready. We simultaneously take a deep sigh, let go and travel to our separate inner healing planes, especially when listening to relaxing guided meditations.

A couple of days after speaking to Marianne, I visited a local health food shop and found a pot of dandelion coffee. Eager to try it I put the kettle on as soon as I got home.

'What have you got there?' asked Simon.

'Something new to me, suggested by Marianne. It smells good,' I replied smelling the steaming liquid. Adding a little soya milk I sipped the hot liquid; it tasted so comforting and good, after well over a year without tea or coffee.

Two weeks after Charlie had gorged the supplements, while resting and stroking behind his legs, I noticed his scabs and rash had entirely disappeared. Delighted and astonished, I couldn't wait to tell Simon, Marianne and Yashu. It looked like the supplement helped other living creatures too, with different health conditions.

Next time I spoke to Yashu, she said, 'Please make a note of this interesting and exciting discovery, and when we give a presentation to inform doctors of our findings with Carctol, would you please join us and share your experiences of what it has done for you, and Charlie!' She laughingly put the phone down, as she was busily planning a seminar on Carctol. Over the next few years, I spoke at a number of seminars, including one in Baden-Baden, or 'Baden and Baden' as Yashu called it.

Meanwhile Helen, my friend working at the local hospital, and her husband Nigel were secretly arranging an outing.

'Please put something nice on,' said Simon, 'we're going out to London for the evening.' Filled with secrecy he wouldn't be coerced into saying more. I took it easy for the entire day, feeling mildly apprehensive about being out later than was usual.

'Come on, hop in the car. We're meeting somewhere, and going on from there,' Simon said smiling. Before we reached the end of the communal drive Simon was parking.

'Do tell me what is going on?' I asked perplexed.

'Just be patient, you'll soon find out.' With that a black stretch limousine turned off the main road into the driveway.

'Gosh, someone's going out tonight,' I said unknowingly. The limousine pulled up alongside our car and Helen and Nigel stepped out looking smart.

'Come on, Gill, and sit in here,' urged Helen, laughing and patting the seat beside her. As I gingerly climbed into the car, it felt as though I'd died and gone to heaven. The midnight blue roof sparkled with star-studded lights. A bottle of champagne nestled on ice next to a bottle of water, which I drank while the others sipped champagne throughout the journey.

'Where are we going?' I asked.

'To see *Aida* at The Royal Albert Hall,' said Helen. 'We wanted to surprise you.' They succeeded. Sitting back as everyone chatted, I enjoyed every precious moment. We were dropped at the entrance and, as we alighted from the car, I noticed how chilly it was. The hall was filling up with people, all dressed beautifully. We found our seats, in a private box, and sat back admiring the stunning Egyptian scenery; the performance was marvellous, transporting me to another world. Glorious music filled the auditorium and many became deeply moved. Walking down the stairs to leave, with one arm on Simon's, the other on the marble banisters and chatting to our friends, I glanced up at the glass dome roof. Snowflakes were falling; in that instant I felt as though I was encased in a magical children's Christmas festive shaker. What a happy evening we all had. I marvelled at the plotting and planning that had gone on behind the scenes, and thanked everyone for their thoughtfulness and generosity.

Soon my next appointment arrived to visit Professor Thomas. 'How are you?' She had my file open and took notes as usual.

'Since last seeing you, my confidence has been shaken as I've had some sort of healing crisis, which I don't understand as friends with germs thoughtfully stay away, yet I've got a nasty rash.'

After examining me Professor Thomas said, 'The rash is a recurrence to a lesser degree of shingles.'

'Oh, I had that in my twenties when stressed from working too hard.'

We continued talking before she looked at Simon, asking how he was, and I listened while they chatted.

After the appointment she wrote the following letter to my GP:

I saw Mrs Gill at the Guildford Nuffield Hospital on 30th January. She remains extremely well in herself. She recently had a re-activation of shingles, which she has had in the past, but did not notice any pain, simply a rash across the left upper abdominal area.

On examining her she seemed slightly less distended and certainly says she is feeling more comfortable. She is now taking 2 capsules of Carctol 4 times a day, which is the full dose.

Clinically the findings are completely unchanged with a large mid-line abdominal mass. Her liver remains impalpable.

I have checked her baseline bloods today, full blood count and profile, but have not checked her tumour markers as I think there is little to be gained from this practice, given that she is not having any conventional intervention.

She has also told me about a private seminar to learn about the use of Carctol which will take place in London on 2 March. Unfortunately I am unable to attend, but I understand that Gillian will be attending as a case example. Dr Rosy Daniel, who works from the Harley Street Clinic, believes she is the only person having this treatment in the absence of any conventional medical treatment.

A while after this appointment Simon said, 'We should think about going on holiday. I recall Rosy saying how for some people with cancer she's noticed they deteriorate after flying, so it's best to think twice about flying. No one is sure why it happens, it's just an observation she's made.'

'Then how will we travel?' I asked confused.

'Train is a good alternative. We can travel to Lausanne in Switzerland that way and meet your friend Lindsay there and stay somewhere close by.'

'What a lovely idea,' I replied, 'especially as Switzerland is renowned for its pure mountain air acting as a tonic.'

'I think we deserve a break; and I know you're struggling coming to terms with Irene being about to retire and move to the coast.'

Having become dependent on Irene, I was feeling apprehensive about going it alone without my regular visits to her healing clinic. Time for another challenge, I thought. In my heart I knew I could still phone her and chat, and realized she'd already filled me with her belief in my ability, amongst other things. Yet I still felt shaky.

Over the next couple of months I remained steadfast to my new regimes. My abdomen still stung and gurgled alarmingly, and at times I felt an uncomfortable tugging sensation around my 'lump'.

Springtime came and one morning as I walked the dogs close to a pond, a favourite spot in the corner of one of the fields, I noticed the entire surface was covered in bubbles. Riveted to the spot, I suddenly saw tadpoles midway into becoming frogs. Hundreds of them were swimming to the surface, using their newly grown back legs, and then gulping air before diving back down into the pond. Later on that evening our nature-loving friends Melinda and Trevor joined Simon and I for a dog walk. We stood by the pond totally absorbed, laughing at the beauty and abundance of nature, as new life emerged before our very eyes.

Soon I was due for an appointment to see my nutritionist. 'I'm off to see Marianne for a check-up,' I said to Simon before leaving the house. Driving locally and regaining a sense of independence felt good.

'You look well,' she said hugging me warmly before I lay on the couch. 'Oh, this is so exciting. As I'm muscle-testing you, I can tell that you have natural bacteria busily gobbling up and clearing matter. If you experience small amounts of increased abdominal bloating, it's a good thing, nothing to be concerned about. Your body may be trying to heal itself this way. It has its own ability to heal itself if permitted.' Again, I was hearing affirmation.

'I was concerned about the bloating,' I said, adding, 'I've noticed if I cut myself, curiously my wounds heal faster than they used to.'

Marianne knowingly replied, 'This can happen with all that you are putting into healing yourself. There is one thing, though. Your emotions are rocky and I have just discovered these wonderful new animal essences. They are similar in principle to the wide range of different flower essences and are doing marvellous things for many of my clients. Would you be interested in my muscle-testing which one would be appropriate for you?'

'Yes,' I replied, trusting her completely and fascinated by her description of an animal's spiritual essence, combined with love, being used to help humans via means of a prayerful ritual conducted by a Shaman. Shamans, after all, are the ancient natural healers, finding from nature what is required to heal people within their community.

'Your body wants frog,' she smiled. Then I told her about my recent walk. 'Nature is trying to help you. This essence helps embrace seeing the world through the eyes of a child, filled with awe and wonder. It is easy to take and should support your emotions at this time of your healing transformation.'

'Thank you, I'll let you know how I get on,' I replied.

Marianne continued, 'I've just had a cleansing enema and wondered what do you think about having one? They are so good for the body.' I flinched at the idea. 'I know how you feel,' said Marianne, nevertheless pressing the point, 'but you can buy DIY kits instead of seeing a practitioner if you prefer. I can order one for you and have it sent. The directions are easy to follow. You wouldn't believe the rubbish that gets stuck in deep corners of the body; they emerge like black rubber bands.' She'd somehow convinced me to give it a go.

I was apprehensive when the kit arrived. Charlie was barking his head off as it was being delivered.

'The policeman was right about getting a dog with big ears,' said Simon hastening beside me to see what the commotion was.

'Lucy's barking, joining in again!' I said laughing.

'What's that parcel?' asked Simon.

'A DIY enema kit that Marianne ordered,' I replied, disappearing to study the instructions.

The following day Simon went to a meeting in London, as I was improving health-wise. He was noticing others in the office were also beginning to spend the occasional day working from home. Meanwhile, the downstairs shower room was being transformed with layers of rubber-backed bath mats. I phoned my friend Jo, a two-time cancer survivor using conventional medicine. She had just lost her father when I was diagnosed so I hadn't told her my dismal prognosis, just that I had cancer. She's a born survivor with a strong will to live and warned me against taking an unorthodox approach, as she was so worried for me. Her directness and humour are a pure tonic. 'What are you doing now?' she asked.

'Lying on the floor with a tub of lubricant in my hand,' I replied.

'Gill, I don't want to know any more!' she said. 'What about the poor bathroom floor if you get it wrong?' That did it. Somehow she'd fortified me for the task. I hastily said goodbye in case I changed my mind. I looked at the jug of tepid camomile tea and the mountain of towels, which for some strange reason made me fleetingly think of The Princess and the Pea fairy tale. The coat hanger held the plastic bag now full of tea. My hands shook as I took the rubber nozzle at the end of the long tube, ready to receive the enema. The tea stung in what I perceived to be the liver region, and I'd barely started before deciding I'd had enough. Feeling a complete failure, I burst into tears. Grabbing the loo roll to mop them up, I fought the sense of defeat, struggling to realize my body was trying to tell me something.

When I phoned Marianne, she laughingly told me not to worry. I felt better listening to her as she said, 'It was worth a try.'

Well, I thought, we only know what we want in life when we know what we don't want. 'It's all part of learning,' Marianne said.

Yes, I thought, she had had a good experience with the procedure, but I hadn't. Our bodies were different, that was all. That night, when contemplating the issue before going to sleep, I realized each of us possesses a quality that is unique to us. Marianne does things her way; I must do things my way and be true to myself, we're individuals. One of life's gifts is recognizing one thing we each can do well. After speaking to Marianne I realized that, for me, it's being prepared to have a go; something Jane, my sister, had taught me during our childhood, and which was now being validated. Listening to others, I realized it's best to avoid comparing oneself to another and to strive to retain a sense of inner contentment by living a life true to oneself and enjoying small things, simply. Listening to a buzzard calling while soaring over the adjacent fields always fills me with delight, I thought; so does listening to pigeons cooing. At those times I become aware of an underlying strength, uniting with a power outside myself, no matter what emotions ripple across the surface.

Marianne told me something else during our telephone conversation: 'You may like to try Essene bread now your digestion's improving so much. It's made with sprouted wheat and is easily digestible. It's similar to malt bread in texture.' A while later she told me about Artisan Bread Organic, a company that produces a range of biodynamic and organic breads suitable for those with sensitive digestion. Following her recommendation, I tentatively bit into the toast. It was heavier than normal bread and comforting to eat, and after two years of no bread at all it was a treat. Later still, other varieties of Artisan Bread were easily digested and savoured, providing a most welcome addition to my diet. I was also now able to reintroduce small amounts of low salt bouillon powder into my cooking.

Around this time my menopausal hormones were rampant and it must have been terrible for Simon on occasions, though he did his best not to show it. He just went out cycling more often. Restraint is so hard to learn, particularly with one's nearest and dearest. With Marianne's help I tried to view the hot flushes as a positive sign, rather like a rite of passage when becoming older, and hopefully wiser. She taught me to view some of the alarming physical changes as a plus, imagining deeper levels of unwanted matter leaving the body via this natural means. She also suggested some soya-based supplements, which helped.

When I spoke to my oncologist about some of the menopausal side effects she offered reassurances that they were normal.

At this time I was in great discomfort with my bowels playing up, which coincided with our septic tank doing the same thing. Rosy was later to tell me that it's not uncommon for our physical environment to mirror internal disturbances. I found this most comforting and it was something I became aware of and found happening repeatedly.

By now the Carctol seminar was looming. 'Hello Ma, just thought I'd phone to wish you good luck with the seminar,' said Clare phoning from Newcastle.

Preparing for the seminar, in order to distract myself from my nerves, I focused on what to wear and settled on a jonquil yellow top that the moths hadn't found. The colour lifted my spirits and the cotton jumper was comfortable. Then I sat quietly praying, asking for help. Afterwards I remembered Gee telling our group years ago how sometimes in life we're called forth to make personal sacrifices, overcoming emotional challenges, and that if we persevere, something naturally occurs: we discover something of greater value, heralding a sense of deeper inner fulfilment.

'I'll be right beside you,' said Simon squeezing my hand, bringing me out of my reverie, 'and Claire, your acupuncturist and yoga friend, is coming to support you too.'

'I know it's ridiculous. I just want to help and do my best in any way I can, but I feel nervous speaking in front of so many doctors.'

Everyone attending the seminar wanted one thing: to help find natural ways of combating cancer. Yashu had reassured me she would be there with her husband, Chandra, and many family members. Dr Daniel would be the guest speaker; she would guide me by asking questions, then throw the floor open to questions from delegates.

'Look at all the brightly coloured Indian saris,' I said quietly to Simon and Claire as we walked into the hall filled with people, some standing in groups talking, others already seated. Then Rosy, coincidentally dressed in bright colours that matched the saris perfectly, came over and introduced me to Yashu for the first time. She looked radiant in her sari with her lustrous black hair plaited perfectly for the occasion.

'Gillian, you look beautiful. Doesn't she Simon?' said Yashu bending forward, her hands in prayer and touching her heart, greeting us before warmly embracing me. 'Chandra, Gillian and Simon have arrived with their friend Claire,' she continued, as her family gathered around to meet us all. Warm exchanges of Namaste followed.

With everyone seated Rosy got the seminar off to a good start as she charismatically delivered her introductory speech.

'I'd like to introduce Yashu Amlani MBE.' She proudly pointed at Yashu, who acknowledged the introduction by standing up. Yashu gently touched her heart with both hands, while lowering her head, saying Namaste. 'She brought Carctol, the Ayurvedic Indian herbal medicine, to my attention and arranged a meeting in India with Dr Tiwari. She was determined to bring that meeting about. I confess to being impressed by Dr Tiwari's findings with the extraordinary combination of eight herbs, which taken separately achieve little.' Papers rustled, as some people looked at their notes listing the herbs. Rosy continued to mention the good results from Carctol in some of her patients. One particular lady had a nasty cancer which conventional medicine had only helped so far. She'd decided to integrate Carctol into her health regime as a last resort and managed to beat her cancer.

Believing in the path one chooses can affect one's recovery, and finding a new way of living can increase positive mental attitude. After all the sadness and illness around cancer that I've seen, I like to think that many of us, given the chance, would be willing to try holistic or complementary medical treatments when conventional methods have failed. Some people respond to certain forms of medication, others do not. Of course, I can only speak of my own experience.

'Gillian,' said Rosy, 'please stand up.' My eyes locked with Simon's, then Rosy's, and as I stood, with Simon seated beside me, I felt a sudden calm raining down on me like an invisible shower.

'Look everyone, Gillian is wearing the identical colour to my other patient who is doing so well on Carctol.' Everyone applauded and laughed at the coincidence, relaxing the atmosphere.

My mind cleared as I spoke before fielding questions. Then I asked a question: 'Does anyone know how acidic tomatoes are?' I missed them on my alkaline diet. There was some discrepancy over their acidity when cooked, but the consensus of opinion was they became less acidic.

'Gillian,' said Yashu, 'tell everyone about Charlie your dog's experience with Carctol.' After having done so the place erupted with laughter. I mused at how each day now started with a warm greeting of two wagging tails, from Lucy and Charlie.

An Ayurvedic doctor, dressed in a smart pinstriped suit, stood up proclaiming, 'Your dog would have a good reaction to those herbs; one of the ingredients is renowned for calming and soothing the skin. That's clearly what has happened to him.'

'How have you found Carctol helping you?' asked a discerning doctor.

'Apart from the physical aspects of frequently going to the loo, I noticed shortly after taking the prescribed dosage that mentally I felt calmer. Carctol acted like a splint to my mind, which had felt uncomfortably stretched at times.' I was too embarrassed to go into further details publicly. Truthfully, I knew my regime was doing me good, and my progress checks with Professor Thomas supported this, but intellectually I couldn't work out all the answers. This puzzled me on occasions. Sometimes we have to put our trust in something and stick with it, especially if it works. I was learning to stick to my instincts and follow my heart; a bit like Charlie.

Carctol seemed to agree with me and people kept telling me that I looked better than I had for years. I put that down in no small measure to my change in lifestyle and diet.

One of the Ayurvedic doctors continued speaking: 'The herbs in Carctol, when separated, don't do anything significant, but when put together then something entirely different happens, and one or two of the herbs I recognize from the list here help calm the mind. It's good that you've recognized this and felt the benefit.'

After the seminar we said farewell to Rosy and then Yashu, who squeezed my hands saying, 'Gillian, you know you feel like a soul sister to me. Our long telephone chats, as we get to know one another, mean so very much to me, more than you may realize. When you have recovered from the seminar please will you include all those taking Carctol in your healing prayers? They need many prayers; it's power is not to be underestimated.'

'It will be my pleasure to do this for you. I feel honoured to be called your soul sister and feel likewise with you.'

In Yashu's traditional way we then parted with the Namaste. In the car on the way home I thanked Claire for coming along with us, and after an initial chat about the seminar and then her acupuncture work, we fell into amiable silence. I drifted off to sleep feeling tired, recalling something Claire had read in a healing book and passed on: 'Tapping the thymus gland, in the middle of the chest, approximately twenty-three times lightly with your fist, first thing when waking and last thing before bed, stimulates the immune system.'

Yashu was busy staying with relatives after the seminar but a few days later, when chatting on the telephone, she asked me, 'You mentioned at the seminar that you feel mentally stronger. Can you tell me more about that, Gillian?'

Doing my best I replied, 'I'm living a quieter, simpler life and in doing so notice more acutely how one thing or another affects me. With things pared down, it's easier to pinpoint the specific causes of my body's different reactions and make the necessary adjustments. I strive to focus my mind far more than previously, by living increasingly in the present instead of going back in time, reliving and picking over disturbing events, or imagining future scenarios. With Rosy's help I've learned about vibrational exchanges, especially with different people. Some drain me, albeit innocently; others do not. In the process of turning increasingly within, in order to find my way, I've discovered that my body and mind, if I listen, will give me clues. It doesn't mean I always listen, but if I do, it usually shows benefit.'

'That action reaps its own reward then,' said Yashu.'

'Yes, but I'm acutely aware that not everyone would wish to do this.'

143

'Quite so,' replied Yashu continuing. 'It's more a question of leaving it up to each individual to use their own free will to choose a direction, after consideration and reflection, when facing challenges and making choices. With health issues, if one wants to stay alive – and I think that the majority of people do, at least those I work with – from what you're saying, if I understand correctly, one can learn to refocus and redirect thoughts accordingly, finding useful tools along the way, as guided meditations and holistic practitioners are more widely accessible nowadays.'

'This is what I believe and am finding,' I replied.

'Chandra sends his love to you and your family. Many blessings be upon you all.' We bade one another our customary farewell.

Another appointment was due with Professor Thomas at the Nuffield Hospital. No matter what I did, I always felt a degree of anxiety before such appointments; in truth we both did. One day, to quell my mounting anxiety, I chatted to another patient in the waiting room.

'I've lost at least a stone in weight,' she said. 'That's the plus side. My name's Diane.' Her husband chatted to Simon as we briefly shared our different approaches to cancer, exchanged phone numbers and thereafter kept in touch.

'Please come in now,' said Professor Thomas opening the door.

'How are you?' she asked.

'Everything's going well and I've introduced something new, animal essences, that my nutritionist recommended. They're similar in principle to flower essences and they are helping me become stronger emotionally. My bladder is usually more comfortable nowadays. I find your interest in all I'm doing enormously supportive.'

'Since I last saw you, I've met Dr Daniel. She came to give a talk at St. Luke's Hospital, next door to the Nuffield. We spoke about you and how well you seem to be doing with all you're embracing. You certainly look very well,' she replied while making notes in my file. She then invited me behind the curtain to lie on the examination couch, while Simon remained the other side, listening.

The following is a letter she wrote to my GP after the appointment:

I saw Mrs Gill at the Guildford Nuffield Hospital on 5th June. She remains very well in herself, continuing to take Carctol along with the enzyme therapy. She is also involved in healing and has been researching into animal essences. These appear to be an animal form of something like the Bach flower remedies.

Whatever the whys and wherefores of these different treatments, Mrs Gill remains well in herself. On examining her, the lump in her abdomen has not changed in size over the past eight months – indeed if anything it may be slightly smaller.

I have stopped checking her tumour markers but her other blood tests show that these are all in the normal range. She is not only an advocate of alternative therapy but an advertisement for it. I feel that my role in continuing to hold her hand is reasonable and appropriate. She tells me she finds support from this, and I have to say I believe my education is being broadened as well!

She is planning to see me again in approximately four months' time and I will then book her annual CT scan as she will then be two years out from her original diagnosis.

Shortly after sending me this letter Professor Thomas wrote the following with my latest blood test results:

Just to let you know that your recent blood tests were essentially normal. The bilirubin level was a little elevated.

This may suggest that the liver is not functioning as well as it could. The only thing I would warn you about is to watch the colour of your eyes. If you think that the whites are in any way becoming jaundiced then please do get in touch.

Other than that I hope you continue to keep as well as you have been.

With some concern about my liver, I contacted Marianne and she put me on a metabolic clearing programme, telling me, 'This programme allows your digestive system to rest and to heal itself. It's hypoallergenic and sensitive and includes a rice-based protein nutritional drink. Stick to the accompanying diet, contained in a booklet, and this helps detoxify pathways in the liver, removing unwanted waste from your body.' The programme was tiring, but I adhered to it in the short term as advised, and rested more while continuing with everything else, gently integrating the programme.

Meanwhile Simon continued planning and fine-tuning our holiday. 'Over the last couple of months I've enjoyed looking into our holiday and booking the train tickets to take us to Lausanne. It's given me something to look forward to. David's excited and is looking forward to paragliding off the mountains.'

'I can't believe all the trouble you've gone to working this out, so I don't have to fly,' I replied.

'It's no trouble; in fact, it's been fun planning to travel this way. The views should be good from the train, especially once we're the far side of the Channel Tunnel.'

'I can hardly believe how this goal to go on holiday, that I set myself ages ago, is on the threshold of happening.'

The day arrived. As we climbed aboard the Eurostar in London I settled back in my seat watching David and Simon's excited faces. The journey was relaxing and pleasant as we were able to walk about freely. The boys visited the buffet car to stretch their legs and enjoy a drink; with all the water I drink, I frequently visited the loo. In no time at all we arrived in Paris Gare du Nord.

A taxi ride across Paris took us to Saint Lazare station for our onward connection to Lausanne. As we were pulling our luggage into the station we smelt the most delicious food.

'Those filled French sticks look good,' said David, his mouth watering. 'Oh, and they've got crepes over there,' he added excitedly.

'We'll share both,' said Simon, heading towards the French sticks while David queued for the crepes.

'I'll wait with the luggage and eat my picnic,' I told them, finding a bench to sit on. As I opened up my food bag I noticed the oil dressing that I'd covered my avocado, lettuce and walnut salad with had leaked. Using some tissues to mop it up, I still managed to spill some on my top.

'That's typical of you, Mum,' said David, as he and Simon laughed, quite accustomed to such incidents. After we'd eaten we climbed aboard the

TGV to take us to our final destination, Lausanne. Finding our seats, I sat back comfortably while Simon stowed our luggage with David's help.

Shutting my eyes I drifted off, tired from all the excitement. As the train pulled out of the station gathering speed, I felt as though I was between worlds, everything seemed dreamlike; I couldn't believe it was actually happening. Lucy and Charlie were happy at home, with Philippa kindly house sitting and working mostly from there. They knew and loved her. Charlie always sang her a song in greeting whenever she arrived for a visit.

Waking with a jolt I looked out of the window and saw a typical French square-walled graveyard, set on the edge of a meadow, and silently gave thanks for not being in one myself. The train sped along and, as we approached Switzerland, meadows of Alpine flowers flashed past, with vast mountains looming one behind the other in the background.

'You look happy, Mum,' said David.

'I am. I've been looking forward to this for such a long time. It's wonderful being here with you and Daddy.'

'Would you like to walk about the train, David, and have a hot chocolate in the buffet car?' Simon asked, as David's face lit up.

'Yes, please.'

Pleased to stay in my seat, I admired the glorious views, marvelling at how my once dulled senses came to life. Beneath several heavy layers of concern and fear, joy and happiness simply bubbled to the surface. I reflected on the many bubbles I watched on the pond only weeks ago, made by the hundreds of developing frogs.

During my childhood, we'd had an explosion of frogs during springtime on the farm one year. Hundreds of young frogs had squeezed beneath the back door and dropped down the step into our kitchen. They had found their way into our shoes, and gave us all such a surprise as we watched them hop across the red floor tiles. Jane, Joanna and I had scooped them up in jam jars and returned them to the pond.

'Look at that field of sunflowers,' said David returning to his seat, as we looked out of the window, 'they're following the sun and all turn in the same direction.'

'We're almost there now, in case anyone wants to go to the loo,' said Simon.

'Oh, look at that man,' said David, 'he looks like Mr Bean.' A French man was walking through the train with a very distinctive walk and intense expression, totally absorbed, lost in thought.

It felt as though we were alighting from a time capsule. The hours had passed blissfully. I'd felt totally protected, sheltered and away from the world I'd immersed myself in since my diagnosis. The doors opened. Sounds and scents from the station thrilled me.

'I'll carry these two bags,' said David, with his rucksack on his back.

'I'll take the rest,' said Simon heaving them onto the platform. What a new experience this was for me, and I was enjoying it. Everything I saw and experienced in those first few moments took on an entirely different hue.

'There's Lindsay,' I said, pointing to our friend. She ran towards us along the platform, with an enormous smile on her face.

'Oh, Gilly, I can't believe you're here. It's wonderful to see you. You look marvellous!' We embraced in a bear hug. We'd known one another since my teens. Even though we didn't see one another often, when we did get together we just carried on in our familiar way with great ease.

'This is Reynald, my husband.' We knew of Reynald, her new Swiss husband following her sad divorce, but hadn't met him. He drove us to the Hotel du Signal, which they'd recommended. It was a traditional family-run Swiss hotel, a short distance from Vevey. We drove along the clear, open roads winding our way up the hills overlooking Lake Geneva. Glancing out of the window I noticed that in place of my usual terror of heights I was admiring the breathtaking views.

In the hotel we glimpsed an elegantly dressed, grey-haired woman, apparently the owner. The manager was charming, taking pride in his work, and he arranged for us to be shown to our room, which had a balcony. Throwing the doors wide open I strode over to see the view. What a lovely surprise! We'd been given an upgrade with a view of the lake, which was surrounded by majestic, snow-capped mountains, the Alps. I breathed in the glorious, invigorating mountain air, deeply inhaling it into my entire being as I felt it surge through my bloodstream. David was delighted with his room, which also had a view of the mountains.

'Do you mind if David and I go off to explore?' asked Simon once we'd unpacked our cases.

'Of course not. I could do with a spell alone, to be honest,' I said. Throughout our marriage we'd become accustomed to spending time separated, largely due to Simon's punishing work schedule. It was now a pattern ingrained in each of us; and we both knew how to best make use of it. 'Go and have fun,' I said, 'and take your time. I won't be going far.'

'Shall we go and hire the car now?' suggested David as they bustled from the room. I went to sit on the balcony and watched the calm lake, reflecting mountains and clear blue skies above. It was like heaven and earth combining, I thought, sitting there losing all track of time. I breathed in the Alpine air, oxygenating my blood stream, in the belief it would shrivel my 'lump' and purify any unwanted toxic matter, while recalling stories I'd heard of people visiting Switzerland to take the air as a tonic.

'Shall we go for supper?' said the boys in unison, hungry after their outing. 'The menu looks typically Swiss, with different meat and cheese dishes. But look, they also have salads and eggs,' said Simon looking at my grave face.

'I'm so pleased you spotted salad. I hadn't got that far and was just beginning to panic.'

'Go on, Mum, have a chip,' said David as his meal arrived, after regaling me with their afternoon adventure.

'Just one,' I replied, savouring the taste. 'Lindsay said she'd take me to Vevey tomorrow, to see Charlie Chaplin's grave. His wife Oona lies beside him apparently.' After a good night's sleep in a comfortable bed with the softest pillows, I awoke refreshed.

Following a simple breakfast of nuts, seeds and muesli, accompanied by the soya milk I'd taken with me, whilst the boys enjoyed sampling the buffet of meats, cheese and bread, we parted ways for the day. Simon and David were going off to explore the region and do some paragliding from a mountain top.

Lindsay and I caught a train to visit Charlie Chaplin's grave. As I stood beside it I thought what a glorious spot to lie in rest. He'd had a hard early life and gone on to become an amazing mime artist. It was comforting to know he lay alongside his beloved wife Oona, surrounded by great natural beauty. A fitting tribute, I mused.

That evening we all met at our hotel for supper. 'We had a great day, didn't we Gilly?' stated Lindsay. 'What did you boys get up to?'

'We went paragliding,' they said, looking elated.

'What was that like?' Lindsay and I asked in unison, and laughed as we looked at one another.

'Well, we each had an instructor harnessed to us ready to fly, and when we got to the top of the mountain we had to run along a sort of runway, wait for the wind to be right, then launch ourselves off the edge and into space; it was amazing,' said David. 'The wind just lifted us higher and higher. The views were breathtaking. Then the instructor taught Dad and me how to steer the paraglider. Coming into land was a bit scary, as the ground raced up towards us.'

Simon stood proudly grinning while listening to David's experience, nodding in agreement.

One morning we all took the mountain railway up Les Pleiades where I marvelled at a rainbow that arched across the entire skyline. It was breathtakingly beautiful with snow-capped mountains as a backdrop.

The time flew by, with me visiting Lindsay for long chats each day in between maintaining my disciplines, while the boys went off mountain walking. Then we'd all get together in the evening, at either the hotel or Lindsay and Reynald's home, for supper.

Upon returning home refreshed from our holiday, I decided a dental check-up was overdue and booked an appointment with both a hygienist and the dentist. Karen was new to me as a hygienist; the previous one I'd seen made me feel like a naughty child, giving me marks out of ten. Karen was different. Lying in the chair listening to classical music, I mentioned why I hadn't had a check-up lately.

She listened sympathetically before saying, 'You have been through a bit, haven't you? Well, let's see what's going on in here. Please open wide and I'll give your mouth a thorough going over. Having clean teeth is important. I'll just floss between your teeth as plaque carries bacteria which you certainly don't want in your mouth.'

After cleaning my teeth she said, 'Your gums are bleeding, probably due to all the stress you've undergone. You need to repeat warm salt mouthwashes throughout the day until that stops.'

I noticed I'd been less tense while in the chair listening to the music with Karen chatting. I had a thing about dental visits, tracing back in part to the fact that as a child I'd had extensive dental surgery at Guy's Hospital in London, my mouth being too small to carry all my teeth. This had included not only the removal of a few teeth, but also dealing with an unusual one that grew in the roof of my mouth. Thereafter, I'd required follow-up visits for years for ongoing treatments, including the removal of other teeth using gas as an anaesthetic. Once, I'd woken up unable to move, hearing the dentist telling the nurse to pass the needle as he was about to stitch my gums, and I then felt every agonizing stitch.

'Please wait there a moment,' Karen said disappearing through the door. Returning she said, 'The dentist is ready for you now, and I'll see you again in six months' time.'

Walking into the dentist's room I heard more classical music. That certainly hadn't been the case when I'd last visited.

'I hear you've had a bit of a time of it. I am sorry. Let's see what's going on in here,' said Chris, someone we'd got to know well over the years.

Peering into my mouth Chris said, 'We'll leave that troublesome tooth at the back that we had earmarked for major work. I think you've got enough going on in your life without adding any more strain. Are you aware that you've been grinding your back teeth?'

'No,' I replied bewildered.

'That's stress coming out in your sleep. I'm sure Karen told you your gums are inflamed, so take care of them as she advised; look after yourself and we'll see you again soon.'

Over the next years, interestingly, the troublesome tooth never did require major rework.

After the dentist I decided it was time to make an appointment with my Italian hairdresser and went along for a trim.

'Hello, how lovely to see you,' said Fausto. 'Your hair is looking in better condition. I see you won't need that wig you mentioned over a year ago.'

'No, I seem to be managing another way.' After discussing our families and holidays, we chatted about what I was doing to help myself.

'Your hair seems to be not only thickening now, but it's shinier and healthier, and appears to be growing faster. You may want to think about seeing me more often.' Being in the hairdresser's relaxed me. Leaning my head carefully over the basin to have my hair washed and scalp massaged was heavenly.

During the school holidays, Ben, my late sister's little boy, came to stay. David was as excited as I was. The weather was good so the boys set up a tent to sleep in the garden. 'Let's go out for an early supper in the local pub,' said Simon. Both boys smiled at the prospect of chips!

'That would be nice,' I replied, not quite believing the turn of events and us going out for a meal that included Ben.

Sitting in the pub garden with the dogs quietly beneath the table, we enjoyed a drink while looking at menus. There was only one thing that I could eat: jacket potato and salad. I noticed Ben looking quizzically at me: 'What can you eat, Aunty Gillian?' By now his parents had had a chat with him about my health and what I was doing.

'It's a bit challenging eating out but there is plenty I've learned that I can eat,' I replied. The food arrived and after a happy evening we went home.

'Let's take the dogs into the garden,' said David. They zoomed across the lawn, sniffing the tent before diving between the entrance flaps.

'Looks as though they think that's there for them!' laughed Simon. Dusk was fast approaching and with it the bats were coming out.

'Oh! One just skimmed past my left ear,' said David looking electrified. 'Aunty Gillian, I've never seen so many bats. Where do they live?'

'In the roof of our neighbour's garage. It was once a hayloft. It's a perfect home for them.' We stood marvelling at the bats in fading light.

'How did Ben's visit go?' asked Clare, phoning a couple of days later and sounding happy.

'Very well, thank you, and he sends his love.'

'I'd like to bring Ashleigh, someone I've met at university, home to meet you and Dad. We've started going out together.'

I was so thrilled when Clare bought him home, but was embarrassed at being caught off guard. In the kitchen I was berating David's old cat Tom, a green-eyed ginger who had opted to live with our elderly widowed neighbour. He'd brought a dead rabbit into the kitchen and was disembowelling it. He must have known it was a special occasion, bringing us a rare gift. However, the air was blue as I cleared body parts and blood.

'Mum, this is Ashleigh,' said Clare, as I turned wearing rubber gloves with cloth in one hand, bucket in the other. That dispelled any tension there might have been and we took off from there.

CHAPTER 8
Facing the Fear

The Burden Bearer
[...] The little sharp vexations,
And the briars that catch and fret –
Shall we not take them to the Helper
Who has never failed us yet?
Tell Him about the heartache,
And tell him the longings too;
Tell Him the baffled purpose
When we scarce know what to do,
Then, leaving all our weakness
With the One divinely strong,
Forget that we bore the burden,
And carry away the song!

Margaret E Sangster 1838–1912

(Bequeathed to me by my dear friend Lilian Ingleson, herself a spiritual
healer of many years standing)

October 2002 – April 2003

'I think the time has come when you really should tell your parents and
Jane the truth; it's simpler in the long run,' said Simon. How I struggled
listening to him. In my heart I knew he was right, but I didn't know how I'd
find the words. However, with happy memories of Clare's visit I felt more
buoyant and prepared myself.

As with most things these days, I increasingly prayed for help and inspiration. Both phone calls were distressing but I made them. My parents listened and accepted the shocking news as well as could be expected. My memory of the exact conversation has now faded, but I do remember telling my mother that my ovarian cyst was in fact a tumour.

Jane was both understanding and forgiving, offering to help in whatever way she could, including lending a sympathetic ear, though initially there were sharp words and high emotions when unavoidably painful memories of our sister's death from cancer were stirred. Fresh layers of grief arose in the ensuing months for us all, and sometimes we talked about them.

By now we'd all met Ashleigh a few times and got on well, so well he seemed like part of the family. He and Clare appeared very much in love and devoted to one another, seeming to bring out the best in each other.

During this time Daphne phoned. She had helped me with housework after we were married, having first 'interviewed' me, and then became like a surrogate mother figure. After David was born she would shoo me out of the house to have a break. I'd go for a drive somewhere, park the car and cry, as my fluctuating hormones took hold. The tears were natural, a mixture of fatigue, happiness and sometimes sadness. Merely sitting quietly in the midst of nature replenished me. A couple of hours later I'd return feeling stronger and walk through the front door to be greeted by delicious smells from the kitchen. Daphne would have both the children happy and laughing, and something tasty cooked for supper.

'Gill,' she said, 'it's Eric. The hospital has just called. His leg infection has got worse, and he has suspected gangrene and may have to have his leg amputated. It only started with a small infection in his foot, but what with his diabetes…'

I could hear the desperation in her voice as she continued. 'And you know since he's retired from driving those huge concrete lorries, his only passion is for his allotment and growing things.'

I talked about their predicament with Simon, and he came up with an idea: 'The best thing before going into hospital for major surgery would be giving him a new exciting project to look forward to. Why not ring

Daphne and see if they want to share our vegetable patch? It's looking neglected.' So I phoned Daphne back.

'Gill, what a lovely idea of Simon's. Please thank him for us. Sharing your smaller patch will mean less work for him; and the allotment's expensive, so it'll save money too. Our pension is a bit stretched at times. Hang on… Eric says what can you eat? He'll try and grow what you like on that odd diet of yours. Make a list for him.'

'Looks like this arrangement might suit everyone,' said Simon, pleased.

Thoughts of an orderly vegetable patch reminded me of the one we'd had on the farm when I was a child; it was enormous. I'd taken it for granted then, the neat rows of every vegetable throughout the seasons, and fruits too. That was when I'd seen my first ghost. One Sunday evening, when washing up the supper things, I'd looked out of the kitchen window and had seen someone wearing old sackcloth walking down the farmyard through the open gate. He was heading for the vegetable patch. My mother told me that Jack, our gardener who had died years ago, had put his heart and soul into the kitchen garden and he was still obviously overseeing it.

With the approach of Eric's operation I silently prayed that a spirit surgeon would help his earth surgeon and all those in attendance in the operating theatre to bring about the best possible outcome. Others also prayed. Daphne was concerned about the effect the anaesthetic would have on Eric.

'Gill,' said Daphne happily, phoning following his surgery, 'his leg is saved! It's a bad infection, nothing more.'

Eric went on to renewed health and vitality and recovered sooner than expected. At the bottom of the garden, beneath ancient yew trees, our old shed filled up. Eric put a garden chair into it so he could sit back and watch the garden after working in it, often having tended a bonfire. A black coffin-like box containing many tools and a protective plant fleece acted as a refuge for mice, which nested amongst it. The 'coffin' was placed next to the greenhouse Simon had constructed for me after Joanna died. There I'd found many an hour of solace while tending seedlings. I had once been surprised when growing lettuces in the greenhouse to pull one out and see nine pairs of eyes staring back at me. A toad was rearing her young in that dark dampness. I had put the outer leaves back to cover them.

The notebook in which I'd been jotting down my successful kitchen experiments was getting fuller. An idea took hold to produce a recipe book for those in a similar situation to demonstrate what I was learning, which is that a vegetarian alkaline diet needn't be lacking in fun and flavour. Food and cooking has always been a passion of mine and, even though the list of permissible ingredients was limited, I'd found some great combinations and loved the idea of sharing them. A particular pick-me-up favourite treat when feeling tired and low is a bowl of banana crumble. This recipe is enough for two.

In an ovenproof dish, spread a little vegetable oil, then mash 3 bananas and sprinkle over a handful of mixed pumpkin, sesame, sunflower and hemp seeds together with a cupful of ground almonds. Bake for 20 minutes in the middle of a moderate oven, then savour every mouthful! Adding half a cupful of oats to the topping is delicious too.

Having mentioned my alkaline recipes to Rosy, she had told us there was demand for them, so with the help of our close friends Ed and Susi, who are graphic designers, we set to work on compiling the recipes. Ed, having recovered from testicular cancer after successful conventional treatment, volunteered happily. Clare helped with illustrations. Rosy asked her colleague Jane Sen, a cancer nutritionist and published health cookery writer, to check each recipe, and she endorsed their nutritional value.

'I'm going cross-eyed proofreading,' said Simon reading the final draft for the umpteenth time. 'Have you got the measurements correct? I think you should try cooking this recipe again and make sure.' My method of cooking is the intuitive approach, where measurements are judged by eye and feel; plus I simply didn't have energy to spend hours weighing everything initially. However, the book called for more exact instructions so each recipe was re-cooked, checked and had its ingredients weighed as by now I had more energy to do so. Simon unstintingly corrected mistakes, and still there were some that had gone unnoticed.

We decided that we would like to self-publish to be certain that it would be available as soon as possible to help those requiring an alkaline diet, especially if they were taking Carctol.

Throughout this time Lucy and Charlie stayed close when we were working, giving contented sighs as they lay together using one another as pillows. Charlie, we were noticing, was nervous and liked to stay close to one of us when not with Lucy.

David was taking exams and preparing to go straight to university in the autumn, opting not to take a gap year. 'I'm finding it so hard coming to terms with David growing up and I am going to miss him when he leaves home. It was bad enough adjusting when Clare left for university. I feel anxious and wrenched apart with thoughts of both children leaving home.'

Simon reassuringly said, 'It's the next stage to their growing up. It's not easy, but remember how we visited Clare at university? We will adjust in time. Look how well Clare's done graduating and getting a job.'

An uneasy feeling remained nevertheless; an irrational part of me wondered if I would be redundant as a mother.

Meanwhile, I had another CT scan, which made me feel unwell for a few days afterwards. My system was more sensitive to the revealing fluids I had to drink beforehand.

During my next appointment with Professor Thomas she told me how pleased she was with my progress. By now there was a significant shrinkage of my abdominal mass, which she again measured in her unique manner. It was during this appointment, while sitting in her familiar office, that Simon and I were staggered to understand from Professor Thomas that my tumour had taken on the characteristics of a benign cyst.

Simon and I looked at one another, hardly able to digest this news. Such was the enormity of this statement that, for some inexplicable reason, both Simon and I were just stunned and could not begin to process it, let alone comment on it at the time. Later still, it never occurred to us to question it further; it was just part of the complicated circumstances that we were living under. Our diverse emotions did their best to accept this news but our intellects appeared to have deserted us completely. Our senses were overloaded and disbelief and bewilderment were the feelings that won out. At some remote level we knew it was good news, but that was all.

We'd been working hard to achieve that result, but now it had happened we felt confused and deflated. We'd quietly anticipated the possibility of bad news; one could never be sure.

The following is a letter Professor Thomas sent to my GP after that visit:

It is now some 26 months since I first saw Gillian Gill with her large abdomino-pelvic tumour and multiple liver metastases.

As you know, since that time she has managed herself with a combination of nutritional therapy and complementary therapy. Her recent CT scan shows no real change compared with the scan performed a year earlier; indeed the 8 cm metastasis in the liver (the largest of several) is unchanged but the pelvic mass is, if anything, smaller on the sections which I measured today. This is quite remarkable.

On examining her I can now place 13 fingers' breadth between the xiphisternum and the upper limit of the tumour, which suggests that the tumour is genuinely smaller than it has been. When I first saw her in October 2000 I could only insert 4 fingers' breadths!

Mrs Gill is understandably slightly concerned about the raised bilirubin [the yellow pigment associated with jaundice], which we found when I saw her in June. She has since received some 'metabolic cleaning programme' through her nutritionist and hopes this will have improved her liver function. Other than that she eats a fairly vegetarian diet and no red meat. She continues to take Carctol and other supplements but has reduced the dose of these recently.

We did talk about the possibility of embolisation. Mrs Gill has always been firmly opposed to surgery, but the thought of having the mass in the pelvis and possibly one liver metastasis shrunk through embolisation was quite appealing. I have therefore agreed to write to my colleague Professor Chris Sutton to find out more and I will then let Mrs Gill know if he has any suggestion to make.

Other than that she will arrange to see me at her convenience as usual.

Embolization is a surgical procedure to deliberately tie off blood flow to a vessel or to a tumour.

Quite coincidentally, following that appointment Simon had booked a table at a favourite vegetarian restaurant in Brighton. Far from celebrating, we both felt strangely downcast, unable to fathom the good news, and we drove to Brighton in virtual silence.

Once in the restaurant we sat staring at one another across the table, all thoughts of enjoying a tasty meal gone. 'I feel strangely low, as though I've been hit on the head,' I said perplexed. 'How did this result happen?'

'Well, we've focused to achieve these results, but I feel deflated too. I don't understand it. Logically, I know it's good news. Like everything, this is a process and right now we're reeling from this sudden turn of events. We hadn't expected it.'

After mulling the news over during lunch we decided to walk on the beach. 'It's very cloudy and chilly but the sea air will be good for us,' said Simon. Walking along the sea front with the tide out, I found a sandy patch but hadn't noticed a deeply embedded stone. Tripping over it, I could feel myself falling and braced myself, fearing damage, but was stunned to feel I was free falling, as though helped by an invisible parachute. Time slowed right down. Stranger still, the ground beneath me, far from feeling hard and hurting, felt like a cushion. This was the third fall since my diagnosis when I'd braced myself expecting to be in real pain after hitting the ground, yet had felt nothing other than the peace and grace of my spirit guides and guardian angels watching over me. Rather than yelp in pain, I found myself laughing where I landed and giving silent thanks. Simon was bending over me looking concerned, then relieved as I took his hand and stood up unharmed.

In the car my mind again returned to the unfathomable news. I felt a headache coming on, fast turning into a migraine. When home I was violently sick. Trying to soothe myself, I ran a bath. I remembered how Philippa, after giving me a relaxing aromatherapy head and shoulder massage, had taught me to add a couple of drops of geranium oil for balance and lavender for calm. Someone else had suggested to first put the oil drops into a small cup of milk to disperse better in the bath. Lying in the deep fragrant water I gradually noticed tensions easing. I shut my eyes after briefly watching a flickering candle flame at the foot of the bath. Years previously, when living in London and volunteering for the trolley run at the Great Ormond Street Hospital for sick children, I remembered the prematurely aged, brave children I'd met. Their faces were filled with compassion, wisdom and mirth as they carried their pain-wracked bodies, linked arm-in-arm, around their specialist ward.

The next thing I knew almost an hour had passed and the water was cool, but curiously my migraine had gone. I felt exhausted so went to bed to try to sleep. As usual, my feet were cold, so I put bed socks on to warm them and made a hot-water bottle as I was shivering. My sleep was definitely improving, and using one of the teddies to support my shrinking 'lump' while lying on my side made it more comfortable. I drifted off to sleep.

We were gradually coming to terms with the latest good result. The following is an extract from a further letter that we received from my oncologist:

Dear Mrs Gill

Just to let you know that I have recently heard from Professor Sutton, one of my colleagues here at the Royal Surrey who has an expertise on embolisation. He has also discussed this with a specialist Radiologist who has undertaken a large number of such embolisations.

They both feel that you would not be a candidate for embolisation. They felt that it might make matters worse as you would be left with a lump in the pelvis, which would be dying off due to its lack of blood supply, and this could cause more problems than doing nothing at all...

I look forward to seeing you again in due course.

Sharing the news with Simon, he suggested, 'Why not make a telephone appointment with Rosy and discuss it with her?' I did and she came up with a good visualization instead of the surgical embolism. Thereafter, I repeatedly conjured up a vivid image of a cauterization in the form of a snare gently cutting off the entire blood flow to my 'lump' with minimum side effects, thus trusting my body's intelligence to achieve the best results. At times when practising this visualization, especially when I combined it with my hands-on healing, I felt increasing internal stinging and tugging in my abdomen and fleeting electrical charges of shooting pains, similar to an internal punch.

By now I was also seeing my friend Sarah for reflexology and, after I had been regularly practising this visualization, she commented, 'I've found an open channel to the ovary where the lump is attached.' I was doubly astonished, as I hadn't yet mentioned my visualization technique to her. This was something new as previously the 'lump' had blocked this channel. I continued including this visualization for the next few months as part of my routine.

December 2002

On Christmas day it snowed briefly. Watching the flakes fluttering down I felt a childlike happiness and was finally able to fully recognize the 'cyst's' transformation as a cause for celebration. This was the best Christmas present I could have wished for; it was miraculous.

January – April 2003

Much of what I was going through had been torture for the family to witness. The fallout was huge, leaving them feeling alone at times, desperate in their own ways. They had to cope separately as best they could with the love and support of those closest to them. David had received tremendous support from the school staff, and Clare from her close circle of friends. I worried I was no longer the stoic one to turn to during that time, and it was hard watching their suffering and bravery. Every step I've taken has been with their unstinting love and support, along with other family members, friends and neighbours.

I was also gradually noticing that the changes I'd integrated into my life were affecting those nearest and dearest to me in a positive way, giving rise to new ways of looking at problems, health issues and life itself. Many I know changed their diet and experienced improved health as a result.

This inner struggle of no longer living with ovarian cancer but living with a 'lump' with the characteristics of an ovarian cyst went on for some time. I still felt those same old fears that were deeply ingrained, being alert for signs of trouble. Fear of the unknown being one of the worst fears, I queried how long it takes to move from the fear zone back into the safe zone. Then I realized you never do fully manage it, but with time that fear gradually fades. I had to find a way of continuing onwards.

I thought, I am alive but what now? I'd been taught by Rosy to sit quietly and reflect and to ask myself 'What have I to learn from this?' Yet, I had reached a new crisis of faith and wondered how I would suddenly live in the world again, when I'd reshaped my own world so dramatically to help and heal myself.

Simon said, 'You have to find a way to live without the dread of cancer hanging over you. Learn to listen to your fear and remember how to function normally in the world, keeping up your regime.'

'I worry every time I get a sudden pain, though,' I persisted, driving Simon crazy at times with my need for constant reassurance. He was right, though; I just had to stick at it and stop imagining every pain or ache heralded my cancer's return. I knew something as innocent as trapped wind could be responsible for extreme pain and discomfort and remembered Marianne had told me peppermint oil capsules could alleviate that, as Simon had born witness to many times.

CHAPTER 9
Breakdown to Rebuild

The Rose
In the days ahead when all around appears darkness,
remember: a rose in bud is tightly furled, but when a
ray of sunshine smiles from afar, that same rose bud,
kissed by warmth, unfurls. At its centre, the light
shines out. That same light, hugged tight by petals
formed with delicate stamens, remains throughout both
inwardly and outwardly, forever a major structure of
that rose.
Gillian Gill

May - August 2003

It was by now late May and, despite a huge milestone being reached in my recovery, which had been a significant victory over cancer in the physical sense, I had over-stretched myself mentally. I had conquered my struggle to come to terms with these latest results, though it had been a confusing and disorientating time. I had also become obsessive about a relatively new writing project with a friend after receiving a rejection from a publisher for another book I'd been writing. Stealthily these issues began to overtake me, and the next eight weeks would bear witness to a very challenging, different and unexpected part of my healing process; there was a new storm brewing. Simon has had to help me remember this period of my life as my memory of the facts is a little hazy.

Simon had just returned home from a brief, and by then uncommon, business trip abroad. I was feeling the tremors of agitation and anxiety that had become so familiar but thought little of it. These feelings were increasing, as was my feeling of remoteness and detachment from reality. I have very little recollection of the following events but Simon told me I threw all the jewellery that I wear every day away in the garden and began yelling incoherently. He phoned Natasha, our psychotherapist friend, for her professional opinion and she warned him that it sounded like I was entering a dangerous psychotic state. As he then began calling doctors on the phone, I took the car and drove so fast that Simon, who gave chase in the other car, couldn't keep up. Later on I'd put my old worn-out things in the dustbin and filled black bin liners and boxes with keepsakes, thinking I was on my way to heaven, waiting for the moment of death.

I remember lying down in our bedroom, with the phone constantly ringing as Simon rallied support. I felt unable to leave the bedroom, which I'd turned upside down putting everything out of place, and I played loud music. Throughout that surreal day, ambulances came and went. The sitting room filled with officials arranging for me to be sectioned, which was necessary to take me to hospital, and by the evening Simon finally coaxed me downstairs and into one of the ambulances. Although there is a part of me that always wants to fix things, I wasn't reasoning or even thinking straight.

Some years later Simon told me that he had to endure listening to the team of officials assembled in our sitting room to conduct the sectioning process. He still vividly remembers a consultant saying, 'Undoubtedly, the cancer has spread to the brain and in my experience very few patients in this situation survive for long.'

My mental breakdown included an identity crisis. Old avoided issues, many surrounding life and death, heaven and hell, rose to the surface, where I couldn't make sense of them, and I became confused and fixated on death. Was I following in my father's footsteps and his father's too, I wondered, thinking of their mental breakdowns and all I'd heard and witnessed as a child? My breakdown was reminiscent of my father's, which he suffered after the trauma of losing his entire livestock on the farm in the 1960s from a foot-and-mouth outbreak.

Looking back, it's as though there was an expectation for me to have a mental breakdown at some level. As a child, I recalled frequently being told by my mother that such traits were inherited, and that thought had often troubled me. It's as though we attract the very thing we don't want by giving it thought power.

I was admitted to the psychiatric unit of the local hospital. When wandering about I discovered a corridor that had an empty wing attached to it; it was the secure psychiatric unit. I thought it was barbaric, the stuff scary movies are made of. Luckily it was due to close, though images of it haunted me. The fabric of the building seemed vile to me; however, I dare say it served its purpose. I was troubled by thoughts of the many previous patients with their own anxieties who had passed through these corridors. The mind seemed to me to be a very fragile thing.

The nurses were dedicated and kind, and care shone out from their eyes; one could see many of them had a calling to their work. Sue, the wife of Tissa, the Sri Lankan radiologist who had held my hand after my first CT scan, was a nurse at the hospital. She heard I'd been admitted and appeared by my bedside one day, plumping pillows and talking sweetly, and her familiarity and kindness touched me. She gave me green grapes, which I knew I mustn't eat but couldn't grasp why. People thoughtfully sent me flowers and many bouquets arrived in the first few days. I asked that they be shared with others to spread their beauty and the love that accompanied them around the ward.

One day while looking out of the window I saw on top of the far hill a beautiful vision of a white building surrounded by trees. That was a welcome vision, but one I didn't fully comprehend at the time, for I was soon to be moving to a similar place. After two weeks the hospital were about to discharge me. Fortunately Simon recognized I needed considerably longer to recover and made arrangements, after first consulting my GP and Rosy, to move me to the Priory Sturt Hospital, a local unit of the famous Priory mental health hospital in London. I agreed when Simon mentioned going there, recognizing that at some level I wasn't myself, but then I doubted my decision until I finally remembered my vision.

The day before my move Simon quietly strolled into my room, reaching out to gently kiss my cheek, saying, 'Look out of your window. Someone has come to see you. Through the misty layers of my confusion I saw a welcome sight. Right outside was my Nigerian friend Dr Eli Mama. He beamed in through the window, standing resplendent in his crisp white shirt, dark tie, blazer and slacks. In one hand he tightly held his walking stick; in spite of his back and hip trouble he wouldn't be deterred from seeing me. Beneath his other arm was his wife's adored miniature longhaired dachshund, Fifingi, which means little shadow, adorned with roses interwoven into his collar. Those roses were some of Eli's prizewinning specimens. I wasn't easily able to access my scrambled feelings at that time, nevertheless I felt something akin to elation for those brief, precious moments. Eli waved cheerily, swishing his walking stick with his free hand, and held Fifingi up in the other hand for me to see more clearly. Eli and his wife are dear friends. They had fled for their own lives from their home in Kaduna, Nigeria, during a period of vicious religious conflict where there was mass slaughter of innocents. Now being residents here, they shower me with their love and abiding friendship.

During my spell in the first hospital I received good care and medication as my fragmented mind gradually began to reassemble, and soon it was moving day.

'It's time to go now,' said Simon, as I felt mounting nervousness. 'Clare is outside in the car. Today is the day for your move.' Sitting in the back of the car with Clare, she gently held my hand while chatting quietly, as she had many years previously when we'd been on the way to the maternity unit after I went into labour with David. We seemed to be speeding along the roads; the car's movement together with the medication made me feel slightly twitchy, strange and distant. In my 'altered state' it appeared that we were going faster than we were.

'We're almost there now,' said Simon as the car slowed and turned a corner in the road. There was a parting in a thick hedge that led up a driveway, and at the end was the beautiful white building surrounded by trees exactly as I'd seen in my vision.

'Hello,' said a friendly receptionist. Simon completed the necessary paperwork as Clare stood quietly next to me.

'Please come this way,' said a nurse, smiling at Clare and me. 'I'll show you to your room. It has an adjoining bathroom and a nice view of the garden.' It was unfamiliar yet strangely welcome. As far as I could remember I had never had time in my life without responsibilities of one sort or another.

I sat alone in the room while Clare and Simon disappeared briefly. During the interlude I was convinced I had already died and was between two worlds, perhaps in purgatory, which I'd learned about from my Catholic schooling, although my family upbringing was Church of England.

Sitting by the window, I remembered Diane, wondering if I might see her. I'd met her outside Professor Thomas's consulting room and we'd become friends. When she was well enough Diane had come over to visit me at home following her surgery and chemotherapy. We sat chatting. Suddenly Charlie moved closer to Diane and, sitting on his haunches, placed his paws delicately on her abdomen. She juddered and then cried. Opening her eyes she said, 'Charlie looks like the ancient Egyptian dog Anubis; his eyes penetrate my soul. How does he know I've just given away my horses and all but one dog? I can't look after them any longer. Charlie's given me permission to let go. I felt sad and grief-stricken but now all I feel is his love.'

Diane continued to live for some time, longer than was expected, but eventually accepted her fate. Before her passing we chatted about life and death and her fears and anxieties. She had realized her dream of living out the remainder of her life quietly in her dream bungalow by the sea with her husband and dog. Her grown-up children visited. She reconciled herself to the inevitable and eventually let go of her anxieties and found peace in their home by simple, everyday living.

I came out of my reverie as Simon came back into the room with Clare and a doctor. 'The doctor is going to take a blood sample for testing.'

Unknown to me, Simon was wondering if I had a brain tumour. He had been speaking to Rosy, who was extremely helpful and supportive to him throughout this period. Clare took time off from her work in Newcastle to help at home. She was marvellous and instinctively knew how to treat me. David was in the middle of exams; it couldn't have been more difficult for him, though caring staff at school supported him. Being private by nature, he didn't want his friends to know I had cancer, never mind a mental breakdown. Simon was great with both our children. Ashleigh, Clare's boyfriend, was wonderful throughout this period, both with Clare and the whole family.

My mind was repairing to some extent, though there were times of great sadness as I realized I couldn't do anything for the family.

I was having vivid dreams. One night I dreamt a nurse was placing maggots in certain parts of my brain. The following day Simon came for his usual visit and said, 'Kevin the builder has just been working in the attic today. As he climbed through the hatch door into the attic he discovered hundreds of maggots and flies. He said how maggots were once one of the most effective wound-healing agents.'

Convinced my father was dead, I grieved his loss deeply. One day a bouquet arrived from my parents. I marvelled at his ingenuity of being able to send flowers from heaven, thinking how heaven and earth must be closer than I'd ever realized.

I sat for hours in the garden on sunny days listening to the birds singing and the bees buzzing. There I planned what I'd do in the garden when I returned home. I would resume ironing and cleaning the house. The birds all looked brightly coloured, vividly so; this was due to the medication I was on creating an altered state of mind, as I later discovered.

I was encouraged to attend groups to talk with therapists and other patients. After my initial resistance I reluctantly joined a small group one day, and was glad I did, as I was still worrying about the heartbeat I'd continuously felt in my 'lump', fearing it was a monster. Airing this fear, a nurse said, 'That's the aorta. It is the motorway of the blood system. It travels down the front of your body and can only be felt when you're ill.'

That night I had a dream that my 'lump' had softened and flattened and that I could do up my trousers with ease. I dreamed of a gold builder's chute placed next to me, taking all the waste matter away. Then I dreamt my 'lump' separated from me and hovered like a golden orb above my head. A golden light was pouring into me, liquefying my 'lump' as it naturally passed out of my body. Five angels were flying over me holding hands.

During this time I was hardly eating; for me this is rare. I had lost my appetite, one of the side effects of the medication. The staff, who ate in the same dining room as the residents, encouraged me to eat, including chef, who cooked me special tasty vegetarian dishes. The other residents encouraged me to eat too. Sleep came easily now and I slept deeply for hours every night.

Simon and the children visited me again. Clare sweetly sat hugging me and then softly stroking my hand. She could see both Simon and David felt awkward and unsure of how to be tactile under the circumstances.

'Mummy, you've been sent so many cards from your friends and our relatives around the world. Everyone's praying for you, including congregations around the world. Oh, and I've brought you some clothes, as I thought you might need some more.' The following day I put on the pale green trousers she had brought. I hadn't been able to do them up before my breakdown, but now the zip did up effortlessly, though I thought nothing of this at the time.

One day after lunch, while queuing in the nurses' office for my medication and chatting to others, I suddenly heard music coming through loudspeakers; the popular radio station Magic FM was playing. Something inside me stirred. I went and sat in an armchair to take my medication, including Carctol, which I was continuing to take at Simon's insistence. I had been on my way to my room for a rest.

A nurse stood mesmerized looking at me, smiling broadly. 'Gillian, you look so happy and radiant. Do you like the music?' I could only nod in response as my spirit soared and body swayed in tune with The Beach Boys belting out 'California Girls'. This was a turning point. At the time I hadn't realized it, though I saw a vision of someone kneeling on one knee with the weight of the world on their shoulders, and then it was lifted off.

The next day I enrolled for another therapy group. Sitting there listening to others talk about their childhood, I suddenly felt confident to explain, 'I had a Catholic upbringing at a convent school.' Then I remembered I hadn't applied myself wholeheartedly to lessons; I was more interested in the teachers' characters and how kind or strict they were. I was easily distracted by others in the class, acting the fool behind the teacher's back while she wrote on the blackboard in scratchy white chalk which set my teeth on edge.

When I was ten years old I lost my best friend in a riding accident, on an occasion I wasn't with her. During break time I was often alone if one or other of my close friends weren't about as I didn't belong to anyone's 'gang'. I wandered over a bridge, pausing to look into the stream below at the dancing dragonflies on top of the water lilies. For some reason they always reminded me of my late friend. On rainy days I'd wander into the little school chapel.

This was an early awakening to my spiritual side. I'd find a pew at the back and settle down on my knees, inhaling the candle smoke. I felt peaceful there, becoming enthralled by looking at the candle flames. Our family isn't deeply religious but I just enjoyed basking in the atmosphere. This sense of peacefulness when entering the silence has stayed with me throughout my life to varying degrees.

I continued talking to the group therapist. 'I've often puzzled over ideas of heaven and hell. I remember chatting to my father about heaven and hell when we were once set homework to write what we thought about it. My father told me he thought hell could be here on earth at times. He said life could be filled with struggles and what didn't kill you made you stronger. He said he thought purgatory was like a waiting room, where you were sent until you were ready to be moved on to heaven. He also said he thought heaven could be felt right here on earth, experienced when he felt a salmon tug on the line while fishing on the River Tay, when he got a hole in one on the golf course, or when he had a particularly good harvest when the elements worked together to perfectly ripen the crops.' My father always instinctively knew what the weather would be like, though he habitually tapped a barometer every morning as he walked downstairs.

It helped having the support of everyone in the group, going through their own dilemmas with the therapist conducting us, and it helped to make sense of what I was going through somehow by talking about it and then listening to others. Some, I discovered, suffered with similar issues.

Returning to my room I found an envelope sitting on the dressing table. The post had come. Inside was a beautifully colourful Celtic Mandala drawing of someone encased in chains. Then I read the message inside:

With all our love from Tony and Sara, our prayers remain with you throughout. When I worry sometimes I imagine them all being parcelled up and put into a pretty gift box full of transforming loving prayers. Then I tie a silver ribbon around it and put it away. We also have the whole community praying for you. Take care – get better soon. XXX.

Puzzling for days over that image of a person encased in chains, I learned to focus my attention beyond myself and into the picture, finally concluding that limitations don't necessarily have to be viewed as confining. That realization was liberating and I had all the time in the world to quietly reflect on it.

A new yoga class started and many, including myself, enrolled. The spacious lounge, with furniture pushed back against the walls, was crammed full and everyone enjoyed stretching their bodies and being led by the sensitive female instructor, who spoke quietly, leading us into different postures, which inspired and helped me so much. I practised yoga daily in my room, which I continued when I returned home, even if it was only for ten minutes a day. The discipline requires focus on the breath and bodily stretches at the exclusion of all else. It's another way I strive to find inner harmony, uniting the opposing forces within my nature.

Philippa arrived to visit me one day with her partner Ron. He always liked a good joke. Sitting in the communal lounge I could sense his unease. Nevertheless, he smiled and proceeded to tell me jokes, making me smile and then I couldn't help myself laughing. With laughter I felt something inside relax and just let go.

Prior to their visit I had reflected on everything that had happened in my life, similar to life flashing before your eyes. All I wanted was peace and quiet, so I avoided any stimulation such as the television and reading.

When Clare visited one day she told me about a disturbing phone call she'd had when someone inquisitive phoned for all the wrong reasons; she fielded that call as best she could. Such were the challenges for the family at home. Simon became increasingly protective and adept at fielding calls, having to preserve his own energies for the sake of the family, who were now entirely dependent on him as he also struggled to keep working.

One day while sitting in the garden, listening to the distant pheasants calling and reminding me of my childhood on the farm, I closed my eyes. The only sound now was of the wind through the leaves on the trees above me; it was as though they were whispering. I thought of an earlier summer when I'd been walking our late rescue dog Jack through remote woodland. There I'd heard a cracking sound echoing around the treetops above me. Looking up I'd noticed the sky filling with pinecone seeds. The fir cones were opening up in the sunshine releasing the seeds, which gracefully spiralled downwards, drifting on the breeze.

Simon and the children visited me with Lucy and Charlie one day. We were in the garden; I was sitting on a bench and felt overwhelmed by the dogs' exuberance as they ran towards me. They showered me with love, licking my face and hands, tails wagging excitedly. Nervous, I asked Simon to put them back in the car, as I couldn't respond normally.

During another visit, my loyal friend Philippa spotted a book in a stand, written by one of the psychiatric doctors at the Priory Sturt. It talks about mental illness, particularly depressive illness, as being the curse of the strong. That thought had never occurred to me before. Philippa went on to tell me how the limbic system in the brain plays a role in the nervous system, the emotions, especially love, and the sense of smell, and when overloaded results in depression, a physical illness, often triggered as a result of dealing with stresses and pressure, which build up until the body shouts *enough*! A breakdown is similar to a broken limb and takes time to mend.

I bought a copy of that book to read slowly at home. Later on, I lent it to a friend suffering from severe depression, who ceased to need medication due to its impact and reading how Carrie Fisher and Stephen Fry cope with their depression.

My sister Jane and her daughter Alice drove from Norwich to visit me. She thoughtfully brought a picnic and we all sat chatting on the lawn in the garden on a sunny day. She handed me a beautiful gift wrapped in soft turquoise tissue paper. It was a turquoise glass dragonfly, which I hung in the window of my room, and when the sun shone it filled my room with rainbows. On one level her visit helped me immeasurably, yet I was still feeling confused and vulnerable.

Jo, my cancer-surviving friend, came to visit me one day with her son Toby, a school friend of David's. He was sad seeing me like that. I've always loved Toby like an aunt; he's sensitive and caring and was determined to see me. I was glad Jo was with him; even though my feelings were dulled at the time and I couldn't communicate with them in my usual buoyant way, it didn't matter.

One or two other close friends also visited me, including Lindy and Susi. Sarah also visited me, overcoming her own anxieties to give me reflexology, at Simon's suggestion.

Midway through my stay at the Priory Sturt, an ambulance arrived to take me to hospital for brain scans. Simon looked worried, having kept this news away from family and friends and taking the full brunt himself, but supported by Rosy.

'Just relax,' he said. 'I'm staying right by your side. Give me your hand to hold.' The hospital corridor was busy with people as I lay waiting for my scan. Such was my fragile mental state at the time that I didn't feel the foreboding sensations in my body that usually accompanied a hospital scan. Simon was told pretty quickly that I didn't have a brain tumour.

He phoned Rosy to let her know the results. It was clearly 'just' a mental breakdown I was suffering.

Walking alone around the tranquil gardens at the Priory Sturt helped me, then one day I carried on walking, even though I wasn't very good at geography, nor did I comprehend my exact location. I had a bee in my bonnet that I wanted to go home for a visit to see the family and our beloved garden as I hadn't been able to do any gardening. As I couldn't work out the signposts by the roadside, I asked someone for directions, and several hours later arrived home.

I was so anxious to leave the hospital that I didn't realize how much I needed to be there. I was unable to deal with ordinary things, yet I felt trapped and useless in hospital. At some level I was deeply worried about the family and couldn't imagine how they were coping. Preparing to walk the seven miles home, I donned my trainers but forgot my usual bottle of water; I was fixated on going home. I attempted this walk more than once.

During my walk home, I passed through a churchyard and paused beneath a cathedral-like yew tree to soak in the natural sanctuary. It was a place of special tranquillity and focusing my mind entirely on my immediate surroundings overrode my desire to get home for a while. The peace I felt there banished all memories of my confused mind prior to my breakdown and I began to feel better.

That feeling didn't last long because when I arrived home and walked into the garden I felt bewildered. I couldn't understand how it had become so overgrown and neglected; that sight deepened my confused state and distressed me. Simon came out and found me and took me into the house to chat until a car arrived to take me back to the Priory.

A couple of weeks later when chatting to my psychiatrist before being discharged, he gave me two good pieces of advice: 'Don't revisit your breakdown too closely. And one more thing. I have to say this to everyone, so please understand. Don't experiment with recreational drugs. They can do untold harm to the mind, especially after such an episode as the one you've just had.'

I was in Priory Sturt for six weeks before being well enough to go home. Only days before my discharge Simon had unexpectedly bumped into my psychiatrist at London Bridge station and had a brief chat about what a remarkably quick recovery I had made from such a severe breakdown.

Late June 2003

I am sure that my swift recovery was largely due to all the prayers and distant healing, from those in both this world and the spirit realms. Also, I know now that it is a testimony to Simon's tremendous love for me, as well as that of our children, family and friends. So much of my recovery has been about accepting love, which is a powerful force. Once home, love came in many shapes and forms that I could now more easily recognize. It was as though emotional blockages had cleared and I was more responsive, even than before my cancer diagnosis. My breakdown began increasingly to feel like a rebuilding of me without the old, self-limiting ideas, which, along with many other toxic ones, had dissolved.

Having hired a metal detector, Simon found most of the jewellery I had thrown away and returned it to me, then to celebrate my first evening home he took me on a lovely evening stroll with the dogs. There had just been a shower, the sun was setting and, as we walked along our usual well-trodden path, ahead of us was a stunning, vibrant rainbow and we were walking straight into it.

Simon said, 'This is nature's special way of welcoming you home.' It felt beautiful. Wings wide open, a hawk drifted overhead on the warm thermals, and I marvelled at its effortless flight.

I set about cleaning and clearing up the house, and it felt good. So many things had found new homes, especially in the kitchen, so I put everything back where it belonged. These simple acts helped me readjust. Vacuuming the house was particularly satisfying. I regained my appetite and remember standing in the kitchen eating a naughty cheese and pickle sandwich, something my father and I had once enjoyed. I'd been strict with myself for so long. Although that sandwich was forbidden on my alkaline diet, I couldn't help myself; it was my way of celebrating the fact I was home. Had Simon known he would have chastised me, as he acted as my food policeman on rare occasions when temptation arose.

Over the next few days I tended the garden. 'I'll help you,' said Simon, working tirelessly despite not being a keen gardener.

'My wheelbarrow is full again,' I called across the garden, still feeling slightly out of sorts. 'I'll go and empty it at the bottom of the garden ready for a bonfire.' After several weeks of living apart, gently working side by side helped us both.

As I built a bonfire I thought of all the people I'd met in the Priory Sturt as they too came to terms with their recovery. I let go of the frustration of feeling trapped, useless and a burden. Those feelings had built up to a tremendous guilt about leaving the family and the stigma attached to mental illness. I'd missed being a wife and mother. Such thoughts floated around my mind as the flames flickered from the bonfire; I imagined all that I'd been through being transformed by flames, as though letting go, cleansing and clearing, preparing me for whatever lay ahead. That was cathartic because while in hospital I'd often thought of what I would do when I first got home, and much of that revolved around everyday things such as cooking, ironing and gardening.

I was acutely aware of the prescribed medication I was still taking. 'I really want to come off it all,' I said to Simon.

'You have to be patient and discuss it with your psychiatrist.' However, I didn't wean myself off the medication as gently as perhaps I could have. Some days I just left it out altogether. Realizing it was chemical-based, I wanted to resume my holistic regime. Also, I wanted to find another way to help myself, other than becoming reliant on such medication, as my father had for the latter forty-odd years of his life.

I talked to the psychiatrist, who explained how the pills were helping me, including the ones I'd already come off. He told me to gradually stop the remaining pills, saying, 'I must warn you you'll suffer from cold turkey or withdrawal symptoms. You'll feel unwell for at least a week and may feel as though you have a bad cold.' I thanked him and resolved to immediately start cutting down.

Meanwhile Simon was planning another holiday for us to Switzerland in August, which coincided beautifully with the medication coming to a complete end.

Bit by bit, Simon coaxed me back into the fold of everyday life, starting by taking me next door to see our ninety-year-old long-term neighbour, Dodie. Tom, David's ginger cat, had elected to live with her some years previously. She pampered him, cooking fresh fish every day. Greeting me warmly she opened her front door, stretching her arms open wide for a hug. 'Gillian, it's so lovely to see you, please come in. I've got tea all ready.' It was like entering a time warp as we walked into her sitting room, the former billiards room to the adjoining manor house. A tea tray with her silver teapot, cream jug and sugar bowl sat proudly on a lace cloth with her best china tea set. In my slightly altered state, I couldn't help but notice how Dodie looked youthful and radiant despite her years. I had a glimpse of her pure, strong spirit shining through and the courage and tremendous beauty of her younger years, and of the suffering she'd borne after tragically losing not one but two husbands early on in both marriages. She was elegantly dressed with large diamonds sparkling on her wedding finger. Tom was stretched out in a pool of sunshine on the faded floorboards beyond a tapestry rug, and kept glancing over at her in between stretching his toes, blissfully happy.

I noticed the plate laden with rich chocolate biscuits and cake slices, and couldn't resist eating one, then another, in spite of Simon's protests.

Returning home Simon said, 'Now, over the next day or two, we're going to visit Daphne and Eric to plan the vegetable garden.' Within hours of eating the biscuits and cake, my stomach was gripped with pain that made me breathless, and I was forced to sit up for most of the night just waiting for it to subside. Eventually it did, by nature taking its course and evacuating it from my body. My still recovering liver clearly couldn't process an overload of certain forbidden foods.

A few days later Daphne welcomed me into her home with, 'Hello, Gill. Lovely to see you, isn't it Eric?'

Eric greeted me before regaling me with his plans. 'I've got a variety of seeds ready to plant for a good harvest next year, and I've already planted some vegetables you can eat, including beetroot. They're doing well. Have you seen them?'

'No, so far we've been blitzing the rest of the garden, all the flower beds,' I said uneasily.

Simon kept reassuring me and I relaxed. 'Picking up the threads of life will continue at a steady pace,' he reassured.

'Time to go now,' said Simon standing up. In the car he said, 'That went well, didn't it? And when you feel ready I'm going to take you for a quiet evening drink to the Seven Stars. We'll sit in the pub garden with the dogs.'

This felt like another challenge, although it wasn't long before I was sitting there on a fine summer evening. While I recognized the familiar surroundings, I still felt slightly on edge and disorientated. Learning to relax, trust and just be with Simon and the dogs, although not having to strive to do anything, presented me with a slight struggle initially. With time I finally overcame this obstacle and eventually learned to enjoy sitting in nature just for the sheer joy of being able to, and of simply being alive. I was relearning so much on a deeper level than ever before, and was more conscious and appreciative of my surroundings as a result.

All these experiences have taught me so much of value in life, how fragile life is, how beautiful life is and how important the people in our lives are. To draw breath and feel love, whether it's for a sunset or 'a someone', is a gift to be treasured.

July 2003

'I think we should make an appointment to go and see Professor Thomas,' Simon said one day.

'Do I have to?' I answered, feeling my tummy do a somersault at the thought.

However, I did make an appointment, knowing I couldn't run away from it. After my physical examination, Professor Thomas told me my 'lump' was roughly the same size it was at the beginning of the year, and queried that it felt softer, confirming there was no suggestion of progression. She was unable to feel an edge on my liver.

The following are extracts from her letter concerning this appointment sent to my GP:

I saw Mrs Gill with her husband at Guildford Nuffield Hospital on 7th July. She immediately volunteered that she had recently had a nervous breakdown. I was aware of this as I had been contacted by the Psychiatrists from the hospital.

She was certainly rather more timid and withdrawn than her usual bubbly self, but entirely appropriate and sensible. She has been back at home for about a week now, attending the hospital as a Day Patient. I understand that she had a CT scan of her brain, which showed no abnormality....

I suggest that she has her usual annual CT scan in the Autumn, and I have checked her blood for tumour markers... The only agent which she is receiving which might be therapeutic is the Indian ayurvedic medicine Carctol.

I will see Mrs Gill again in November with the result of her scan.

Our next big hurdle was travelling to Cambridge to visit my parents before going on holiday. I had been thrilled to learn my father hadn't died as I'd been convinced whilst in the Priory.

'How are you, darling?' said my father, holding my hand tightly in the back of the car on the way to their favourite pub on the outskirts of Cambridge.

'I'm feeling much better, thank you. I'm getting more involved with the garden. Eric is teaching me what flowers to grow in the vegetable patch to act as a natural deterrent for carrot weevils, so we've planted marigolds. You used to grow borage and the bees, especially the honey ones, love it, so we've planted some between the potatoes.'

'You've been through so much, Gilly dear,' said my father, uncharacteristically tactile and emotional. He looked thin and frail and held back tears. I felt his body tremble as he thought of our parallel breakdowns. After that we had an exceptionally happy lunch.

We skirted around major issues in the main, as we all wished to simply enjoy being together at the table. Simon and my mother stood at the bar ordering drinks and food and chatted, while my father and I sat talking over old times. He told me how when resting in the afternoon and drifting off in his armchair he visited beautiful places where he met old friends. Sometimes he played golf with them and won. Other times he met and chatted with friends who had fought in the war and looked so young, well and happy. 'I feel your sister's presence in the warm breezes when I am out walking and standing on the bridge looking down at the fish in the River Cam. Sometimes I sense her sitting at the foot of my bed.' He paused before continuing. 'When I have these experiences with my old friends,' he said mistily, 'it feels so real, it takes me a moment or two to realize I'm in the armchair at home with your mother.'

As hot, steaming plates of food arrived, my father's face lit up.

Brightly, my mother commented, 'Your father's appetite is exceptionally good today. He's eating everything.' He then proceeded to eat two puddings.

As Simon drove us home I commented, 'My father has never been so openly affectionate before.' I'd also noticed my mother's hands shaking, making it difficult for her to hold her knife and fork; the strain of his frailty was taking its toll.

'He is suddenly looking very old, and your mother quietly told me at the bar that he is increasingly suffering from dementia. Their neighbours help them when it gets difficult. Apparently your father's adjusted to the respite care he goes to periodically, which helps them both in different ways.'

When we got home Lucy and Charlie welcomed us warmly, excitedly jumping up and barking. Later, when sitting quietly on the floor, they lay either side of me taking deep contented sighs as I rubbed their tummies, feeling all tiredness and tension from the day drain away and basking in their love.

I was just about off all prescribed medication from the psychiatrist by now and realized how they had balanced my brain. My father continued taking medication throughout his lifetime, as his brain was unable to manufacture certain chemicals. He'd been in hospital for months following his breakdown and had undergone electroconvulsive therapy, whereas I would now sit in my healing room and focus on inviting calming healing to my mind and imagine a waterfall gently flowing through the top of my head, cleansing, clearing and harmonizing my entire brain to encourage it to function optimally. I also learned to recognize the times when I needed more rest.

Claire, my yoga friend, had also begun giving me acupuncture after I'd eventually overcome my fear of needles.

'I know you don't like needles,' she said, 'but you'll hardly notice them, they are hair thin.' When I had stuck my tongue out for her to assess my health she'd commented on how acupuncture 'assists the body's innate intelligence to self-heal itself'. She said, 'Many illnesses have their roots in past traumas and stresses. This method helps to relax the mind and body, thus aiding the healing process.' We hardly stopped chatting throughout the treatment and at the end she generously said, 'Please only pay a mate's rate.' I tried to press the point but she remained fixed, so I graciously accepted, though acceptance was something I was still coming to terms with.

I was feeling so much better that Simon decided to take a chance and booked flights for us to go to Switzerland on holiday. We revisited the same small family-run hotel and were warmly greeted in a charming manner; they remembered us from our previous visit. Once we had settled in we arranged to see Lindsay and Reynald for supper. We chatted and told them of our plans for the following day, a trip on a paddle steamer across Lake Geneva, and they told us about their gardening project, Lindsay's book writing and Reynald's work. We had a most enjoyable evening.

'Here comes the paddle steamer,' said Simon expectantly, as it glided across the lake towards the jetty ready for passengers to board. As we walked across the gangplank onto the steamer Simon said, 'What a timepiece this is. My father, the frustrated engineer, would love it. Look at the magnificent paddle wheels, dripping with water from the lake.' We found a seat and the boat set out across the lake. I watched the ripples in our wake, feeling calm and soothed.

This was a change from the shakes I'd awoken with prior to breakfast, a side effect of coming off the medication. To help detoxify my body I drank increasing amounts of water, taking a bottle with me wherever I went.

As we continued, the weather deteriorated and visibility was hampered by a low mist eerily spreading out across the lake's surface. Above the mist rose tall brooding mountains, almost black. Perhaps reflecting the weather, my mood began to change to a sense of foreboding that I couldn't shake off.

The following day, after a quiet evening, Simon said, 'Let's go for a gentle walk. I've got a map we can use. There's a secluded valley I'd like to visit.'

'How lovely,' I replied, reaching for my walking boots and stowing them in the car boot. It was a clear day with a few clouds scudding across the sky as Simon drove up the mountain roads and around hairpin bends, surrounded by cattle grazing on the lush grass. Wildflowers in the meadows gently swayed in the warm breeze.

'My boots feel tight,' I said putting them on.

'You haven't worn them for a while. They'll soon feel more comfortable when we start walking.'

'Oh, doesn't the air smell sweet?' I said, inhaling deeply. We walked through a farm where the family lived above the barn. Pretty lace curtains hung from the windows, heart shapes were carved into the classic Swiss wooden shutters and logs lay neatly stacked against an outside barn wall.

'It's so peaceful; the only sound is insects and occasional bells ringing from the grazing cows' necks.'

'Glorious, isn't it?' replied Simon.

We were walking slowly as I tired easily, another of the side effects as I readjusted to coming off the medication. Suddenly I felt mounting apprehension and noticed a movement from a dense copse beside a ditch on the edge of a meadow. Pointing at the movement, I urged Simon to look and we both simultaneously noticed a man from a bygone era, dressed from head to toe in old-fashioned black clothes. He wore a pointed black hat and held a sickle, cutting the grass in long, rhythmical strokes. Even though the sun was out I felt a shiver run down my spine. He glanced up and we waved to one another. Simon drew me closer saying, 'Obviously the old ways of farming are still alive here.' To all intents and purposes he reminded us both of the legendary 'grim reaper'.

The next day Simon's mobile phone rang while we were having supper with Lindsay and Reynald. He looked grave as he listened then left the room to stand outside, speaking in hushed tones. When he returned, Lindsay rushed from the table towards him. I sat silently looking at his white face, unable to move. He came and stood beside me and gently told me, 'Clare's been trying to reach us, as your mother in her desperation couldn't find our telephone number to break the news. Your father has just died.'

I felt faint listening to the news. Simon apologised to our friends, who were sympathetic as they accompanied us to the door, and we bade farewell as Simon, arm around me, steered me towards the car.

Driving back to the hotel, lights all around the edge of the lake were flashing. I couldn't fathom why and I felt numb. The sky was darkening with large thunderclouds rolling in as far as the eye could see and lightning flashes signalled the start of a powerful storm. We reached the hotel in no time and returned to our room. Flinging the double windows wide open, I stood on the balcony staring across the lake. The darkened water was swelling as the mighty storm gathered pace; the lights I'd noticed around the lake earlier were signalling an alarm. Spectacular bolts of forked lightning, the like of which I'd never seen, ripped through the sky in between deafening rolls of thunder. I stood transfixed.

'Come on in now,' called Simon. 'It's pouring with rain.'

I hadn't noticed the rain splashing off the overhead awning, nor the tears tumbling down my cheeks. Walking hazily back into the bedroom, I slumped down onto the end of the bed, then sat bolt upright as I heard a thud and felt a chilly blast of air. A local information guide, falling open on a golfing page, had jumped off the desk and landed squarely at my feet. I knew in that instant it was my father's way of letting me know he was okay. He was so close I could sense his presence. It was as though he didn't want me to mourn and grieve his loss, but rather to celebrate his life knowing that he was now happy and free from his suffering and that he was surrounded by golf courses of an entirely different hue!

I fell into bed exhausted and slept fitfully that night. When I phoned my mother the following morning, she insisted we remain on holiday, saying she had all the help she needed. I told her I'd phone her every day.

We checked out of the hotel to move to a quieter area near Chateaud'Oex where Simon had discovered an English-owned small hotel that reminded us of a cuckoo clock. No sooner were we in our new bedroom than I promptly started shivering, feeling queasy and unwell. Putting myself to bed, I urged Simon, 'Please go for a walk and enjoy the mountains.' They'd been calling to him.

I fell asleep, and when I awoke I couldn't get out of bed to go further than the adjoining bathroom, as I kept being sick. It hurt to lift my head off the pillow I had such a bad headache. As the day wore on I got a violent tummy upset too and had profuse sweats with a high temperature.

When Simon returned and saw me still in bed, he said, 'Grief comes in many forms; it affects everyone differently.' Breaking my dietary rules, I drank a bottle of lemonade to rehydrate and nibbled a slice of dry toast. Shortly after, my headache disappeared, having been thoroughly purged.

During my breakdown I'd had a premonition of my father's death and had been wracked with grief, believing it to be true. I'd already done much of my grieving then, having sensed he didn't have long left to live, though nothing prepares for the deep sense of loss of someone close.

Phoning my mother, she told me, 'Your father was eating his favourite Sunday roast a day early on the Saturday he died. I'd cooked roast lamb, roast potatoes, leeks in cheese sauce, gravy and redcurrant jelly. During lunch he started to cough, though there was nothing unusual about that. He then just gently slipped to the kitchen floor and closed his eyes. He never woke up. His time had come to join his friends. You know he'd been becoming increasingly weak, and in spite of his normally healthy appetite he couldn't put weight on. But you know, dear, he lived to make eighty and died in his eighty-first year, so he achieved his goal. He passed so very peacefully and I was right there beside him.'

It had been a terrible shock for my mother, in spite of living with his increasing fragility. Latterly, he'd suffered not only dementia, but also had a prostate problem and my mother was feeling the strain from looking after him and from the shock of him dying right before her eyes. Speaking to her for an hour every day throughout the remainder of our holiday helped us both. 'Please don't rush home,' she repeated to my suggestion otherwise. 'I'm getting help with the funeral arrangements, which will be simple, family only. I've agonized over it and can't manage anything else.'

I continued processing my grief without the everyday interruptions of life at home. That alone helped to hold me in a protected space. The hotel was enchanting. There was a patio adorned with festive umbrellas so diners could eat outside at the top of the garden, protected from the elements and surrounded by beautiful plants and wildlife.

My father would have loved it.

CHAPTER 10

Regeneration

When we are tested by life,
It's almost as if we are being asked:
'How strong can we be?'
Gillian Gill

Late 2003

Returning from Switzerland, my only thoughts were about supporting my mother in the lead-up to the funeral. Over the phone she'd admitted, 'Old farming friends are asking me when the funeral is, but I just go to pieces at the thought of your father's send-off being anything other than a quiet, small family affair.'

Respecting her sensitivities and limitations I replied, 'Then why not do just that and keep it simple? It's what you originally decided, but it's natural to doubt.'

The day of the funeral finally arrived and Emma, my sister-in-law, brought late summer roses from their garden to dress the coffin. I'd found bulrushes, which reminded me of the pond on the farm where I'd played throughout my childhood, together with a bunch of wheat. Jane, deeply grief-stricken, brought roses too. We supported one another throughout the service, shedding tears in spite of our knowledge that it was a celebration of my father's life. When we were back in my mother's sitting room having tea after the funeral the atmosphere subtly lifted.

'This is the room where Daddy used to drift off to sleep and dream of his old farming, fishing and golfing friends. That's the chair he sat in,' I said wistfully to Jane.

'I'm just going out of the room for a moment,' she said preoccupied.

She reappeared carrying a huge plate. On it sat a large chocolate cake adorned with roses, gold dust and gold candles.

'What a cake!' said my mother wide-eyed.

'Daddy would have loved that,' I said. 'Chocolate was his favourite.'

The time came for everyone to leave, to give my mother space to quietly reflect on my father's send-off now he had gone on to join so many of his old friends. In his own way, since passing he had already paid each of us a visit in spirit form. Jane had felt his presence when two geese had unexpectedly flown low overhead while she was walking in a local park. My mother sensed his presence around the house, especially in the early days, when her favourite coffee mug would move from its usual place. During the drive home I remembered how my father had taught me, aged ten, to drive the Land Rover and tractor on the farm roads.

Life carried on. During October I had another CT abdominal scan and the results were as set out in this letter from my radiologist to my GP:

What is seen in the lung bases is normal. Multiple metastases are seen in the liver, the largest of which replaces the caudate lobe and involves much of the anterior aspect of the right lobe of the liver. This lesion measures approximately 10 x 8cm. There is a huge mass arising from the pelvis displacing the bowel superiorly and this mass extends up to the level of the lower pole of the kidneys. A few septa are seen within it and this unquestionably represents ovarian carcinoma. Some unopacified loops of bowel are seen on the left but this does not represent further mesenteric disease. The par-aortic regions are normal. Some small lymph nodes are seen low down in the pelvis bilaterally.

CONCLUSION: There is a huge cystic mass arising from the pelvis occupying much of the abdominal pelvic cavity to the level of the lower pole of the kidneys. There are further multiple metastases in the liver. Although I do not have the previous films or report for comparison I am sure the disease is progressing.

This letter was written by my radiologist, not Professor Thomas. His opinion is different from hers. Perhaps he had not compared this scan with the previous one, and I respect the difference in their viewpoints, however they came about. It is only more recently in the writing of this book that these letters have come to my attention.

What has kept me going throughout is constantly endeavouring to banish any negative thoughts of my internal organs being crushed or unwell and instead to focus on imagining my body healthy and well.

'We've done it!' said Simon a few days later. 'Your recipe books have been printed and will be delivered by courier in a day or two. When they arrive we're going out to celebrate all our hard work and achievement. We'll invite both the children and, of course, Ashleigh to join us for the part they have played. Susi and Ed too; without their input the book wouldn't have happened nearly so well.'

We'd gathered at a favourite restaurant in a small hotel surrounded by dense woodland and a lake. Jolly faces sat around the table.

'Cheers, guys,' said Susi and Ed almost in unison.

'This is such a special place, where we occasionally come for family celebrations,' I said wistfully, joining in the toast with my wine glass filled with water.

'Come on, Mum,' said Clare, 'let's take a break for a moment and have a stroll around the garden.'

Her timing was perfect. This wasn't the time or the place to become teary, but I was so moved by the love and support of everyone and the achievement we'd made between us all.

My prayers continued to be that the book we had given birth to would help others in a similar predicament to myself and that they'd find nourishment, inspiration and healing from the recipes within.

'Thank you everyone for coming along to mark this occasion,' said Simon rising from the table, arm outstretched, raising his glass to thank not only those present, but also Rosy Daniel and Jane Sen for the part they'd played in helping us with their encouragement, belief and support.

Over the next few years those books circulated far and wide to many other countries, helping people with cancer who wanted to include a dietary element in their battle against the disease.

Home again, Simon said, 'Now we have celebrated, let's think about how you can quietly refocus on helping yourself a little more.'

'I just don't seem to be able to return to my old practices in quite the same way since my breakdown.'

'Then approach them gently. You've been through a great deal of processing, so do what you've always done: trust, be yourself and have confidence.'

Something inside me shifted after listening to Simon's words. I walked quietly into my familiar healing room and sat in the high wingback chair that once belonged to his late father; the chair felt infused with his love. I settled down after first lighting a candle to focus on. Immediately, I entered a deep prayerful state, offering gratitude for all that had happened and all I had survived. Then I stilled my mind, focused on my breathing and stated my intention clearly that now I truly wished to restart meditation. I let my mind still and sank into a deep, familiar rhythm of peace, and when thoughts or feelings arose that weren't particularly comfortable, I watched them in a detached way, letting them quietly come and go, rather than letting them take over.

'You look different suddenly,' commented Simon after my first day's practice.

'I took your advice and resumed my meditation, without the shadow of doubt about my ability hanging over me.'

'Well, whatever happened, it shows in your face. I'm so pleased for you. As you know all too well, cycling and walking are my form of meditation that always clears my mind.'

By November it was my mother's birthday and she celebrated it quietly at home. At the same time, I was due to visit my oncologist for a routine check-up and to hear about my latest scan results. The following is a letter she sent my GP:

I was very pleased to see an extremely well-looking Mrs Gill on 5th November. Unfortunately her CT scan performed about five weeks ago was not available to me, and I have promised to contact her with the results.

In the meantime, clinically she is clearly stable. The mass in her abdomen is smaller than before with now fifteen fingers' breadth palpable above the tumour. It is also narrower laterally. Symptomatically she is well and thriving.

I will see her again at her request in the next few months.

As I had no idea at that time of the differences between the letters from my radiologist and Professor Thomas, I kept going with my lifestyle changes and diet, doing the best I could every day of my life.

On my return home, Simon said, 'This is a year for celebrating your body's regenerative powers. It's incredible that your 'lump' has so evidently shrunk.' He was visibly moved after such an encouraging visit.

'I think I've got some extra help on my side now that my father has gone to the spirit realms. He believed he would be closer to us all and in a better place to give us a stronger helping hand.'

'So it seems. I'm going to plan another holiday for next April, take you somewhere special. I'll ask the children if they want to join us.'

'Mum, that's such fantastic news about your further shrinkage,' said Clare phoning home. 'I am moving back to London to live closer to home. Ashleigh wants to do a course at a London university and I'm coming to be with him.'

'I am so happy for both of you. Your relationship is obviously deepening.'

'We have our moments, but then don't all relationships? We work well together. So many of our friends are now in London it seems like the next natural step.'

Simon was delighted when I told him of their plans.

One evening while sitting quietly with the dogs lying at our feet I said, 'Darling, I feel so tired now the evenings are drawing in and it's getting dark earlier.'

'Well, you've always told me it's the time of year for hibernation. Maybe nature is telling you something? You need more time to rest and relax and let nature run its course in keeping with healing your body. Just follow your own natural rhythm; don't go against it.'

So I entered my own 'hibernation' period that winter, with its deep meditations, reflective silences and gentle pace that culminated in a quiet, and very happy, Christmas surrounded by the children and dogs.

CHAPTER 11
New Horizons

Life calls us to achieve many tasks,
Some we are unprepared for.
Let us at such times merely
Trust and like a fast-flowing river
Go with the flow.
Gillian Gill

January - September 2004

I gently and gradually gained renewed energy, continuing to walk with the dogs and feeling replenished and uplifted by doing so. My other daily disciplines also remained in place, sometimes requiring great effort and control. Interestingly, I noticed that the rash on my groin, mirroring the site of Joanna's trouble spot, had completely healed.

By June I began seeing an old friend again. 'Hello, it's Sarah,' said a familiar voice down the phone. We'd met shortly after I married Simon and instantly got on. In spite of having lost her husband many years previously, Sarah was always bright and positive and kept smiling the entire way through her own battle with breast cancer, as well as working when she could. We frequently chatted, catching up on news.

'I'd love to see you,' she said. 'I'm feeling quite strong at the moment as I'm in between chemotherapy sessions. I'm managing to make some curtains and do a little upholstery for my clients, whilst taking life gently.'

'In that case why not come over and we'll walk the dogs gently around the meadows?'

As she pulled into the driveway I noticed how Sarah's hair was growing back thick and curly. Stepping from the car she held me in a massive hug, crying and laughing all at the same time. Sarah's dog, Dusty, an enormous rare breed Picardy Shepherd with long blond fur, happily joined Charlie and Lucy as we set off up the drive.

'How do you do it?' she asked.

'Do what?' I replied.

'Carry on. You look amazing in spite of your breakdown and your tummy is definitely flatter.'

'There are several things that keep me going. For starters, my daily routine includes meditation, and I find the best time for this is as soon as I wake, very early in the morning. But just before that I do half an hour's body visualization, seeing my body cleansed by a beautiful waterfall then receiving rejuvenating energies.'

'Hmm, I might try that myself. Do you meditate in the evening too?'

'Sometimes, but mostly I contemplate my day after stretching my body with yoga.'

'How long do you do yoga for?'

'It depends on how I feel; sometimes ten minutes, sometimes an hour plus.'

'I find meditating helps me, especially with my hospital visits…'

Sarah broke off, watching Dusty and Lucy up ahead chasing through the long grass while Charlie, taking his time, trailed some way behind them, closer to us.

'Something else I do', I continued, 'is keep a stone in my pocket at certain times. It's called my worry stone. I share my worries with it, which gets them out of my system and into the stone. Then I visualize the stone being thrown into either a pond or river, in the belief that all the worries are then washed away from the stone, and from me.'

I paused, taking a breath before continuing, 'That's the sort of ritual practice that helps empower me. As I said, I don't literally throw the stone away, but rather imagine throwing it into the water. If you really want a stone to use for this purpose, I find there's always one particular stone that stands out from the rest. Perhaps it's a pebble found on a beach or a path when out walking.'

My extended response to Sarah's question allowed me to realize how often I rely on simple rituals to control my stress levels and steady myself. Over the years, Sarah had witnessed my battle with ovarian cancer and all the dramatic lifestyle and dietary changes I'd made on the road to recovery, but there are still small things that seem hardly worth a mention that have constantly acted as props. These small rituals, like carrying the worry stone, help to bring balance and keep me going. They help to take my mind off the enormity of what seems at times to be an overwhelming task. It's a coping strategy.

I continued speaking: 'Another coping strategy involves a hypnotherapist that I recently met at one of the seminars I spoke at, who I am now seeing. I find I need support from time to time, and repeatedly learn the necessity of reaching out to ask for it. As you've always told me, I'm very lucky to have Simon's love. I've found that loving him gives me a strength I never knew I possessed and, in turn, his love gives me courage to confront things I'd never imagined I could face. I'm beginning to understand a little about the difference between love as a sentiment and love as an active force that has a power of its own.'

'Look,' said Sarah suddenly, laughing and pointing to the sky, 'those clouds have darkened and it looks like it's going to rain. Let's make a dash for home.' Neither of us had run for some time so we launched ourselves into a jog as it started to rain hard.

'It's lashing down,' I said laughing. I couldn't help but stare at her, saying, 'Your hair is plastered to your scalp.'

'So is yours! And look at poor Charlie. He hates the rain; his ears are flat back. Neither Lucy or Dusty seem to mind though.' We fell into a steady rhythm, moving as one in a pack. We arrived sodden back at the house, with Simon opening the front door and looking astonished to see us giggling, with tears of hysterical laughter pouring down our faces.

That is one of my happiest memories of Sarah, for she didn't survive. Before she died she said, 'Please will you have Dusty? He loves being with you, and Simon makes him feel safe. He's the best rescue dog I could have had and has never fully recovered from the abuse he received earlier in his life. He gets on so well with Lucy and Charlie.'

So Dusty came to live with us for nine months, during which time he ran off into the bushes chasing rabbits and pheasants and gave us all the runaround.

'Every time I take him out for a walk,' said Simon, 'Dusty proves to be a real babe magnet, stopping ladies in four-by-fours in their tracks. They ask, "What breed is that incredible-looking dog?" They can't take their eyes off his extraordinary face and long blond fur. But seriously, I think as Charlie is suffering from extreme territorial issues we must try and find Dusty another home. I know it's difficult for you as you gave Sarah your word but, trust me, it's not fair on Charlie. I can almost hear him pleading what about me?'

Before we knew it I was due to see my oncologist again. I was sitting on the sofa preparing for the visit, feeling melancholy about Sarah and Dusty's plight, when Dusty surprised me by wandering over and pressing himself against my leg, resting his head in my lap. As I stroked him I felt a tremendous shift in my emotions. It was as though he was trying to reassure me that everything would be okay and was just as it was meant to be.

With my next hospital appointment looming, anxiety emerged beforehand. Perhaps that edginess is part of what motivates me to persevere and carry on doing my utmost to help myself. There's some driving force that is beyond me and, although I persistently try to unravel what that is, in the end I just humbly thank 'it' and learn to live with it.

The following is a letter my oncologist wrote to my GP following my early June appointment:

This remarkable lady remains extremely well on nothing more than an Indian Ayurvedic medicine known as Carctol. She has also been seeing a hypnotherapist recently and is clearly keeping her 'disease' under control.

On examination of her abdomen the lump is still up to the umbilicus but does seem slightly narrower than before. Certainly there has been no dramatic change since she was last seen.

We talked about a mutual friend who was also under my care and who passed away recently, having abandoned Carctol treatment.

I have now been following Mrs Gill and her progress since October 2000. She has had no conventional treatment in that time and for what appears to be a tumour metastatic to the liver on her CT scans, this is a remarkable story.

I am due to see her again in the autumn when she will have a further scan. I am still negotiating with her that when she reaches the five-year mark I would like to persuade her to have a biopsy. This is such a highly unusual situation it would be helpful to know what precisely we are dealing with!

When I next spoke to Rosy after that appointment, I brought up something that had been troubling me: 'I'm feeling well now but in the spring we went to Grenada and my entire body swelled up and felt sluggish as a result of the flight.'

She replied, 'Listen to your body and remember that flying for whatever reason can cause disturbances.'

Following that conversation we resolved that if I was ever to fly far again it had to be business class. We were fortunate to have accumulated lots of air miles from Simon's business travel, so we could afford it.

Planning holidays, and the ensuing anticipation, was something that lifted my spirits and delighted us both. Simon had worked hard all his life and travelled far and wide. For him travel had become second nature; he was always comfortable wherever he was in the world, reminding me of a chameleon. His motto had become 'It's the life in your days, not the days in your life; therefore let's live for the day and enjoy our health while we have it'. So we weren't about to put a ban on our travels together; we just had to pick our destinations wisely.

At the end of the summer towards harvest time, we flew business class to Montreal, using a vast number of air miles, to visit some friends living in a rural area in Quebec. For a change our friend and part-time gardener

Nick came to house-sit to look after the dogs. He is a keen fitness fanatic who happens to love dogs, although his lifestyle prevents him from owning his own.

'Edwina will be so delighted to see us,' I said excitedly to Simon.

'I know she's one of your oldest college friends, and she's had quite a time of it herself. I remember the photos of you two and Helen, beaming in your tall chef's hats and long white aprons at college. It'll do you both good. She was so sensitive with you about the children at the onset of your health issues, not knowing what the outcome would be.'

'That's typical of her. I'm so grateful that you've booked us somewhere near the airport to stay for the first night.'

'Well, I know how tired you get when travelling, and that your emotions will also take their toll. It's best to take precautions to try to prevent you becoming overly tired.'

I got into bed the moment we walked into the hotel bedroom. After a short rest, we ate a light meal then I went straight to bed again and slept until morning.

'Look at the mess on my clothes!' I said to Simon, rummaging in my suitcase to find fresh clothes to wear.

'Charlie has obviously curled up in my suitcase before I shut it and somehow dislodged the lid from the pot of my dandelion coffee and it's gone all over my clothes, together with his fur!' Missing the dogs, I was delighted in a strange way to make this messy discovery.

Thoughts of him made us both smile.

After breakfast we drove to Edwina's home, where she greeted us with an enormous grin, in spite of working all night at a care home.

'Come here and let me give the both of you a hug,' she screeched in her adorable Canadian accent.

For the next few days we spent much of our time sitting in rocking chairs on the deck surrounding their house, bordered by fields of tall maize. It reminded me of the television programme *The Waltons*.

'What are you two up to?' asked Simon striding out to join us after a shower following a long walk.

'Catching up on old times,' said Edwina. 'Look, there's Chippy the chipmunk. He's popped out of his hole at the edge of the flowerbed to see what we're up to.'

'I'm not a bird feeder!' said Simon astonished as a hummingbird swooped down and hovered in front of his bright red polo shirt. 'Look, it's up there.'

There were several bright red feeders containing sugar water hanging from the house, and clearly Simon had been mistaken for one of them by the hummingbird. We were all helpless with laughter.

The day arrived for our departure. We bade our farewells, hugging and laughing, then Simon drove us for several hours towards our next destination, a hotel on the St. Lawrence River. The scenery was beautiful, with belts of tall fir trees lining the river, and on clear, sunny days their reflections on the water were stunning.

During our first evening the waiter came to explain the menu; it included blue potatoes, which are packed with minerals. As I tasted the first mouthful I was in raptures. Simon's fish was cooked beautifully and he'd chosen a delicious wine to accompany his meal, which I couldn't resist tasting. During dinner Simon said, 'This remote part is known for its natural beauty, and if you're lucky you can see whales at this time of year. Let's book a boat ride tomorrow and see if we can spot one.'

The following day we stepped onto a small tourist boat and set off in calm waters. Walking down the narrow steps leading below the water line, I suddenly grabbed the handrail. A glassy eye was staring right at me – a minke whale! My initial fear dissolved, giving way to awe. The water was full of them. I hastened upstairs to stand beside Simon as we held hands and stared at the bubbling water, surrounded by whales.

Our time away was a tonic and I didn't have any side effects from the long flight this time. Being able to stretch out to sleep on the aircraft had made all the difference, along with my visualization techniques. As we walked through the front door on our return, Charlie's excited vocal cords erupted as he pushed his way forward in greeting with Lucy and Dusty by his side.

Nick followed in their wake saying, 'The dogs have helped keep me fit, especially Dusty when he runs off. I kept him separated in the house sometimes, to give Charlie and Lucy time together.'

We thanked him profusely, glad of his intuitive way with the dogs.

The next few weeks passed with me paying greater attention to Eric when he visited the vegetable patch, as he passed on some of his knowledge and experience. Clare and David continued with their lives independently, coming home for visits when time allowed.

Then one day out of the blue Rosy phoned, saying, 'Gillian, I'm preparing a press release on my findings with Carctol. You are my star patient, having achieved all you have without conventional treatment. I know you are a private person but would you please consider speaking to the *Daily Telegraph*? They wish to do a piece on our findings with Carctol. You, along with some other patients, are doing extraordinarily well. You've met Steven at one of my seminars and he has already agreed. But no pressure, please think about it.'

Before I had time to think I answered, 'Yes, I'd be happy to help in any way I can.' As I confidently put the phone down, I wondered where that instant response had come from. Then fear took hold, causing me to doubt myself. But I realised I was living proof that my drastic changes in lifestyle, diet and thinking had brought about positive changes in my health. So many people I knew and had worked with had been less fortunate. By then I also knew others like myself who were breaking into new territory and incorporating complementary medicine into their own health regimes with success. Surely the public had a right to know this?

I put into practice my self-hypnosis techniques to calm me, and also stepped up my prayers and meditation. An illicit bag of milk chocolate buttons was also bought and hidden at the back of the fridge; eaten sparingly, these forbidden fruits gave me a psychological lift.

As I swallowed a melting button the phone rang. It was a pleasant reporter introducing himself before interviewing me. A day or two later a photographer called at the house at an appointed time.

'Come in,' I said, not knowing what to expect and feeling a bit edgy, yet he had a way of putting me at ease and I was able to be true to myself and say that I would prefer photos to be taken in the garden. As Carctol consists of herbs which grow naturally, being outside is so much a part of what has helped me.

'Mum, I'll come too,' said David, who was then in his last summer off before university. I was so glad to have him about. Simon was in London visiting his office.

'Okay,' said the photographer, 'the weather's fine, so would you please stand in the flowerbed amongst those purple Michaelmas daisies for me?… Yes, that's good. I like that.' He kept his camera clicking until satisfied he'd taken enough photos.

What he didn't know was that David was standing right behind him pulling faces at me to help me relax. We both felt it was a bit surreal and could hardly believe what was happening, yet on another level it felt perfectly natural too.

When the article was due to appear in the newspaper Simon rushed to the front door to pick it up, placing it on the kitchen table. 'I'll start at the back and see if we can spot it,' he said.

Working quickly through the pages, I said, 'I think they must have changed their minds about printing it. It doesn't appear to be there.' Both our spirits sank.

Turning to page three, Simon exclaimed, 'Look, here it is. There are photos of Rosy, Steven and you. You're standing in the flowerbed. How appropriate for you is that?' We laughed, as I'm passionate about the outdoors and tending the garden has been a mainstay in my life, whatever my ability. The article appeared under the current news heading and took up the entire page. The article was a fair write-up: 'I've seen herbal remedy make tumours disappear, says respected cancer doctor.'

Following that, Simon had to go away for two days on business. 'I'm off to Bulgaria. I'm sure you'll be fine; you're so well now. Take care and don't be tempted to overdo it. Remember, if you need help, ask for it.'

'Good luck,' I replied, waving Simon off in the taxi after a hug farewell. I already missed him and was busy planning how I'd indulge in eating quantities of garlic, which couldn't offend him, and cover his side of the bed with books when I heard the phone ring.

'Hello, this is GMTV.'

'Don't be silly,' I replied. 'Who is this acting the fool? Is it you, Ron?' Philippa's great friend Ron is a true jester and loves nothing more than making people laugh.

'This is GMTV. Is this Mrs Gill I'm speaking to?'

Something inside me knew in an instant that it wasn't Ron, or another friend having a laugh. I was stunned into silence, then replied 'Yes'.

'We'd like to invite you on air to talk about the Carctol and how it's helped you with your cancer, following the recent newspaper article.'

The nerves kicked in instantly, but my voice replied calmly enough. 'When will you be sending the camera crew over?' I thought that's how it would be, based on what I'd seen of some early morning television interviews with the public.

'Oh no, we won't be doing that. We'd like you in the studio and will send a car to collect you.'

'I can only do the interview if I can bring my son with me,' I replied, clutching at straws. My fear of going on live television was very real, but I remembered how I'd made a promise to myself long ago not only to help myself, but also to do what I could to help others. This was an opportunity that I couldn't turn away from and I forced myself to focus on that.

I mused over all the distant healing prayers I had sent to those I knew of in need, and the few referred to me by Rosy, my oncologist or my GP, when I did my level best to inspire and answer questions. 'When will this be?'

'Tomorrow morning. We'll send the car at 4.30 am.' I am an early bird, but that was earlier than even I was now accustomed to. But I was glad it was that end of the day as I struggle with late nights and always take a day or two to balance back up after them.

As soon as I'd put the phone down I tried calling Simon. Luckily he hadn't yet boarded the aircraft.

'Guess what?' I blurted out, telling him everything.

'I'm sorry I can't be with you.'

'I understand.'

'Just be yourself, and never mind what you wear. You are the living proof that what you do works, and at some level that will inspire others.'

Next I rang Clare, speaking with a mixture of disbelief and excitement. She was sweet, wishing me luck and saying she'd have the television on at work anyway, as that was all part of her job as editor of an online lifestyle magazine. I was so proud of her as she was the youngest to hold such a job in her organization.

I still couldn't decide what to wear but worrying about that took my mind off all else. In the end I opted for a friendly old pair of white jeans, left unbuttoned as they wouldn't do up but held in place with a sturdy belt. The pale coral sweatshirt I wore hid my improvisations nicely. Throughout the day GMTV phoned several times.

'We've read the article in the *Daily Telegraph* and we want to give plenty of airtime to the report on Carctol to inform people of this exciting, new to the West cancer-defeating agent.

I coughed nervously and then replied 'Good'.

'We'd like John Stapleton to interview you at 6am, Fiona Phillips around 7.20 and Lorraine Kelly after 8. We want to give maximum coverage.'

'Yes,' I agreed without question, wondering how I would cope with my nerves and what on earth was going on with so many phone calls from them. It appeared that the *Telegraph* article had created strong interest.

I spent the day in prayer and meditation asking for Divine help and inspiration. That night I hardly slept at all, but it didn't matter. By the time the alarm clock rang I was wide awake. Neighbours kindly helped us by walking and feeding Lucy, Charlie and Dusty.

The car arrived in good time. The driver, a man in his mid thirties, was keenly interested to hear what I was being interviewed about. He wished me good luck, saying the public had a right to know of anything that could help them when confronting cancer. He knew several whose lives were touched by it.

As the car swooped to a halt in front of the studios, David and I exchanged a look of bewilderment, smiled nevertheless, and felt a tinge of excitement as we walked towards the lady waiting for us. 'Please come this way,' she smiled, opening doors and showing us to a lift.

'You'll be taken straight into make-up then shown to the green room,' she informed us.

A man in his fifties, dressed in a flamboyant Hawaiian short-sleeved shirt, whisked me into his make-up room and sat me down, then studied my face. I'd already passed Fiona Phillips in the corridor coming out of make-up and ready to go on air.

'You've put a touch of make-up on already,' he smiled into my eyes through the mirror.

'Yes, it's one of the things that helps to get me going in the morning.' Just like Gee, my spiritual teacher, I thought, who had told us she always went to bed with an emergency bar of chocolate hidden beneath her pillow and with her eyeliner on, just in case she died in the night!

'Well, you don't need very much. I'll just put a dab of blusher on your cheeks. You do have such wonderful skin, like a peach!'

'Thank you, it's all the fresh air,' I replied, knowing I was lucky to be born that way, but also thinking how since my change in diet and lifestyle it had become even better.

We chatted on until I was whisked out of make-up to join David waiting for me in the corridor, where Lorraine Kelly was strolling along with her hair in large rollers. We were introduced and struck an instant rapport. Her face immediately filled with compassion as she said, 'My friend Caron Keating tried to beat cancer incorporating some holistic approaches.' Her eyes became misty. 'I'm especially interested in the Carctol story. What is your diet like?'

'Restricted, but I love cooking and have created some alkaline recipes to support the diet.' As she seemed interested I went on to tell her about some of them and she listened intently.

'What's it like for you?' she said jovially, looking at David. 'How do you cope with that diet?'

David joined in the conversation and laughed. I was so proud of him; he was relaxed, confident and enjoying himself.

'I don't stick to the same diet as Mum, but I incorporate more fruit and vegetables in my diet and have noticed a great improvement in my health, boosting my immune system. I don't get nearly so many colds.'

Afterwards, we were shown to the green room, where President Bush's aunt sat holding court while waiting her turn to be interviewed. Next, a girl who hadn't washed her bra for a year, and who was causing a sensation in the press, joined us and sat down waiting her turn to be interviewed. Finally, Cybil Shepherd swept in wearing a full-length hooded red velvet cloak. My eyes swivelled in my head as I tried not to stare. It was impossible not to. She arrived with an entourage of young men, all glitzy and attentive.

My nerves were getting the better of me so I went in search of the loo, where I took some deep calming breaths. I mused over my belief in angels and how at strategic moments in my life I'd often find a feather in an odd place. Glancing down I found one on the floor and lightly touched it. It was pure white, soft and downy. I recalled Gloria Hunniford saying that finding white feathers was a sign that her daughter Caron Keating was watching over them. Those encounters had helped her after her daughter died so tragically young.

When such moments occur I feel secure and calm. Then follows a wave of serenity and certainty that life carries on, and those who have passed before us are trying to make their presence felt to let us know they are close during a time of need. Little did I think that I'd ever meet Caron's dear friend Lorraine Kelly.

It was now fourteen months since my mental breakdown, and I had been so very tired during my recovery, but I had grown stronger as a result and accepted more readily whatever happened in day-to-day life. Resuming my meditation practice had helped me with that too. Entering with sincerity into silence and seeking help by prayers is enormously empowering, whatever happens. I had repeatedly discovered that I couldn't alter others and that world events were outside my control, but what I could change in life was myself, by thoughts and actions. I strive to achieve this, to retain an inner sense of equilibrium, and I drew on that balance while waiting for the interview.

'Gillian, would you come this way please?' said someone behind the scenes, ready to escort me through to the studio. Butterflies kicked in.

'You'll be alright, Mum,' said David, confidently walking beside me. He was led towards the cameraman and stood just behind him. There he repeated his magic by pulling discreet but delightful faces at me throughout each interview. Looking into his smiling eyes helped take the edge off my nerves as I was steered towards a sofa.

'Hello,' said John Stapleton smiling. He then introduced me and started the interview. I had seen his wife, Lynn Faulds Wood, on television and knew that she too was a survivor of cancer. He instantly put me at ease and continued to ask questions.

I was disconcerted by the questions from Doctor Hilary, the health and medical advisor on GMTV. In my naivety I hadn't realized someone has to play the part of devil's advocate, giving the alternative point of view. He politely explained this to me after the interview as I was upset, not so much for myself but for Rosy. She was being linked in from a television studio in the West Country and my heart went out to her. This is the way of the world. I silently prayed that one day it would be otherwise, when everyone could work in harmony for the collective, greater good.

Doctor Hilary was implying that Rosy claimed Carctol was a cure for cancer and this offered false hope to desperate people, when in fact Rosy hadn't claimed to have a total cure, rather a new medicine that had shown remarkable results when used to treat cancer in quite a few cases. This was a positive step in the ongoing fight against cancer, but any sensationalist claims of being a wonder cure were entirely the media's own.

'Please sit here next to me,' said Fiona warmly, patting the sofa. Eamonn Holmes sat beside her, looking intently at us, waiting for his cue.

I can't remember all the questions that Fiona and Doctor Hilary asked me, but Rosy was brilliant fielding and answering from her end. Once off air, Fiona reassuringly patted my knee, congratulating me on my courage in choosing the holistic route.

Later, I was shown to Lorraine Kelly's sofa, where she interviewed me in her unique, friendly style, concluding by saying she'd like to do a follow-up on my case one day.

I gave Doctor Hilary a copy of my recipe book, which I'd brought with me in the hope it would inspire others on their cancer journey.

Someone working in the studio rushed up to me saying, 'We've never had so many phone calls from members of the public; our lines are jammed. Too many people's lives are touched by cancer. More has got to be done about that to inform people they have power to help themselves and take some control for their own well-being. Far too many people feel helpless.'

'Yes, I know,' I replied, before David touched my elbow signalling that the lady was waiting to return us to our driver.

As we walked dazed towards the car, David and I noticed someone running towards us.

'Clare!' I shouted, before bursting into tears and falling into her arms. Clare burst into tears too.

'Mum, luckily you were on early enough for me to surprise you before I left for work. Congratulations, you were great! I brought you these flowers,' she said extending both arms, hands clutching a large bunch of brightly coloured, fragrant lilies and freesias.

'They are gorgeous,' I said, burying my face into their glorious fragrance. David stood by, mystified by the ways of the fairer sex.

I wiped my tears dry and fell into a hug with both children. My heart almost burst with their love. Love is what I'd always been seeking unknowingly. I realized all I'd ever wanted to know was how much I was loved. I hadn't realized it before, but startlingly I could see this was what my cancer recovery was teaching me. No matter what state I was in or how I was, Clare, David and Simon clearly loved me. They'd put up with so much from me. I honestly don't know how they did it, but I was only too grateful that they had.

The next thing we knew, Rosy was phoning to ask if I'd mind doing another interview, this time with the *Daily Express*. We agreed a date and I sat ready for the reporter to call at the allotted time, whilst trying to keep my nerves in check.

'Hello, this is Christina Robino,' came the voice of the journalist introducing herself over the telephone.

She asked questions passionately, making the interview as easy and comfortable as she could, and I knew where her heart lay. The photographer also called to make an appointment. He was keenly interested in what I'd done to achieve such results. Not knowing about my request to the *Telegraph's* photographer, he suggested, 'As Carctol is made from herbs I'd like to take a photo of you in the garden.'

David and I exchanged a look and both smiled. Again the weather was clear and dry. Lucy, Charlie and Dusty wandered out ahead, leading us to the end of the garden where they sniffed about. Over a privet hedge dividing the lawn from the vegetable patch stood a row of tall sunflowers grown by Eric. Spotting them the photographer said, 'Perfect, that'll do nicely. Would you please stand next to the sunflowers?'

Once again David came to my rescue. He pulled his now familiar faces and I felt my nerves give way to humour; the smiles came easily.

When that article appeared we were even more surprised to see it taking up two entire pages, and there was the photograph of me by the sunflowers. The article appeared in the Your Health section of the *Daily Express* with the title 'Is this a cure for cancer?'. The article covered the different views of members of the medical establishment and Dr Daniel, calling her a respected doctor who promotes an integrated approach to cancer, combining conventional medicines with other therapies. It presented arguments on both sides, including comments that a large number of cancer patients in India have had significant benefit from Carctol. How I prayed those articles would help others with cancer.

CHAPTER 12

Grace

Can it be possible?
Rather than hasten towards death
To live, extending towards a healthier life.
Gillian Gill

October – December 2004

'Her brother is dying of cancer,' Philippa said, while chatting and driving me to meet her holistic massage therapist.

'I'm so very sorry,' I replied.

'Thankfully, her family and friends are joining one another supportively, doing all they can under the circumstances to help him. It's tragic for such a young man to be suffering like this.' As we pulled up, Philippa continued, 'We're here. Enjoy your treatment.' She knew I'd never have found my way alone through the maze of streets, especially as map reading isn't my strong point, and I was grateful for her insistence at driving me.

Walking up the stairs into the treatment room, I was greeted by my friendly therapist. The only sound was of water trickling from an ornate fountain in the corner. Once the preliminaries were over, I changed out of my outer clothes and wrapped myself in a thick, warm towel and climbed onto the couch ready for treatment.

My heart was moved as I looked into my therapist's sad eyes. She knew Philippa had told me about her brother. She smiled stoically, saying with a soft voice, 'My family come from the West Indies, where we believe that when God calls you home, it is because your time here is over.'

Before I could reply she continued, 'Now just relax and go into the silence as I prepare myself mentally, for this is your time and I want the massage therapy to help heal you.'

An hour had slipped by and my tense muscles were yielding to her professional touch. I couldn't have spoken if I'd wanted to.

'Please turn over,' she quietly invited.

As she massaged my back I suddenly felt most peculiar. The room spun, I felt nauseous and knew something wasn't right.

'I'm going to be sick,' I stammered. She rushed to fetch me a plastic bowl and thrust it into my hands just in time. I couldn't stop vomiting. Sweat was pouring from me and my entire body hurt.

'I need the loo but can't move on my own, the pain is excruciating. Will you please help me?' I pleaded. She held me tightly as we inched our way to the bathroom.

I collapsed onto the loo as the world repeatedly poured out of me, while clutching the plastic bowl, retching and watching bright yellow bile floating around. Something definitely was up.

'I'm phoning for an ambulance,' she said, peering around the door to make sure I hadn't passed out.

'Thank you. Will you please help me back to the couch?

As I stumbled back, the violent sweating continued. I clutched a towel around me while feebly trying to dress. I could barely focus on the two ambulance crew as they walked in.

A paramedic reached over, touched my brow and said, 'You're burning up. What's happened here?'

My therapist told them. I could see she was traumatized herself.

'I can hardly breathe now,' I panted.

'Just try to stay calm, and nod if you've had a baby,' said the female paramedic. I nodded.

'Remember those magic breaths you took during labour? Well, concentrate on them now.'

Half an hour later they lay me on a stretcher and carried me out to the waiting ambulance. I was freezing as we set off and still finding it painful to breathe. 'Please don't do anything to me,' I pleaded as she began monitoring my blood pressure and covering me in blankets.

'It's okay. I just happened to switch on GMTV the other morning, having come off a shift, and I saw you. I admire the choices you've made. I won't force anything you don't want on you. Try to remember what you'd do in this situation,' she sweetly suggested.

Both stunned and relieved by this unexpected turn of events I replied, 'Phone a friend,' and gave her Philippa's telephone number.

'That's good, remembering her number,' she murmured absentmindedly while dialling the number. I didn't want Simon worrying at this stage; he was in his London office today.

By the time we reached the Mayday Hospital in Croydon, Philippa and Ron were waiting to greet me at Accident and Emergency.

The paramedic held my hand as she helped wheel me into the hospital building. Her farewell words were, 'Remember, you've got help from above, as well as in the hospital.'

As I watched her back disappear towards the ambulance I saw a feather spiralling out of the sky above her.

I was transferred onto a bed in a curtained-off bay. Philippa held my hand while I drew my knees up to try to ease the intense pain. Ron ran through some jokes, despite being ill at ease in the hospital surroundings. I was glad of their company and my mind began to adjust to the sequence of events and cope with all that my body was experiencing.

When a nurse appeared I asked for a muscle relaxant rather than a painkiller, and could have hugged her when she readily agreed.

Once the injection began taking effect, I asked Philippa to let Simon know I was okay but in hospital. Next thing I knew, a saline drip was being hooked up to rehydrate me.

Ron and Philippa eventually left for home and I was moved to another area. A beautiful nurse replaced the empty saline bag; her smile reminded me of the rising sun.

'We'll soon make you more comfy, honey,' she crooned, tucking the sheets in.

'A doctor will be along to see you just as soon as he can.'

I didn't have to wait long before a tall white-coated doctor arrived and began to read the notes at the foot of my bed.

'What have we here? Let me see…' he said, feeling my swollen, fluid-filled abdomen.

'Please don't press me there, it's excruciating.' But he appeared not to hear and carried on. 'Please don't take samples either,' I implored when I regained my breath, as he suggested a procedure to test what the fluid was.

I willed my mind to let go of fear, to trust, and that was all I could do. I was never more relieved to see his back receding as he heeded my last request.

Simon soon appeared looking worried.

'Hello, how are you?' After listening he continued, 'I think you're suffering from toxic shock.'

'Is that what this is?' I realized how much I relied on Simon to explain the unfathomable to me.

He continued calmly, 'I thought you might like your slippers and toothbrush and some money for a payphone; then you can make a list of other things you may want and I'll bring them in tomorrow.'

The hours ticked by slowly until around midnight, when I was wheeled into an area filled with distressed people, all either in beds or chairs. Some were weeping, others groaning or calling out in pain. I felt myself overcome by the assault to my senses. I thought how I'd love to run away and be somewhere else, and then realized there's no running away because you're always with yourself, with your own thoughts and feelings. Just as I was wondering how much longer I could cope, a nurse appeared by my side. She asked my history, looked shocked and proceeded to wheel my bed into a quieter side bay. Having first drawn the curtain, she disappeared to find a thermometer.

Staring at the curtain, and thanking the powers that be for the latest intervention, I saw a shower of silver stars. Then I passed out.

'Come on, you're okay,' said the nurse having reappeared.

'I'm just going to take your blood pressure... As I thought, it's a little low. Now I'm going to take your temperature, assess you and get you moved up to a ward where you can try and sleep tonight.'

The memory of the silver stars nourished me. To me they were a sign that my spirit guides and sister were close. I felt a renewed strength as I lay alone in the quieter bay.

A night porter drew the curtain back announcing, 'I've come to take you up in the lift to a ward. It's one for post-operative people. Tomorrow you may be moved again.'

As he wheeled the trolley along the corridor I noticed a sign saying 'This ward has MRSA'. Something inside me stirred and I resolved to discharge myself as soon as it was daylight.

The porter gently assisted me into the bed, positioning the drip beside me.

'Hello,' said a teary young woman in the next bed. She was trying to watch a screen but seemed easily distracted and upset.

I listened to her until my eyes felt so heavy I could not keep them open. I slept fitfully, praying for the woman next to me and myself.

When I awoke a tea trolley was doing the rounds. I was 'nil by mouth' and, strangely for me, I didn't feel like anything anyway. But as the trolley passed I asked where the nearest payphone was. I tentatively climbed out of bed, shuffling my feet into my slippers, then clutching the saline bag contraption attached to my arm proceeded to awkwardly push it towards the corridor.

'Simon, thank goodness I've reached you,' I said as soon as my money connected us. 'Would you please come and collect me? There's an outbreak of MRSA here and I just want to come home.'

'I'll collect you, but I insist you visit the local hospital after we get home.'

I agreed, relieved, then dragging the drip beside me walked to the bathroom to brush my teeth, after first getting tangled up trying to go to the loo. The odour had me wincing. My urine had a cancerous odour that

I had become familiar with when volunteering at the hospice, and it was dark coloured. I practised deep breathing to regain calm and counted the moments until Simon arrived to collect me.

After the journey home, walking gingerly in through the front door, Lucy greeted me, tail wagging, and proceeded to sniff my abdomen with greater interest than usual. Charlie meanwhile tilted his head back and sang his loudest welcome. My body hurt too much to do more than merely stroke them; I couldn't manage a big cuddle.

'Now you're home,' said Simon, 'go and get into bed and I'll come up and see you in a moment.'

I tried to lie flat but couldn't. It was too painful to breathe.

'Are you feeling better now you're home?' enquired Simon walking into the bedroom to see how I was.

'I'm glad to be here, but I can't lie down without hurting. The pressure on my diaphragm from my swollen abdomen makes breathing painful. Would you please fetch me one of the large cushions from the sitting room?'

A moment later, 'Here it is. Lean forward and I'll prop it behind you.'

I sank into it with tears of relief and murmured, 'Thank you, that helps.'

As Simon left the room his leg glanced against the side of the bed causing a tiny jolt and sending me into fresh spasms of pain. My body seemed hypersensitive. Throughout the day I noticed even his voice grated and hurt as he said, 'Come on, where's your fight?'

I smiled feebly at his receding back. Sinking deeper into the large cushion, I asked myself the same question. It seemed all fight and resolve had deserted me. No matter how I tried I just couldn't muster it. I felt so awful I began to wonder if this was it. Was I going to die? Would this be my final hour? At least my own familiar things in my own bedroom, in my own home surrounded me, and that alone gave me comfort.

Having given up on the idea of trying to find my 'fight', I did the opposite. I surrendered, completely and utterly. It just happened as I lay there. I prayed, 'Almighty Heavenly Father, Divine Mother, Eternal Spirit, Bearer of Light, if my time has come then please take me...'

214

Then I lost all sense of time and space and appeared to inwardly free fall beyond a dark void, before feeling a wave of divine grace cushioning me.

While I rested Simon had rung my GP, who arranged for me to visit my radiologist at the local hospital in a couple of days. In the meantime Simon slept in another bedroom so as not to disturb me.

During those two days I spent most of my time resting and praying and trying to focus on fresh spasms of pain as they arose, particularly in my abdomen. This appeared to take all my time and energy. I lay in bed for most of the day, except to gingerly get up and go downstairs to the kitchen to prepare a boiled egg for lunch to cushion my Carctol, which I ate in spite of having no appetite. Moving my body, however slowly, made me become sharply aware of its fragility.

To stem my anxiety I stroked the dogs before slowly returning to bed. There I lay with the wind gently blowing through an open window and I prayed that somehow I might come through this. My whole body hurt and was incredibly sensitive, but lying as still as could be and focusing on my breathing helped.

Two days later the pain was less intense and after frequent visits to the loo my abdomen was noticeably less bloated and my breathing had become easier and less painful. On the third morning when I awoke something had shifted; suddenly I felt my spirits revived.

When the appointment was due, Simon drove me to the hospital, where I saw my familiar radiologist; he appeared concerned but friendly. After listening to what had happened and looking deeply into my eyes, he said, 'Your eyes tell a different story to your body. I'm going to suggest that you go home and do whatever it is that you do, as it clearly appears to be working. We are still unsure what the fluid is in your abdomen. If it's blood, you could have a haemorrhage, and then we have a severe problem. So go home and know that if you need a hospital bed, we will have one for you.'

While there I received a CT scan to try to discover what was going on. Unknown to me at the time, as I could not mentally process everything properly, had the fluid been blood, it could have indicated an internal bleed and proven fatal. Later, he reported to my oncologist that the hepatic

215

metastases (liver tumours) had changed and it looked as though one of them may have ruptured.

Over the next ten days I hardly ate anything, having still not regained my appetite. As I had to eat something to accompany my Carctol regime, I ate simply and sparingly: a banana for breakfast and a boiled egg for lunch, in addition to drinking two to three litres of water a day to keep flushing me through. I tried not to think about my abdomen, which was distended like in the early days of my diagnosis.

Every time I went to the loo I could smell cancer, which I presumed was the fluid from the rupture appearing in my urine. I lost a stone in weight in those ten days. As if my body knew what it was doing, it constantly eliminated waste matter. I rested quietly in between the frequent loo visits and tried to remain comfortable. When alert, I prayed for all I was worth that this was a release of the toxic fluid from a ruptured 'sack' in the liver, rather than blood. I imagined each breath filled with invigorating lifeforce energy charging every cell in my body with renewed health.

The pain continued in waves, yet at times I felt an angelic presence, which brought me relief and comfort between spasms. I was also visited by two friends to give me healing.

Each day I got up and dressed for a spell to try to feel normal, until one day Simon commented, 'Your abdomen seems smaller.'

'Yes, I've noticed all the visits to the loo are helping flush out the toxic-smelling fluid.'

'It's good you're listening to your body and letting nature run its course. I've just bought you some coconut water from the local health food shop and poured you a glass full. Try it.'

'It looks opaque,' I said, taking a first tentative sip, 'but tastes good.'

'Philippa phoned to see how you are. She's heard how coconut water is a natural electrolyte, renowned for its healing properties, and it helps blood circulation. Apparently coconut water is similar to human plasma.'

My irregular menopausal cycle was heavy again with dark blood clots, so I visualized this as another means of eliminating unwanted matter from my body.

As soon as I was strong enough, Simon made an appointment to see Professor Thomas, my oncologist. She had the recent scan results from the radiologist in front of her.

Preliminaries over, pointing at the scans, we remembered her saying something along the lines of, 'No surgeon could have performed such surgery on your liver. It's so much healthier now. That rupture helped your liver in a way nothing else could. But you cannot afford to have another episode like this as it could prove fatal, so from now on you must be extremely careful.'

Another similar episode could be too much strain for my body, weakening it dangerously, especially if another internal rupture leaked blood. Knowing how close I'd come to a potentially fatal incident, I made a mental note to explicitly request the lightest of pressures when next having a massage. However, I left that fragile abdominal area of my body alone for some time afterwards, only having the occasional head and shoulder massage. I was also advised to avoid riding. So, no more riding for me, I mused sadly, which was something I was hoping to get back to.

During the drive home, I silently thanked the holistic massage therapist who had unknowingly helped to jump-start the latest phase in my recovery. That massage turned out to be the ultimate detoxification in a totally unexpected way. I resolved to write the therapist a letter to express my sincere feelings of gratitude. I felt humbled by the extraordinary turn of events and the whys and wherefores of unknown forces silently at work behind the scenes.

After this appointment Professor Thomas sent the following update to my GP:

I saw Mrs Gill at her request on 15th October, 2004. A couple of weeks ago she was having deep massage therapy and developed acute abdominal pain. She was lying on her front at the time and, given the course of events subsequently and the lack of overt pathology (as far as the patient is aware), I think it is most likely that she ruptured one of her hepatic metastases and bled into her abdomen.

She saw her Consultant Radiologist for a CT scan last Friday and he has demonstrated that the hepatic metastases have changed. It looks as if one of these may well have ruptured. There was certainly evidence of free fluid in the abdomen at the time. Her disease in the pelvis has not changed greatly.

When I saw Mrs Gill today she was feeling much better and in fact reported that each day her symptoms lessen and she feels fitter in herself. It is my view that the ruptured metastasis is the most likely explanation of what has been going on. She also reported that her urine had been dark, but when we stick tested it today there was no evidence of bilirubin.

On examination her abdomen was quite soft without evidence of marked ascites [an excess of fluid between two layers of membrane lining the inside of the abdominal wall and outside of the abdominal organs]. I could feel her liver, which I have not been able to feel previously. The mass arising from her pelvis is still below the umbilicus and has not really changed in the last few months.

Mrs Gill is now four years out from a presumed carcinoma of the ovary with a pelvic mass and hepatic metastases. She has not received any conventional treatment whatsoever during that time, nor has she had a biopsy.

My feeling is that there is no indication at the present time for me to intervene and suggest either a biopsy or conventional treatment. I will therefore leave matters until she contacts me again. She does say that with time she is coming round to the idea of conventional therapy, and if she is feeling unwell or feels that she cannot get on top of things by using her other means she is likely to come to me requesting conventional treatment. Until that time I am happy to continue to supervise her.

I have performed some blood tests today and will let her know the results.

It was not until I started writing this book that I had access to these letters, hence my ignorance of the above terms describing my condition. I was holding firmly to the belief that I was 'on the home stretch' healthwise, with nothing more than 'benign cysts', which was all my memory absorbed at this time and was all I worked hard to remember; I didn't want to put energy into other thoughts and resolutely fought against them, doing my best to always view the positive.

My memory is rusty here. All I recall is that my tumour markers rose. Now that I have my oncologist's results I can see just how dramatically my CA125, the ovarian tumour marker, had risen from a previous level of 315 to 6,520; the normal level for a well woman is 35 or below. Frightened, I wanted another blood test in a month's time.

I was still reeling from my oncologist telling me that, had the abdominal fluid been blood, it could have proved fatal by pressing it under examination, as had occurred when I was in the Mayday Hospital, where the doctor ignored my protests that this examination hurt. So I think the fluid was just a burst sack of toxic fluid rather than internal haemorrhaging, especially as the odour when passing matter smelt cancerous.

In the meantime I phoned my nutritionist, Marianne, telling her what had happened. 'Please come and see me as soon as you can,' she requested.

As Simon and I drove to her clinic I sat silently, feeling every jolt of the car throughout my body.

'Gillian, you have arrived on the very day I have a new machine; it's called an Aqua Detox foot spa. First you need to roll the soles of your feet over this small wooden rolling pin to open up the pores of your feet. Then I shall put half a teaspoon of low sodium salt in the foot spa, to which I'm going to add a small waterproof electrical appliance to send a charge through the water. This in turn draws toxins from your body.'

'Thank you,' I muttered, as Simon sat listening intently.

'Within seconds of putting my feet into the warm salty water the colour began to change.'

'Don't be alarmed,' reassured Marianne. 'This is the start of the process, which takes half an hour. You'll be amazed at how the water colour changes. This is a new tried, tested and safe therapy. Relax deeply with the intent of gently releasing excess bodily toxicity. Remember, it's the intention of the mind that is all powerful.'

Glancing down I felt repulsed. The water was now a deep muddy orange with oily particles floating on top. 'Your liver is releasing more toxicity,' said Marianne, laughing at my shocked expression. 'Ah,' she said knowingly, 'now the water's turning dark green and black. This is a very good response.'

As an alarm went off signalling the half hour was over, Marianne deftly lifted my feet, one at a time, onto her lap and proceeded to wipe them, first with a wet wipe then a towel, before disappearing from the room to empty the vile-looking foot spa contents down the loo.

We eventually left Marianne feeling grateful for her continuing resourcefulness and advice on my nutritional and mineral support. During the journey home I felt very headachy and tired and was glad not to be driving myself. I slept well that night and over the next few days I began to feel increasingly healthier than I had for some time.

During the following months, before my next visit to the oncologist, I was noticing that I was frequently passing alarming menopausal matter – dark red blood clots, resembling chopped liver – during my increasingly irregular monthly cycle, and was pleased to be seeing her to discuss it.

After my appointment she reported to my GP in a letter:

I saw Mrs Gill this afternoon. I wrote to her about a month ago to point out that there had been quite a marked rise in her latest CA125 result. This clearly made her nervous, and she came back to have the result checked again.

On examination, much to my surprise her liver seems significantly smaller and indeed the mass in the pelvis was also smaller. She felt that after she had experienced the pain and problems after deep massage on her back she passed what she describes as 'toxic fluid' vaginally and noticed a strange odour about her body.

I have promised Mrs Gill that as soon as the CA125 result is through I will contact her to let her know. As she is very well today I think it is unlikely that I will do anything more invasive at this stage, but I will keep you posted as to her progress.

My body was doing its best to expel the ruptured toxic fluid around the same time as my irregular, heavy monthly cycles. Professor Thomas reassured me that my menopausal cycles were normal.

I spent time reflecting on everything that had happened to me and, again, how some things are outside our control. I couldn't help thinking that it would have been preferable and less traumatic to repair my liver by other methods, such as applying visualization techniques, using my thoughts to imagine my liver whole, healthy and fully operative. But as a result of that rupture – and thankfully I was strong and well enough to survive it – my liver progressed in healing itself. I believe that I had some scar tissue, which our Nigerian medical friend, Dr Eli Mama, suggested I visualize dissolving.

One evening, as Christmas was approaching, I went for a dog walk at dusk. The dogs were lingering some way behind me. I could hear them sniffing around the rabbit warrens when there, ahead on a fence post, was a solitary little owl. It heard my approach and, frightened, proceeded to swivel its head right around so it couldn't see me and froze. I felt immense joy coursing through my entire being as I backtracked to avoid disturbing it, savouring the image and taking the dogs on a different route.

I could sense my levels had dropped and on 1st December my CA125 tumour marker count had come down to 452, but I didn't know this for certain until 7th March the following year when I saw Professor Thomas at my next appointment.

CHAPTER 13
Five-year Milestone

Look to this day,
For it is life, the very life of life.
In its brief course
Lie all the verities and realities of your existence.
The bliss of growth,
The glory of action,
The splendour of achievement
Are but experiences of time.
For yesterday is but a dream
And tomorrow is only a vision;
And today, well-lived, makes
Yesterday a dream of happiness
And every tomorrow a vision of hope.
Look well therefore to this day;
Such is the salutation to the ever-new dawn!
Kalidasa, ancient Sanskrit poem

2005 – 2006

Early in the New Year, Simon had managed to track down a Picardy Shepherd dog breeder in France. 'Through him I'm contacting the sole breeder in this country, who may help us to find an appropriate home for Dusty.' Being a working dog, Dusty frequently took off into the woods when out for a walk, taking us hours to find him. That aside, Charlie was also becoming increasingly unhappy; their territorial issues were growing, and he and Dusty occasionally fought, exacerbated by the fact that Charlie was often left out when Dusty and Lucy ran off together. Matters were far from improving as we'd hoped, so something had to be done.

I felt torn in two, having given my word to Sarah, but I knew Simon was right. Events rapidly conspired towards helping Dusty find a new home.

'There are two ladies working with problem dogs happy to come and meet Dusty to see if they can help us rehome him,' said Simon.

It was as though Dusty knew his fate hung in the balance, as he'd recently found a shaggy toy dog in my healing room and had taken to suckling it, away from everyone.

The ladies arrived. One, named Irene, listened to our story sympathetically before saying, 'I've done some research on Dusty before coming here, and his dog breeder was struck off for cruelty. It just so happens I have Dusty's mother and sister, who I found at a rescue centre.'

I studied her face when we paraded Dusty before her. Her eyes glowed.

After several weeks of supposedly trying to find an ideal home for him, she drew a blank. Her friend had suggested we build an outdoor kennel for Dusty, an idea I instantly dismissed despite its potential merits. Ever since Sarah had found him, Dusty had lived like one of the family, and the thought of shutting him outdoors felt like a betrayal, both to her memory and to the dog himself.

A few months had gone by when we heard that Irene had managed to persuade her husband they could give Dusty a home. She wanted to reunite him with his mother and sister and assured us that her other two rescue dogs, a large Alsatian and a Cocker Spaniel, would accept him. It seemed like the perfect solution, and we agreed to keep in touch to follow Dusty's progress.

The children came home to say a teary farewell when the day arrived for Dusty to be collected. As he was driven off, looking out of the back window of the car, I knew he was going where he would be showered with love and given all the exercise and new life skills he needed. Subsequently we heard, much to our amazement, that with Irene's coaching he had won an award at an obedience class.

Filled with gratitude for Irene's firm resolve, I remembered something Gee had once said to me years ago: 'There are times not to do what you ought, but rather to do what you want – you'll know when such times occur – so as not to live with regret but rather to live with a glad heart.' It seemed Irene had done just that.

We waved them off and, once the car was out of sight, Charlie strutted back into the house looking happier than we'd seen him for months. He and Lucy continued to bark in unison with a new zeal, as they protected their home, and us in it, when hearing any noise outside. My heart lurched when thinking of Dusty, though Simon's voice of reason resounded in my head and I looked at our two contented and now tension-free dogs.

By March I was due to visit Professor Thomas for a check-up.

'You honestly look healthier since your rupture,' commented Simon as we walked through the hospital doors.

My tummy did its familiar flip at the hospital sights and smells as we walked together holding hands to the appointment lounge.

'Hello, Mr and Mrs Gill, please come in,' said Professor Thomas leading the way into her consulting room. None of us had a clue that by the year's end she would be diagnosed with cancer herself.

Following on from this appointment Professor Thomas sent the following letter to my GP:

I saw Mrs Gill for a follow-up appointment on 7th March. She has been remarkably well in herself.

Her recent CT scan showed relatively little change from the previous scan, apart from evidence that the episode which occurred last year is likely to have been due to the rupture of a metastasis.

Interestingly Mrs Gill's tumour markers shot up just after the apparent rupture to 6,520 from the previous level of 315. They settled back down to 452 on 1 December.

As Mrs Gill continues to be so well I will see her again when she makes an appointment.

During my consultation I had told Professor Thomas how Rosy advised me to take an excess of buffered vitamin C capsules to counteract the radioactivity from CT scans and help eliminate it swiftly from my body.

The weeks passed and soon it was my fiftieth birthday. 'Let's have a party,' suggested Simon. 'It's not only your fiftieth but also five years since your diagnosis. That alone is worthy of celebrating.' Inwardly I felt uneasy as I find parties daunting, particularly if they're mine.

Simon, gaining momentum, continued, 'Think of all the people we can invite. So many have helped us, it'll be our way of thanking them. We'll have the party at one of our local pubs and see if Stan, the saxophonist who plays at Ronnie Scott's, will organize a band to play jazz in the background. Yes, it's time to celebrate!'

Stan was a good friend of Georgina, an inspiring woman who beat cancer for years until she sadly lost her own fight, supported to the end by Professor Thomas. She most definitely would agree with Simon, as did Clare and David, so I was outnumbered and slowly began to share some of their sense of excitement.

By now another friend, Jan, had been diagnosed with pancreatic cancer. Initially she was sceptical of my methods but in desperation she and her husband Rob asked for my help; I was so glad. Jan and I spoke several times, agreeing a time for her to come and visit me. We chatted about my own health regime and then healing. After her first healing she said, 'I feel so peaceful, Gillian, when you give me healing.'

'I got a glimpse of a swan,' I said, 'just before I opened my eyes.'

'My maiden name was Swan,' she replied.

Jan's health progressively deteriorated in spite of everything. With my party looming I impulsively phoned Stan to see if Jan could sing a song with the band at the party, knowing that singing is one of her greatest passions. When I asked her if she would like to sing, she replied, 'Oh, I don't think I'd have the confidence, but thank you for asking.'

On the day of the party, amidst great excitement with people gathered from far and wide, Jan's slim figure stepped up to the microphone as my back was turned.

225

Suddenly the room fell into a hushed silence as her husky voice sang in a similar vein to Marilyn Monroe 'Happy Birthday to you…' My eyes filled with tears, as did almost everyone's in the pub.

Yashu and Chandra had arrived early with garlands of flowers, which a beautiful young niece had been up all night making, together with some tasty Indian food. They thanked Jan and then asked for hush. Speeches were made then the garlands were ceremoniously placed around the necks of me, Simon and Rosy Daniel, who also made a deeply moving speech.

My entire family were present along with many friends. It was one of the happiest days of my life, even though I found it somewhat overwhelming. Clare and Ashleigh looked radiant sitting together, holding hands before chatting to others. David was beaming and Simon mingling with everyone, looked elated after his hours of planning.

The party was joyous and jazz fuelled. Jan's husband Rob, discovering my secret passion for fast cars, promised to bring a TVR from his workplace for me to drive. I never expected it to happen until one evening, sometime after we'd quietly recovered from the celebration, Simon said, 'What's that loud rumbling noise?'

Glancing out of the window we saw a heavenly sapphire blue car slowly making its way over the potholes and cobbles to park in the drive. Jan, looking pale and fragile with new short curly hair, which had grown after her chemotherapy, rang the doorbell. 'Surprise, surprise! Rob's brought the TVR Sagaris over for you to have a drive in,' she beamed.

Inviting her into the house, I rushed out to see Rob, saying after an initial hello and hugs, 'I can't open the car door.'

'There's a little button that does that for you automatically,' he replied, opening the door and indicating that I should get into the driver's seat. I was almost lying horizontal and wondered how I'd see out of the window, but such was the car's design I could do so easily. At my urging, Rob talked me through the controls.

The dashboard looked like that of a light aircraft with an array of dials. The chrome handbrake and gear stick were works of art to my unaccustomed eye.

Lifting my eyes to the windscreen I said, 'I'm going to keep my eyes fixed on the road ahead. Please tell me what to do.'

We inched our way forward with my heart pounding with excitement.

'I can't do this,' I murmured.

'Yes, you can,' he urged, 'you already are.'

We turned right out of the drive and after a few miles approached a dual carriageway. The car reached an enormous speed in an instant! Such was my euphoria that I swore, and immediately apologised. My body felt so alive and was tingling from head to toe.

'You're a natural! Are you sure you haven't driven a high-performance car before?'

The thrill I felt was enormous, as I accelerated away from traffic lights, pulling ahead of the adjacent car of young men not yet moving.

'Thank you so much,' I enthused when we got home, climbing out of the car.

'You're welcome. By the way, this is the press car, tweaked to as near racing condition as you can get; this model hasn't yet been released.' Then as an afterthought he added, 'Would you like a job as a test driver?'

I went to bed that night never having imagined that such an experience could happen. I felt uplifted for days and silently sent out prayers of gratitude to be able to experience such feelings.

'Mum, as a belated birthday surprise,' said Clare down the telephone, 'I've got us tickets to see a butterfly exhibition at the Natural History Museum next week. If you catch the train to Victoria, I'll meet you there and we can then travel on together. Knowing how the butterfly has been your symbol of transformation throughout, I thought you'd enjoy it. I've taken time off work, so we won't be pressurized for time.'

I was so moved it took a moment or two before I found my voice.

'That's so very sweet and thoughtful of you, darling. I'd love to come.'

Putting the phone down, my tummy filled with butterflies of its own. I hadn't travelled to London alone by train since my diagnosis and the prospect suddenly seemed daunting. Then I remembered so many of the skills I'd been learning and went to sit quietly to calm myself and mentally prepare by visualizing the entire day flowing with ease and love.

The day arrived. 'Hello, Ma,' called Clare waving from the platform, linking arms when joining me.

I felt fine and had managed well so far. As we stood in the tropical-looking hothouse filled with butterflies Clare said, 'Come with me. There's a confined area where chrysalises are hanging and hatching.'

Standing before them, Clare excitedly said, 'Look at those tiny ones, and those huge ones!' Suddenly a bright peacock blue butterfly landed on her shoulder. She took a sharp intake of breath in awe.

Life seemed so new with a sharper focus. As I stared first at Clare, then the butterfly, next to the chrysalis, I felt like one of those butterflies emerging after a long, dark spell of transformation.

Throughout that happy day butterflies landed on us both, and after a tasty light lunch together, we hugged farewell and went our separate ways, brimming with love.

'How did your day go?' asked Simon meeting me at the station.

'It was simply beautiful,' I replied, regaling him with some details.

'You see, you can do far more than you think you can.'

'I'm beginning to realize that, but I've been thinking how Rosy, with her uncanny knack of dissolving my fear and boosting my confidence, has helped. Along with Professor Thomas's tremendous support, and between you all, I feel elevated to new levels of hope. There's no way I could do it on my own.'

Later on, when alone and quietly thinking about my happy day, I realized how when going through emotional trauma I'd lost touch with my connection to life. Through meditation along with my simpler lifestyle I was regaining this connection.

Despite the day's success, I still wondered if I was doing well enough and remembered a friend saying, 'It's not about arriving at one's destination, rather it's about the journey, so don't just go looking for the end result!' It's like the question how long is a piece of string? There's no definite answer. Then I remembered my friend Suzi, the astrologer, saying to me,

'Everything is a process, it's organic.' Eventually I realized all I could do was try to increase my health and well-being one day at a time.

Sure enough, my health was improving, and as if to prove the point, Lucy again came to nudge my ever-shrinking 'lump'. I loved her for it and for the time being felt greatly reassured.

By December I was due to visit Professor Thomas again, having regained some weight. 'You look so well,' she exclaimed, opening my expanding file to add a recent addition to my regime. Before I stepped behind the examination curtain, she quietly told me she'd recently been diagnosed with breast cancer herself.

Feeling shocked, my heart expanded in my chest, and I had to hold myself in check to prevent reaching out to give her a hug.

'I am sorry,' I said.

'Thank you,' she said. 'Now, let's examine you.'

'There's very little change, but what you are doing is clearly working, so please carry on.'

During this appointment my recollection is that Professor Thomas went through my health regime making detailed notes on all that I was doing.

This is the letter she sent to my GP following that visit:

I saw Mrs Gill on 19th December for the first time in nine months. I am very pleased to report that she looks extremely well. She is currently juicing wheatgrass and has been every morning for the last few months.

On examination the clinical features have hardly changed. If anything the mass arising out of the pelvis is smaller and her liver is about the same.

She is complaining of a small hernia in the left inguinal region. This was not very pronounced but I have suggested she may want to arrange for this to be dealt with before it becomes too big. She is aware that these can now be operated on laparoscopically [keyhole surgery], which made her feel more enthusiastic about the possibility of surgery.

Clearly the decision is up to her. In the meantime I have suggested I can see her again whenever she contacts me. I have checked her CA125 and will let her know the result in due course.

Following that appointment I continued with the fresh wheatgrass instead of dried powder, as I was enjoying buying the seeds, sprouting them and growing my own. After some months, I had the same problems that I'd experienced in 2000. My bouts of sickness and diarrhoea recurred more frequently, so I deemed this a bit of a healing crisis, not understanding at the time that it was in fact a new level of cleansing my body. From then on every time I smelt the fresh wheatgrass juice I felt queasy. Taking this to be a message that my body had had enough of it, I gave my growing equipment to Clare and Ashleigh, who by this time were taking wheatgrass themselves as a form of detoxification, and I eventually returned to the dried powder. When I found that I could tolerate fresh wheatgrass again, I discovered a distributor who delivered trays of growing wheatgrass and placed a regular order. I then established a routine of alternating fresh with dried.

By now I had fulfilled one of my goals which I'd set when recovering from my mental breakdown: to restart the housework fully. Maggie, my friend and home help, had found another job, so I resumed the familiar chores with a new zeal.

My immune system was kicking in too. I anxiously phoned Marianne, my nutritionist, saying, 'I have a sore throat and nasty chesty cold.'

She stunned me with her response: 'But that's marvellous. Look how well you are. Your body is now so healthy it knows it's safe to catch a cold and will repair itself automatically. Congratulations!'

Again I reflected on how thoughtful friends had been by keeping away from me if they had germs, not wishing to spread them.

With Christmas approaching, Simon suggested we go somewhere warm in the early spring to boost both our systems, as he was prone to chesty colds and worsening asthma after a cold winter. We booked a holiday to Egypt, as I'd always wanted to see the pyramids. After speaking to our insurance company about my health issues, I discovered that vaccination against hepatitis was necessary and realized it would be crazy to take a risk with my liver, so we decided not to go.

'We'll make a new rule', said Simon reasonably enough, 'to travel only to Europe or North America to avoid unnecessary health risks.'

'Where will we find that's warm?' I wondered.

'We'll go to Gran Canaria. I've spoken to the travel agent to make the change,' said Simon. 'It'll be warm there and the sea air and sunshine will give us both a welcome break.'

'It's beautiful here,' I said, looking all around on our arrival in Gran Canaria while thinking how my life had changed. My old ways of living had been replaced with new ones, together with a deeper sense of appreciation.

'Have you recovered from the journey?' asked Simon.

'The early start, plus a day's travelling, knocked me for six.'

The resort we stayed at had a running buffet for breakfast and supper. I was relieved to find it included many of the alkaline ingredients from my diet and I enjoyed a variety of salads.

During our holiday we talked about Simon's longed-for retirement. We realised how lucky we were to have changed our booked Egyptian holiday at short notice. Simon found beautiful walks for us to go on, enjoying the different landscapes and plants. I also had time to reflect once again on my daily routine since my breakdown. I mused on the writing skills I'd been learning for the past few years on correspondence courses, and the typing skills I'd learned when younger, and how useful they were for self-expression. Lying in the shade one morning, I recalled the sense of mounting anticipation while waiting for my writing assignments to be returned to me, critiqued by my tutor, in a brown self-addressed A4 envelope.

Throughout the past few years, parts of my correspondence courses had encouraged me to express my innermost feelings on paper as a release. This had helped beyond measure. As I progressed with the writing courses it became a bigger project and I found myself writing a novel that was rejected by publishers. It had been largely inspired by nature while out walking the dogs through meadows. I became deeply moved by the simple things that I saw around me, previously unnoticed, such as slugs carrying white sacks of eggs, and spiders whose threads glanced my cheeks as they hung suspended in the middle of meadows. That mystified me; how could their webs float on air in the middle of a field?

Memories of the ghostly occurrences in my childhood and subsequent encounters had also inspired me to try to write that novel, weaving various strands together into a story. Those long hours wrapped up in my own creative world had given my mind wings in the early days of my recovery, at times becoming one of my greatest joys, and increasingly later on after my breakdown when I became less obsessive about it. My tutor had inspired me to try my hand at new writing skills. This was something I was finding stretching but welcome and the hard work was satisfying in a way I'd only dreamt of. It was a means to express myself fully, something to pour my heart and soul into. These skills led me to writing a small book of meditations for personal use, which I share with others in my prayer and meditation group.

Returning home from that holiday and feeling rejuvenated, life carried on. I continued writing, and had a small article published about Charlie and Lucy in a dog magazine, having been encouraged by my tutor to submit it. After the earlier book rejection that felt marvellous.

Suddenly June and early summer had arrived. It was time for another appointment with Professor Thomas.

'How are you?' I asked, looking at her short, dark, curly hair, instantly recognizable as post-chemotherapy.

'I'm very well, thank you. But I am making some changes and will be moving to a new job, as well as moving home.' Then we chatted about her treatments and recovery.

'I will miss you,' I said with a sinking feeling.

'I can assure you I have someone in mind here who can look after you. I will let them know, if you wish.'

'Thank you very much for all you've done for me. I am so grateful. Good luck with everything in your future.'

'Thank you. I'm sure I'll still hear about you from Simon's cousin.'

How strange it was that they kept meeting through their work. Such a small world, the way everything interconnects, I mused.

Following that appointment, which turned out to be our last, Professor Thomas sent the following letter to my GP.

I saw Mrs Gill on 8th June. She looks as well as ever.

She is now breaking the rules a little bit and having dairy foods occasionally, and was able to enjoy wine while on holiday with her husband in Gran Canaria recently. She continues to take wheatgrass juice every day, either by juicing her own supplies or by using purchased supplies, which she was able to take to the Canaries with her. She also uses her aqua detox system approximately every four to six weeks and takes six Carctol tablets a day. Generally she eats an alkaline diet consistent with Carctol.

On examination her liver seems flatter and smoother than before. There is still a mass arising from the right flank, but again this is no larger than it was and certainly seems more literalised than it did a couple of years ago.

This is clearly a remarkable story. I am unable to persuade Mrs Gill to have a biopsy so that we can actually establish precisely the nature of her tumour. I fully understand her reasons for being reluctant to have the biopsy as she is concerned this may stir things up.

Her last scan was performed at the beginning of 2005 and when I see her next I will encourage her to have a further one, to see whether there has been improvement. In the meantime I have checked her tumour markers again and will let her know the result. Of note on the last two occasions the markers have actually been lower than before.

CHAPTER 14
Death and Dying

The Bridge of Dreams
There is a bridge that leads beyond
The world of time and space,
Through a green and peaceful valley
To a lovely dwelling place
Where our loved ones find true happiness
And joys which never end…
Across this bridge that leads beyond
The peaceful valley's bend.

Anon, bequeathed to me by Lilian Ingleson

Here in the Western world the subject of death and dying is often avoided and for some is too uncomfortable to contemplate. Being diagnosed with a terminal illness forced this unpalatable subject into my life and a large part of my recovery has involved confronting and making peace with my own mortality. Naturally, I still have some fears, but certain memories and experiences have helped to shape more comfortable feelings towards death and dying, and for this reason I'd like to share with you some things that have helped me.

In my capacity as a spiritual healer, I have been privileged to work with many people suffering from cancer and other terminal illnesses and have often been present towards their journey's end. From them I have learned so much. The stories I'd like to share with you highlight how peaceful death can be, and how the initial pain and struggle can be transformed. They show how closely people connect to their spirituality just before dying, and what comfort and acceptance can be drawn from this.

These experiences also illustrate evidence of an afterlife. There are many of us who believe our deceased loved ones move on to a spiritual realm. Evidence of life after death is all around us, if we open our senses to it, but it is purely our choice to acknowledge this. Personally, I've seen enough throughout my lifetime to instil a strong belief in an afterlife, and whilst I accept that spiritual experiences can frighten some people, they can also be uplifting, a comforting sign that the love that's been shared is eternal and does not end when someone dies. Even the most sceptical people that I've met have awoken spiritually when close to death and have felt the peace that accompanies this. It is as death approaches, as one's time on earth draws near the end, that one's spiritual nature can become most potent.

Every day I count my blessings. After celebrating my five-year milestone, I had a renewed desire to return to my healing work, but in a more moderate manner. Without a focus in my life I tend to go to pieces, and healing is my passion. The following are some of my memories of experiences with those living with and confronting dying and death.

Jan

Since Jan had sung at my 50th birthday party her health had deteriorated. When visiting one day to receive healing, she declared, 'That was so relaxing. Do you know what I saw? Angels, glorious angels with big wings; they were beautiful and infused me with love. I floated and felt suspended.'

'I believe you,' I said, sensing her emotions as she peacefully drifted off.

A few days later Rob, her husband, called. 'Gilly, Jan's deteriorated. We're in hospital.'

'I'd like to come and visit, if I may,' I found myself saying.

'Yes, she'd love that,' replied Rob.

I focused myself before visiting, doing all I could to protect myself, both from a concern about germs as well as to help fortify my emotions. I dressed in bright colours, which always helps me feel stronger to lend support.

'Hello, so good of you to come,' said Jan, lying pale-faced in her raised bed with curtains drawn. After saying hello, her children went for a coffee break with Rob. Though struggling with the enormity of their own emotions and all they bore witness to, they nobly strove on, doing their utmost to come to terms with the many difficulties and selflessly giving their love and support to the one they loved.

'I've asked permission to give you some healing if you'd like?' I asked.

'Yes, please,' she replied.

Slowly opening her eyes afterwards she said, 'I saw two men wearing smart suits. They were measuring me. What do you think that means?'

Pausing, I replied, 'That you'll soon be going home, I should think.'

'Oh, I do hope so. But why measure me?'

'Perhaps to see the best way to make you comfortable for the journey ahead.'

'That makes sense,' she said, before serenely falling asleep.

Rob and the children were waiting outside in the corridor and hugged me as I reached them; this simple act helped ease tensions for everyone.

'Gilly, it's so hard to find things to say,' said Rob.

'Why not read her favourite extracts from *Winnie-the-Pooh*? That way she'll hear your familiar voice and the story will distract both your minds. I've got a spare copy. I'll bring it along with me next time if you like.'

'Would you please?' he said.

During my final visit Jan told me, 'After you finished healing me, I saw this glorious vision. It was of a road that rose up to meet me and at the far end it had a bend in the corner. I couldn't see beyond it.' She fell peacefully asleep before she could say any more.

Rob waited for me. 'Those Pooh Bear stories have been a lifeline. We both enjoy them. They not only made Jan smile, but both of us actually laughed. This way she can lie there not having to make any effort but can just relax.'

One evening shortly after that visit, Rob phoned in a desperate state.

'Gilly, I think her time has come. I don't know what to do.'

'Where are you?' I asked.

'Right beside her holding one hand; her brother Steven is holding the other.'

I had learned so much, not only at the hospice years ago, but also from my own near-death experiences, and replied, 'That's everything. Even though she's unconscious, she can still hear you. Have you said everything you need to say to her?'

'Yes.'

'Good. Just keep telling her how much you love her and that it's safe for her to go on. Your and Steve's loving presence will power her for the journey ahead with your deep abiding love.' As they did so, Jan peacefully passed away.

Much later I received a phone call from Rob asking, 'Will you please read at Jan's funeral?'

'Are you sure?' I stammered.

'Yes, she would want it.'

'Then of course,' I replied, again holding my nerves in check.

I again remembered Gee's words of wisdom: 'There's always a part of you that wants nothing more than to help you. Yet another part wants to play games, saying otherwise. Balancing the two is a juggling act, but don't give up. Try and remain steadfastly following the one you desire the most.'

Driving to the funeral we had an accident at some traffic lights with a car that cut across us. We arrived at the crematorium shaken but in one piece. I disappeared to the loo, after saying hello to one or two friends, to try to regain my composure ready for the reading.

I read the familiar 'Death is nothing at all' by Canon Henry Scott Holland. Near the end it says:

I am but waiting for you, for an interval, somewhere very near,
Just around the corner.'

Jan had loved flowers and had asked for them at her funeral, and then for them to be given to guests to uplift them. Walking around following her packed farewell ceremony, I noticed the white lilies we'd sent. Her daughter Lorna was standing by them, saying, 'Look, Daddy, there's a white butterfly fluttering just above those flowers.' Jan's son also looked on.

I hugged memories of Jan around me, of how she'd adapted recipes for my diet, and how she'd smiled her way to the end, letting her family know just how much she loved and cared for them.

Peter

Some months later I had a call from Janet, who'd originally introduced Rob and Jan to us. 'Gillian, my father-in-law Peter has been diagnosed with cancer, melanoma. He recently had a mole removed and tested. He's known you for as long as we have and…' She broke off crying.

Peter became a firm friend throughout his remaining months, visiting for meals and making a fuss of the dogs, while they in turn leant in close and returned the affection. He was spending as much time as he could with his family as he had missed his wife and lifelong companion, Doreen, dreadfully for the past year. Doreen had suffered with various health issues, including cancer, and put up a brave fight before dying peacefully at home in her favourite armchair with Peter beside her.

Towards the very end of Peter's life we visited his home on Christmas Eve.

He was lying in bed, looking pale with his thick grey hair dulled. His grandchildren, Philip and Felicity, were also at home visiting their parents, Tony and Janet.

'Would you like to come with me and we'll offer Pa some healing?' I asked the two children.

They exchanged a nervous look before nodding and following me into his bedroom. 'Hello, Peter,' I said brightly, bending down to lightly kiss his cheek. 'The children and I would like to give you some healing.'

'I'd love that,' he replied, smiling weakly.

'Just lie back against the soft pillows and relax,' I said. 'Philip, would you like to stand with your hands on your Pa's feet?'

'Yes, I can do that.'

'Fizz, would you like to hold Pa's hand?'

'Yes, Gilly,' she said, nervously clutching it with both of her own hands and staring intently into my eyes.

'Now, I'll just say a little prayer,' I said closing my eyes, 'then if you both just send all the love you feel for your grandfather through the sense of touch, we'll begin. If either of you want to tell Pa how much you love him, please do.'

As the healing began, the children took it in turn to speak. They sobbed their words out and tears trickled down Peter's cheeks as he listened. His chest heaved with a sob as he tightly held our hands. Relief washed through everyone. I broke off to wipe Philip's tears, now streaming down his face, his nose running uncontrollably.

Peter eventually dozed off to sleep, so we crept quietly out of his bedroom.

'Gilly,' said Philip bemused, pulling himself together now, 'I felt heat pouring out of me into Pa. My hands stuck to his feet like glue. What happened there?'

'It's hard to describe. Simply put, you acted as an energy source, transferring deep love and compassion through your touch into Pa. It's a force far greater than us and at such times as this can be tuned into, rather like a radio signal, and experienced as you just did. It's a gift when that happens, and you can see the results for yourself.'

'My martial arts teacher has spoken of energy exchanges…' Overcome, he broke off mid sentence and rushed to his bedroom.

During the next few days Peter deteriorated. Rather than going into a hospice, Tony and Janet insisted he stay with them. On New Year's Eve Peter lay in bed listening to an intimate festive supper party downstairs.

'Here you are,' said Tony, handing Peter a small plate of food to taste.

After everyone left in the wee hours, Peter called out.

Tony got up and went to comfort him, remaining until he slept.

By morning Peter had died. He drew his last breath surrounded by his family's love.

The following Christmas, when visiting Tony, Janet and the children in Peter's former home, now theirs, something curious happened.

Standing by the Christmas tree, Janet said, 'Look at those gold angels. They belonged to Peter and Doreen.'

As we stood admiring the tree and the cherished cherubs, listening to the men and children laughing in the kitchen, we suddenly heard a loud noise. One of the angels had fallen off the tree, bounced along the floor and landed squarely at our feet! Startled, we laughed; we couldn't help it.

'What's all the laughter about?' asked Tony, bringing everyone else into the room with him.

After telling him what had happened, he said jovially, 'There's no doubt Mum and Dad are with us. That's as sure a sign as any.'

Bernadette

I affectionately remember our children's surrogate granny figure, Bernadette, who came into our lives when they were young. She looked after them at the start of my healing training every Tuesday afternoon, when I visited a local healing centre to receive instruction and to assist as a probationary healer.

For many years Bernadette was a friend enriching all our lives. We'd frequently discussed life and death matters, which occupied her thoughts. She was divorced and loved her cat, who after dying came back to visit her in spirit form. When quietly reading in the evening, she'd see him out of the corner of her eye, and on one occasion she found a clump of his fur on the freshly vacuumed carpet.

Bernadette had faced many challenges and was resourceful in overcoming difficulties, always maintaining a cheerful outer countenance. Towards the end of her life she was diagnosed with leukaemia, but she kept going right up until the end, which came one bright summer's evening after she'd visited her daughter and grandchildren. She returned to her first floor flat and, as she put the key in the lock, she fainted and lay there unable to move in a semi-conscious state.

When her daughter tried to phone her and there was no answer, fearing that something was wrong, she had called an ambulance and then phoned me, asking me to pray for her mother. She told me how Bernadette had happy memories of visiting our home and spending time with our cats in the garden.

I felt humbled and saddened by this news and immediately went to find a quiet spot to commence praying. No sooner had I started than I became aware of Bernadette's presence in a vision. She seemed serene and looked happy and I started mentally talking to her, as though we were in the kitchen having a cup of tea, just greeting her as usual and asking her how she was.

Astonishingly she replied, 'It's my time now. I've done all I can and I am on the way, Gilly; but I'm afraid and don't know what to do, or where to go.'

I admit to being taken aback, as nothing like this had happened before. However, all I could think was that our close friendship, and the fact that no subject was taboo between us, especially life and death matters, had made this possible. She was visiting me in spirit form at her hour of passing.

I remember then standing beside her, reaching out and holding her hand. It was as though we were in a dream together. She looked totally radiant, healthier than I'd ever seen her. It was as if, having outgrown her physical body, she'd climbed into a new vibrant one. As I held her hand, we became aware of a welcoming, glowing light emanating all around us, and there was a golden stairway, like an escalator. We stood side by side and were automatically taken up it; strangely enough we glided smoothly and serenely. Up and up we went. I was acutely aware of our holding hands, looking at one another and chatting. I don't remember much else, but as we steadily made our way upwards, I felt lighter and more buoyant. Other people were either side of the escalator, and they appeared radiant and angelic.

When we reached the top, we had to step off. I remember that I instinctively knew that I couldn't go any further. Bernadette knew this too and I gave her one big, last hug and she held me tightly; we didn't need words. Someone else she knew stepped forward to meet her, and she looked relaxed as they walked off together and I returned down the golden escalator. Shortly afterwards I received another phone call from her daughter, now safely home from hospital. She told me her mother didn't regain consciousness but passed peacefully in her sleep.

Charles

I remember my friend Natasha's stepfather, Charles, who was a wonderful astrologer. One day I received a phone call from Charles after he'd spoken to Natasha.

'Gillian, Natasha has told me about you, and as I'm suffering with cancer I would very much like to visit you for healing.'

'Of course, Charles, please come and see me. I make no promises, for each time I offer myself as a channel for healing it is like an experiment; I cannot predict the outcome.'

Charles arrived, we chatted and over the next few months, with his failing health, I visited him at his home. He struggled with his cancer yet fought valiantly. Before his demise he told me, 'I've reconciled myself to my inevitable fate. When we are born the surest thing is that each day we are in some way dying. I've had a good, fulfilling life and recognize some achievements. Merely getting through each day is an achievement enough in itself sometimes.' He concluded that, having mulled over his contributions towards life, loving thoughts alone were one of the finest achievements.

Between hospital and hospice visits, Charles told me, 'This is so hard on Suzi, my beloved wife, and the children. Yet when I am at home, it's a luxury beyond measure to lie in my own bed with crisp, clean sheets, put there by Suzi. I lie still, basking like one of our cats in pools of sunshine streaming through the window.'

Acting as his spiritual healer, these are my memories towards the end of Charles's life. Charles lay in his bed at home, drifting off and floating like a cloud, filled with peace as the end drew closer. One of the family cats joined him, lying stretched out on the floor in the same pool of sunshine.

I recall Charles saying, 'I am happiest when lying bathed in the sunshine. It works a kind of magic on me. All my life I've been fascinated by the planets, by their power, by their effect upon us in our lives. At certain times they are like an orchestra playing the most beautiful symphony.' He was reflecting on the entire spectrum of his life. Now he was the conductor of his memories and he knew how to direct them.

Being aware of the spiritual aspect of his nature, and the part this was playing as he gradually declined in health, helped prepare him for his onward journey; he embraced that aspect slowly, while slipping away from this world. This process is hard for anyone to witness, especially loved ones. Many people wish they could change places with the one who is suffering. It's not for us to know the reason why some of us are called forth for such undertakings earlier than we would wish. All we can do is try to work towards acceptance of our inevitable destiny.

Suzi found that she struggled to look after him, witnessing his failing health; at times tensions arose, as is often the case between loved ones. Nevertheless, Suzi poured forth as much love and attention as she could muster while coping with her own feelings of grief and sadness, knowing that she would be left alone with their children. Support from friends was invaluable, especially at that time. It's bad enough for the one suffering from cancer, yet it can sometimes be as painful, if not more so in a different way, for the person living with and supporting them through it.

I read somewhere that a late actor, admired and respected by many, including myself, said that he and his wife had to live in separate houses while he underwent chemotherapy for his cancer. They found it so hard continually living through that experience beneath the same roof. At times, both needed precious space alone to process the enormity of their individual emotions.

Much has been said about those suffering from a terminal illness, though for those closest to them it can present a very different but equally challenging experience. Suzi, to whom I am eternally grateful, has generously revisited this period from her past in order to share her experience as Charles neared the end of his life. She spoke to me honestly and openly, describing the exhausting spectrum of emotions she lived through, from her anger, pain and guilt to unexpected moments of tenderness and clarity, and ultimately how she found peace. This is what she told me:

When living with someone diagnosed with cancer it is not uncommon for problems intrinsic to the relationship to become more apparent under the added pressure. Relationships can go either way, become more distant or closer as each comes to terms with arising factors in their own unique way. So often the one suffering with cancer will withdraw in an effort to process the changes in their body, and ultimately to engage in an inner dialogue with oneself. Charles needed to do this; a man who throughout his life generously looked after so many now had to put himself first.

Suzi was embarking on a storm of emotions as Charles's illness worsened throughout the months. After an improvement and the spark of fragile, new hope, painful disappointment would follow when his illness eventually resisted all the treatments and nothing appeared to be helping. Charles increasingly withdrew into himself, which was one of the hardest aspects of the journey for Suzi, but she came to understand and respect Charles's need for solitude and for engaging with the challenge of his illness in his own way. Invaluable help from wise mentors and loving friends, who bore witness to her struggling and suffering, sustained her and enabled her to hold onto a compassionate understanding of her husband's need for an intimate, and urgent, dialogue with himself. She fully accepted her role, which was to provide material comfort, safety, security, protection of the family routine, and affection and love in whatever form it might be needed. Nevertheless, this was the beginning of one of her loneliest periods, transforming her own perception of life with the passage of time. Suzi knew Charles needed to grapple with what he was undergoing.

It was also a time of dealing with increasingly uncomfortable feelings of anger. Suzi's initial response to Charles's diagnosis had been to muster a kind of 'heroic vendetta against the demon' – they would beat this illness, and they would triumph. But although this courage was needed and helped them cope with the treatments, eventually the harsh realization came that all human efforts to fight the cancer were failing and they faced the bleak alternative. She then felt angry at her helplessness, angry at feeling emotionally abandoned and yet trapped, and also guilty for feeling cheated out of a life she'd had and yearned for, whilst Charles was preparing for death. They both felt the frustrations of their emotional predicament, they both felt angry for a complicated mixture of reasons, and both suffered from what seemed like the growing barriers to emotional connection.

And yet the emotional turbulence of this time was not unusual. In a situation like this, different couples will experience the pressures on their relationships in a variety of ways. The trauma of impending loss may provoke an individual's defence mechanisms, and can exacerbate the 'basic fault line' within a relationship. Having previously been very close, life was now calling each to separate from the other. For Suzi this felt so strange and cruel, and yet eventually it provided her with an invaluable lesson, which was gleaned only slowly and painfully: 'I realized Charles was not mine, that he belonged first and foremost to himself, that he had a purpose mysteriously and uniquely his own…'

Part of her challenge was to let Charles go, to simply allow him the space he needed to digest and assess his life, to have a dialogue with himself. As often happens when one is struggling with the pain of loss, she came to appreciate more deeply the privilege of knowing and loving Charles, and he her, for twenty-two years of their lives. Striving for acceptance of her own fate meant that she saw she needed to view things from a larger, more generous standpoint. This was not easy; only flashes of insight pointed the way amidst the tumult of guilt, anger, fear and sadness. But on reflection, and with hindsight, she felt it was naive of her to have assumed anything more.

There were also their two teenage sons to consider, whom they both loved deeply. As parents, their natural inclination was to try to protect them from torment about the horrendous reality of unfolding events and the prospect of becoming fatherless. They were united in putting on brave, positive faces, but increasingly Suzi wondered if this was right. She hoped that Charles would speak to them more candidly, about both his feelings and theirs. That didn't happen as it was too difficult for father and sons to face, and so 'the need for mutual reassurance understandably allowed the mechanism of denial to hold sway'. Denial has its uses, but the gulf between the reality of Charles's decline and the presentation of positive hopefulness to their boys widened. The containment of the routine of everyday life was enormously helpful, especially to their sons, who were blossoming adolescents with interests and ambitions; but more and more it became clear that every member of the family was struggling with unspoken fears and the sense of impending heartbreak.

With Charles's continued decline, Suzi's intense frustration became more mixed with admiration for the courage and dignity which Charles always found when facing his treatments and then later the disappointing results. Whilst she felt that she was carrying the burden of registering the feelings of their nightmare, her compassion grew for his predicament and the way he needed to handle it. The hurricane of feelings – loneliness, loss, anger, guilt and fear – were hard to bear, but in time, and with much grieving done, she has gained a deeper understanding of the emotions that engulfed her at that time.

Charles's last weekend of life was a crisis point. His already compromised immune system had weakened following medical treatments. Gradually overwhelmed by an internal infection, he became unconscious and was taken by ambulance to hospital on Sunday morning. All the while he lay in hospital appearing lifeless. He was given a massive amount of antibiotics, whilst Suzi sat beside him, speaking quietly but urgently into his ear, reminding him of their first romantic meeting, their special places, the beautiful times they had shared together, the love she felt for him, and the meaning and joy he'd brought to her life. This was all that mattered.

A couple of hours later he revived and, although the medics said the situation was still serious, he did appear to be battling and hope was rekindled for his survival. At that precise moment a friend arrived at the hospital with both sons. Then Charles's adored stepdaughter Natasha and her partner also arrived. With the approach of evening, everyone was seated around Charles's bed, filled with gratitude for the reprieve. Charles told Suzi how in his unconscious state he'd heard every word she'd said before others arrived. He even re-asserted his typically thoughtful personality and put everyone's mind to rest for the night by calling up after the family had got back home to remind Natasha that her favourite chocolate was in the fridge.

However, on Monday morning Suzi was told that during the night Charles had begun to have trouble breathing again, and by the next evening he had deteriorated dramatically. His doctor, always compassionate and strong, spoke with Suzi about what to expect through the hours ahead, and also accompanied her to tell Charles that he was losing the battle. Although devastated and in shock, Suzi's way was to let inner strength, or resolve, take over, and she simply stayed by his side, attempting to soothe and calm his distress and disorientation. They spoke of their love and deepest gratitude for one another, over and over again, and many other things besides.

And then the process of dying took over, and Charles became increasingly less able to speak. Pain relief was administered and the family stayed close by his bedside, speaking gently and stroking him lovingly. As his vitality ebbed he seemed to visually focus on the upper right-hand corner of the room, almost as if he was seeing or becoming aware of something that may have been helping him.

Suzi felt that there was a tremendous tenderness in his dying, and that the privilege of being part of and witnessing this tender mystery opened her heart to a capacity she hadn't realized was there. She came to see dying as 'a huge achievement', and facing this through Charles's death gave her a sense of confidence, a knowing that her own dying would one day be possible. This felt like a gift, this unexpected, humbling new acceptance of what we all must go through.

It can seem obvious to say, but it's true: like being born, dying is a stage of life, a passage, which is to be honoured with a gracious, respectful consciousness. Its mystery perhaps can never be fully understood, but by succumbing to the process, it's as though the mystery of death enters in and can *transform*, leaving a boon and a blessing deep within.

At his farewell ceremony, a certain magic had the last word and cast a warm, rejoicing glow, which paralleled in an uncanny way the warm generosity of spirit that was Charles's defining characteristic. As the funeral procession made its way along the winding, narrow West Country lanes, the weather paid tribute with its own sweet symphony. It was late wintertime, February. All week it had been wet, wild and wintry with rare bursts of sunshine. On the day of the funeral the rain gave way to the sunbeams, and all over the surrounding hills appeared not one but three rainbows that lit the valley below. This appeared to Suzi, and to so many others who loved Charles, to be 'a happy, affirming, synchronous cosmic message, a heartfelt response to the ceremony of huge gratitude for his life' and the way he lit up the lives of everyone he knew.

Simon's mother

My mother-in-law took a turn for the worse in late 2008 after spending several years living in a nursing home suffering debilitating, chronic osteoarthritis, dementia and strokes.

Our relationship had its ups and downs, but she unknowingly taught me so much, including how to be stronger, and for that I am eternally grateful. There were occasions of upset and anger, whilst at other times I felt tremendous outpourings of love towards her. Things somehow worked between us, even though it could be awkward, and we arrived at an unspoken, common understanding. She just didn't know how to give or receive love very well, except to children and animals, where she excelled.

On her final day we received several phone calls from the nursing home alerting us to her rapidly failing condition. The message on our answer phone was unclear, but Simon, who was working at a charity in Bath, had also received a call and departed homeward. It was evening as we prepared to visit. I had already put my pyjamas and dressing gown on, having had a bath to warm and relax myself, so I hurriedly dressed and we drove along the icy roads at alarming speed, with Simon urging me to slow down.

'I don't seem to be able to. I'm filled with a sense of urgency,' I replied, nevertheless trying to drive more slowly.

Miraculously we arrived safely and were greeted by a sweet nurse who told us, 'Your mother is slipping deeper into unconsciousness. We have been popping into her room all day asking her if there is anything we can do. We suggested praying. She didn't want any help, until around teatime. Then, when she could not feel her legs, she called out to us. I rushed in, held her hand and listened. Then I quietly prayed. She closed her eyes and hasn't opened them since.'

Silently she led the way.

Simon struggled to maintain his composure as we walked into the room. His mother lay unconscious in her familiar bed, now positioned against a wall as an added safety measure. My heart lurched as I realized this was the time to say all the unspoken things I'd never said before. A tiny teddy bear sat on the bedside table. I quietly crouched down beside his mother and, holding her hand, told her, 'Thank you for everything you've taught me since I've known you. You are incredibly strong, and I cannot thank you enough for the most precious gift of Simon's life.'

I can't remember what else I said, but I urged Simon to try to do the same. I could see he felt uncomfortable so I turned my back, stood in a corner of the room and looked out onto the garden and up at the inky night sky. Weariness crept into my bones and I suddenly felt a cold blast of air. It came from nowhere. As Simon quietly began speaking I tried not to listen, and again I felt the cold blast. I knew in a flash it was her late husband reaching out to her, as well as us, to let us know he would be there, helping her every step.

'There's no more we can do,' declared Simon helplessly, shrugging his shoulders.

'I'd like to try and help her,' I whispered. I reached out, kissed her cool, dry cheek and, holding her hand, quietly prayed. Once we'd both finished, we noticed a change.

'Look,' said Simon.

'Mmm,' I replied hazily.

'Mumso's face has softened, her body is relaxing slightly more in the bed, and she looks serene. The years are falling away from her now.'

At first I couldn't speak; I'd never seen anything like this before.

'I suddenly feel tired and light-headed,' I said.

Simon looking ashen suggested we leave.

We hadn't eaten supper, but within no time of walking through our front door the phone was ringing.

'Hello,' said the nurse, 'I just wanted to tell you that your mother-in-law has now passed peacefully. After you left I went to check on her and she'd already gently slipped away.'

The following day I did something I never thought I could; I visited her one last time. She looked peaceful. I located her new tights and best clothes ready for the undertakers to dress her in, whilst Simon phoned family and friends. We caught the train to London to tell the children over a long lunch, remembering their Granny. Over the next few days we joined together as a family to prepare for the funeral, consulting our local vicar and each choosing a special prayer or reading. Her oldest friends came to her funeral to pay their last respects, and several commented on the choice of a reading, an extract from *Winnie-the-Pooh*. That book had been her all-time favourite, never failing to put a smile on her face. Over the next week or so I felt her spirit all around me. I went in search of a new dressing gown, and instantly found a festive red one with a Pooh Bear holding a star emblazoned on the lapel. On Christmas morning, I awoke to find a large, floppy teddy bear that normally rests over our headboard mysteriously lying smack on top of the bedding over my heart.

Jayshree

Jayshree was a brave soul, remembered for her dignity and courage when confronting her own ovarian cancer journey, though it was other health complications that finally led to her demise.

Her entire family, especially her daughter Sunita, and I grew close towards the end of Jayshree's life. Sunita told me how she bore witness to her mother's atrocious suffering. Nevertheless, Jayshree had learned to transcend her physical discomforts in order to prepare her family for her demise. She discovered a renewed vigour through prayer. When unable to eat she practised the *mansi pooja*, meaning mind worship, when she would close her eyes and imagine her favourite food, first preparing it and then offering it to God, after which she would feel full up. She embraced integrated medicine along her way.

However, behind her brave face, Jayshree fought a battle between her faith in winning her health and life and her fear of losing the battle to cancer. During the last few months of her life, despite having eaten virtually nothing, she looked beautiful, glowing from the inside.

Cultivating her spirituality, at times she transcended her physical disabilities and saw showers of silver sparkles. One day on a visit she said, 'Gillian, when we meditate and pray together I find enormous strength and comfort and see visions of my Gods. I pray to them constantly.'

Sunita, her middle child, soon became a kindred spirit to me. What a beautiful girl, with brown almond-shaped eyes and long dark hair. Her sister Anita was another beauty, expecting her first baby, and their brother Krishna was a devoted son of hidden depths. Their father, Mahesh, was distraught at his wife's illness, but found deep abiding comfort through his own prayers when visiting the Hari Krishna Temple in Watford, a gift from the late George Harrison.

The last time I visited Jayshree in hospital she said, 'Help me, please.'

Preparing for healing prayers, Sunita said, 'The staff are wonderful here, doing everything to help my mother and allowing me to stay here right by her side. My sister, brother and I take turns. Dad has to run the business and visits frequently. But Mummy is not able to eat, no matter what I prepare to tempt her; it is a worry to me.'

Listening and looking into my eyes, Jayshree said, 'It is my soul that needs nourishment now, and this comes from the love and prayers that I'm surrounded by from my immediate family.' She repeated 'my prayers nourish me and…'. She lay quietly back on the white sheets, smiling valiantly before closing her eyes in anticipation, steeping herself in happier memories of her last longed-for visit to her Motherland, India, where she had made a holy pilgrimage.

Deep peace filled the room as we joined in prayerful harmony. Sunshine streamed through the open windows as fresh air flowed all around. Jayshree needed more than anything to know that to die was not to fail.

Some weeks later Sunita phoned me, saying, 'Mummy has now gone. At times she looked afraid to leave, but we steered her through her difficulties. We simply remained with her, infusing her with harmony and love. The saffron-robed monks from my father's place of worship stood around chanting as she took her last breath. It was very beautiful and she looked blissful.'

Luke

Luke was a young university student struck by testicular cancer.

'I've been forcing him to see you,' said Lillie, his girlfriend. Lillie was a close younger friend of my beloved Sara, whose own husband, Tony, sadly passed after a long illness with pancreatic cancer, though he lived for much longer than expected.

'Lillie,' I said, 'he must use his own free will. I cannot force anything on Luke that he's not comfortable with.'

'But he is desperate and wants to speak to you now,' she humbly replied.

So, prior to my own cancer experience, Luke and I regularly met and spoke on the telephone.

'Gillian,' said Lillie phoning me one day, 'Luke is in hospital now and I've noticed when his friends visit he tires easily. He always tries to cheer everyone up and reassure them he's alright, but of course he's not, he's weak and ill.'

'What energy he has needs to go towards his healing, preserving his energies. A healer colleague, Fran, told me that when her best friend Rosie passed away what helped her the most was not to just have visitors but for them to quietly chat about everyday matters between themselves, leaving her to relax and rest without necessarily giving any input.'

'Can my parents join us?' Luke asked one day as his life was drawing to a close, while lying quietly at home in bed. 'Will you show them what you do?'

Once together in the room we all joined hands, standing around Luke's bed, and prayed together of one mind to help Luke in whatever way possible, to give him added pain relief and control, as well as courage and strength.

Finally, while at home, after being unbelievably brave and surrounded by those he loved the most, Luke took his last breath and slipped away. He was remembered by all who knew him for being the life and soul of every party, having always been the great jester and leaving laughter in his wake.

The hospice

I was privileged to work as a volunteer at a hospice shortly after my late sister Joanna died, which gave me my first experience of working with people close to death and dying. The following are how I recall some of these experiences.

Once I walked onto a ward and a Japanese man opened his eyes and said, 'Are you an angel? Have I died?'

'You're not dead yet,' I replied, gently stroking the back of his hand, the one that didn't have a line going into it. Quietly I began praying for him, and for the relief and release he was seeking.

After a few moments silence he replied 'Then I'll try again,' and he closed his eyes.

Another incident occurred when I was manning the phones on the first floor of the hospice; it was a particularly busy morning with nurses rushing in and out of the rooms.

Glancing up I noticed an exceptionally well-looking man, tanned with thick hair and wearing blue and white striped pyjamas, a dark green dressing gown and ruby-coloured slippers. That was unusual, but at the time I thought nothing of it, until a nurse asked, 'Have you seen the patient from that room?'

'Yes, he just went behind the lift shaft, having come out of that room,' I pointed.

'He couldn't have,' said the nurse looking confused and rushing to search another room.

I didn't realize at the time that the man was one of my favourite television actors from my childhood.

There was an unexpected lull and, finding myself alone with no phones ringing, temptation overcame me. I peeked into the room I'd seen the man walk out of. What I saw took my breath away. There he lay with drips in both arms, face ashen and hollow, and with no hair. His eyes were shut and he looked close to death. I felt like crying, not understanding what had happened, but I held my feelings in until I got home. I phoned my friendly healer, Irene.

'What's the matter?' she asked, knowing me well and being direct by nature.

I told her all that had happened and she explained, 'When a person is preparing to die, they sometimes step outside their physical body and take a look around, as though adjusting to the life that is yet to come. What you saw is a remarkable demonstration of this. By its very nature a hospice is a place for making the transition from life to death, but there is no death really, for life carries on, as you know, and you're a very lucky girl to witness such an event.'

'Thank you so much,' I stammered, drying my tears.

'Don't keep thanking me, Gill; it's what I do in life.'

The following week, as the hospice was quiet, I mustered my courage to ask one of the nurses about what I'd seen. Her reply stunned me.

'Well, that's not at all unusual for us working here. You should be in our cottages at the back of the hospice garden at night; you wouldn't believe what happens on occasions. The scariest thing that's happened to me is when I was in a deep sleep one night, suddenly I was wide awake, with my bed moving about with me in it!'

'What?' I exclaimed, remembering my own similar childhood experience.

'Oh yes, that's not all,' she continued. 'Our windows are opened and shut and the doors are loudly banged.' That also sounded all too familiar.

'How do you cope?' I asked urgently.

'It goes with the territory in this sort of job,' she replied. 'We have one another for comfort, and we discuss it amongst ourselves. We've come to accept it as normal, for when some souls die, they are surprised to find themselves, as it were, not dead at all, merely having easily walked out of their physical body and into a new one! Usually after an illness like cancer this body would be a better, healthier one.'

I could testify to this, I thought, and explained what I'd seen the previous week. She pondered before replying, 'What we do when disturbances occur is to pray for whoever is responsible. We talk to the hospice chaplain and this also helps. Sometimes we light a candle as a symbol of light, to guide the recently deceased soul with love to find a clearer pathway for their journey ahead.'

'Oh,' is all I managed to say, dumbfounded at her natural acceptance of such matters and her ease when dealing with such situations, which would terrify many. What a calling such people have in life; souls like this are a gift to their profession, helping those in their final days.

It has been a huge honour knowing these special souls and being part of their lives at a time of transition. In spite of all pain and struggle, death is an inevitable part of life, a time to be real, and an opportunity to talk openly about feelings and to listen to whatever the ill person may wish to share. Just being with someone you love, just your presence, can be a tremendous help in itself. To know they are not alone and that they are loved and cared for will go a long way towards relieving their fears as they let go. And that alone is a gift, to be with a loved one as they complete their final act on earth, to bear witness to their dying and all that it involves.

All I've experienced has taught me so much about death and dying and that it is important to make the most of the life we have, no matter what, and to say what we feel in our hearts by letting others know just how much they mean to us, and especially how much we love them. When death comes after a long illness, invariably everyone is stretched to their limits emotionally, yet beneath there is an underlying strength that only appears at the end, as though a final gift to help the one departing. I see death as like a graduation, an entire new beginning somewhere other than here. We step out of the physical body and into a new, more youthful one, like changing out of one set of clothes and into another.

CHAPTER 15
Role Reversal

Where there is darkness
Let the soul shine brightly…
And walk with trust…
Gillian Gill

2008

A new cycle was beginning in our lives. Simon had been working part-time as a consultant and was preparing for retirement, as well as looking forward to enjoying the simple, everyday things of life, such as taking the dogs for long, leisurely walks. He'd been given a retirement party at a favourite London pub, which included his immediate family, by his invitation, as well as work colleagues. We all enjoyed meeting one another after years of having been nothing more than voices on the end of a telephone.

Over the next few weeks our dining room resumed its original purpose as files and boxes of equipment were sorted through, destroyed or filed away in another area in the house.

There was also a change going on next door. Our elderly neighbour Dodie had become too frail to live alone and was moved to a nursing home where her sister already resided, both now being closer to their family. We had mixed feelings seeing her go. I was concerned about new neighbours, and silently thought, 'Please may whoever moves in next door enjoy living here and get along with the neighbours.'

Over the next few months various vehicles pulled up as different people viewed the house; it was unsettling. Then one day Simon said, 'A lovely family arrived on bicycles to view next door; they looked like really nice people.' Eventually they moved in and, for the first time in our memory, as they held a small garden party, children's laughter erupted along with the sound of popping champagne corks, which drifted through the yew hedge that separated our gardens.

The same spring, I was just recovering from another bout of sickness and diarrhoea when our friend Tony rang and told me, 'Gilly, you'd have loved our local church's May Day celebration. In the churchyard there was a demonstration called A Leap of Faith.'

This reminded me of how I'd clutched my faith tightly to my chest when telling my oncologist, Professor Thomas, about my choice to forego conventional medicine in favour of the holistic route. 'Do tell me more,' I urged.

'The weather was sunny, bright and cold with a gentle wind, perfect conditions. People gathered in the churchyard, looking up at the tall spire. To honour the occasion children had been invited to bring a teddy bear to the top of the church roof. Parachutes were strapped onto the bears and then the children, one by one, gently dropped them over the edge. The sky filled with teddies, gracefully carried by the wind, floating down to the churchyard. As the relieved children stepped forward, reunited with their teddy bears, they clutched them closely to their hearts while receiving a Certificate of Bravery for the Teddy Bear: Leap of Faith.'

Like those trusting children with their beloved teddy bears, at certain times in our lives we are called forth to face our own challenges, to take our own leap of faith. At such times there is an inherent strength guiding us; we follow what we believe to be our chosen pathway, proceeding one step at a time, while trusting in the best possible outcome, whatever it may be.

I couldn't help but draw parallels with my own personal world after listening to Tony, as many journeys in life start with a leap of faith. The hardest part is taking the initial step. Nevertheless, such was, and still is, my motivation to be healthy and whole, balanced in body and soul that I gathered my beliefs around me to give me the courage to take that first step.

Having decided against conventional medicine, it was as though someone always appeared in my life at the right moment to show me the way forward. Rosy told me about Carctol. Prior to that Simon had discovered Essiac. Each time, when something more needed adding, choices appeared.

Interrupting my musings, I heard Simon's voice saying, 'David's working hard to become an accountant. He's got more exams ahead, but he's determined.'

'Following in your footsteps,' I replied. 'It's ironic, really; since you've retired he's working harder than ever.'

'Yes, and I've just had rather disturbing blood test results back from the doctor. As you know, two sets of my blood test results got lost, now the latest one reveals I've got impaired glucose tolerance, which can easily lead to diabetes. It was picked up as a result of the check-up that I had on retirement. I'm going to make an appointment to chat with my GP to see what can be done. Someone I once sailed with has virtually lost his eyesight due to sugar diabetes and is overweight.'

I felt a peculiar sensation deep within, and it was uncomfortable. I was used to having gripping abdominal sensations, which I always thought was the cancer returning and spreading, but it wasn't that as my 'lump' was benign now; it was my anxious mind overworking and causing tension throughout my body. I suddenly realized how dependent I'd become on Simon. His asthma was under control, but what would happen if he was ill with something else?

'I've done some research since seeing the doctor and I'm going to alter my diet. Will you cook more of your recipes for us both? Look at this list the GP gave me,' he said thrusting a sheet of paper into my hands. 'It lists all foods that should be avoided; it shouldn't be too difficult. Please don't buy any more cheese – you know I can't help myself if it's there – and no more biscuits or chocolate. If we don't have them, I can't be tempted. If I have some meat please cook game as it is low in saturated fat.'

He took advice from Rosy and others on nutrition and supplements, read books on diabetes and increased his exercise. He also discovered that many of us are deficient in chromium, which affects insulin production and is an essential nutrient and a deficiency can result in, amongst other things, glucose intolerance.

Three months later, Simon had lost almost two stones as a result of his dietary changes and increased exercise. The chromium supplements he'd been recommended were also helping.

Nevertheless, I thought he looked tired and pale. Those words were quietly being said to me by many of our concerned friends, together with 'Are you sure Simon's alright? He looks pretty ill'.

'He's making some drastic lifestyle changes and that's taking its toll,' I replied, quietly willing him to go gently. With his retirement he'd agreed to help Rosy's charity and was driving to the office in Bath, a round trip of four or five hours, once or twice a week.

To calm myself from worrying about Simon and our changing roles, I went to find a hoe in the garden shed and spent an hour in the vegetable patch. Eric had all the vegetables lined up neatly at his end; my side was interspersed with calendulas, poppies, borage and lavender, which to some extent overpowered the vegetables. I liked watching the insects drinking their nectar and stood riveted, leaning against the hoe, watching a bumblebee. After drinking its fill from a chive flower, it fell back down the stem three times. I thought it must be drunk as it couldn't manage to fly off, so remained content, lying sideways at the base of the plant as the sun sank in the sky.

The following day Simon said, 'Later on this morning I'm setting up that new exercise machine our friends let us have so reasonably. I'll put it in my den in the gallery above the sitting room.'

'But you're already biking and walking far more.'

'Yes, and I need to do more exercise. That's the key, that way I can burn off excess calories and still afford to indulge occasionally. I've worked it all out, don't worry.' Smiling, he looked at my feet. 'Did you know you're wearing two left slippers from different pairs?'

'No, I must have been distracted when I put them on,' I said removing them.

'Come on, Lucy and Charlie, let's go for a walk,' I called, looking at their friendly faces. It was drizzling outside. 'Come on, Charlie, a drop of rain won't hurt you,' I urged as he dejectedly stood inside the doorway. Dragging him at first, he eventually joined Lucy, enjoying sniffing rabbit holes and forgetting all about his dislike of rain. The sound of large wings low overhead distracted me. Glancing up I saw two Egyptian Geese gliding down, wings outstretched, white backs glowing, into our neighbour's meadow to graze in the rain-sodden grass. Turning to go home, Charlie followed in his own time.

Weeks passed, and suddenly I noticed Simon did look healthier; the colour that had drained from his face had returned.

'Just seen my GP for another blood test result to check my blood sugar level and I'm delighted that my results have reverted to the normal range. Isn't that good news?'

'Yes,' I replied, 'that's all the hard work you've put in.'

'Well, you know secretly I'm a bit competitive. I love going out on the bike with David when he's home and keeping up with him. As he takes less exercise due to working, while I am taking more, I sometimes manage to pass him on the hills!'

As I'd been feeling particularly tired around that time, I was also seeing my GP for blood tests of my own, and they revealed that my thyroid was underactive. I was given a prescription to remedy it, but I was concerned about taking it so I called Rosy for her advice.

'There's another way of treating your hormones – nutrition,' she reassured. 'The most likely cause will be lack of iodine, so include seaweed in your diet, which you can easily buy, and speak to your nutritionist to see what she suggests.'

Marianne had similar suggestions: 'I agree with what you've told me. You can sprinkle seaweed onto soups or salads, it's delicious. Otherwise there's a food supplement called TH207. It's a combination of Siberian ginseng, liquorice and dulse seaweed with vitamins and minerals. Choose whichever you prefer.'

'What a pair we are! Reached that age, I suppose,' commented Simon sagely.

While lying in bed that evening giving myself healing, I noticed how my 'lump' had shrunk further as I again put my hands with wrists on either hip to do a fingertip test. Previously my fingers did not touch, but they now easily overlapped.

Over the next few weeks I began to feel better, and while driving home from a visit to see Philip, Peter's grandson, something strange happened. I found myself strongly compelled to turn into a private drive with a sign saying J A Centre. I'd heard of this local healing centre, but knew nothing about it. Having parked the car I spotted a modern barn-type building with an inviting-looking open door. Walking in I heard a jovial voice call out 'Please come on in…'. Then Gordon, the friendly owner, appeared, greeting me with an extended hand. The more he spoke, telling me he was a retired farmer, the more he reminded me of my late father. I told him how I'd been drawn to pull in off the road.

'You're not the first. My wife Margaret and I decided that, having lost our son Jonathan in his twenties to an oral cancer, we would turn this barn into a healing centre as a tribute to him. I was always sceptical of spiritual matters before his passing. After his death, while walking across the farmyard one day I distinctly heard the words "Out of this sadness will be born a new dawn…". Then this idea seeded itself,' he said pointing all around before continuing. 'There followed extraordinary coincidences, such as blue chairs and matching blue carpets appearing just when we needed them; it's quite a story really.'

We chatted on for some time, and he agreed that I'd be welcome to come along on any Tuesday afternoon to join his team of voluntary healers when the centre is open to the whole community. I felt happy driving home mulling over this strange turn of events. It started a new healing chapter in my life, with the healers working harmoniously in teams of three. Sadly, the J A Centre has now closed.

By then David was taking more exams to qualify as an accountant. Clare was working harder than ever. Both worked long, demanding hours.

Phoning home for a chat, Clare said, 'I'm off to Lake Como to do some filming of a fashion show. I'm really excited, but nervous about making it look professional enough.'

'Good luck,' I said putting the phone down, my heart swelling with pride.

When we next spoke on her return, she said, 'Oh Mum, you should have seen all the little dogs some of these glamorous Italian women at the show were carrying around. The jewels in their collars were real! I've never seen anything like it. And when I pointed the video camera across the square approaching the building for the fashion show, I captured a cloud of pigeons as they rose up all around me. It was incredible!' She was testing the video camera to make sure it was working.

'Mum,' said David, phoning later that week, 'it's the busiest time of year when we've been working flat out auditing, getting up early and working late into the night. We've been staying at a hotel close to work and the food's good. I've got some shirts I'd like laundering. Any chance…?'

'Yes, I'd love to do them for you. Do bring them home.'

My heart burst with joy for still having a place in both the children's lives.

Life moved on, yes, but we were still included in sharing so many of their challenges, and this felt like a gift. Life is filled with precious moments, and often these are the simplest or, in the case of being asked to do my son's laundry, the most unlikely!

CHAPTER 16
Ups and Downs

Strive to meet all things
With equal measure
Gillian Gill, inspired by the poem 'If' by Rudyard Kipling

Late 2008 - 2009

'You really must make a doctor's appointment to get checked again. It can't be avoided, and you shouldn't be eating quite so many of those crisps,' said Simon, acting as my food policeman.

Putting the bag of crisps away into the cupboard was easier now. I knew I could eat just a few for the occasional treat and my body wouldn't suffer. However, it was true I had lapsed in having hospital check-ups.

'Another thing,' continued Simon, 'the compost bucket is too full and Lucy's made a mess with the contents.' Emptying the compost bucket was my job, which I didn't seem to remember every day as I'd intended.

Something inside me snapped and I let rip. Where had my equilibrium gone? I was striving for inner harmony and had just blown a gaping hole in it. Fighting back tears, I stormed off into the garden with a box of long matches in my pocket. Simon's fleeting words were, 'It's not a good day for a bonfire, it's too windy.'

That was all I needed to hear, and Lucy followed as I strode down to the hidden far end of the garden, arms laden and dropping cardboard in my wake.

'Bloody match!' I said to Lucy, who sat on a pile of sand watching me closely.

Several matches later, wind blowing and boxes piled high, the flames suddenly ignited. As they did so my heart rose in my chest. I felt ashamed of my outburst, but also realized it was a healthy release. I now had enough energy to feel strong flashes of anger. Piling more cardboard boxes and pruned branches onto the fire, I stood back to watch the plumes of smoke. Then I started praying for two friends who were extremely ill. Telephone conversations with their partners had been harrowing. Watching the leaping flames, I was engulfed by the billowing smoke, and I began to cry freely as Lucy looked on. She wandered over and nudged my leg. I stroked her head and noticed, as if for the first time, the spreading grey fur beneath her chin.

Feeling awkward, returning to the house I said sorry to Simon.

'It's alright, I know I can be annoying at times.'

Then I remembered how, shortly after marrying, my father had said to me, 'No matter how tired you are, when Simon returns from work, you should make the very best of it. Remember, it's not what we leave behind that's important; it's how we live our lives. He deserves the best…'

'Let's do something together,' I suggested.

Giving me a hug, he replied, 'You smell of smoke. I'll book tickets to go and see that film we've been talking about.'

Several days later, Simon called me: 'There's another email for you about someone needing your guidance.'

For a few years now the pattern continued whereby Dr Daniel, my oncologist Professor Thomas and later still my local GP had asked if they could refer occasional positive-minded cancer patients to have a chat or exchange emails with me. Yashu had also asked me to speak to some people she knew suffering with the disease. We were all familiar with their collective questioning of 'why me?'. It is natural for people to become angry, beneath which lies fear.

I found it rewarding that sharing my own experience with cancer could help people on their own individual journeys, and would always endeavour to make suggestions to suit their personal needs and lifestyles, while respecting their belief patterns as well as encouraging what they were already trying.

I'd heard about the benefits of sound healing and was practising chanting as well as making the sounds 'ooo', 'aaah' and 'eee', which curiously enough felt positive and liberating, resulting in a sense of calm. Whilst attending a workshop, I overcame my inhibitions as our teacher first demonstrated and then invited participants to take it in turn to introduce themselves by speaking while keeping their jaws still, thus making their speech sound bizarre. This broke down tensions, helping everyone relax. By the afternoon our teacher asked if anyone would particularly like to receive healing from the group. I put my hand up. I walked into the middle of the circle and our teacher asked me to lie on a couch, and then with great ceremony proceeded to lead everyone clockwise around me, chanting my name. It was a deeply moving and profound experience.

Life continued and one day Simon, always planning for our future, said, 'It's not long until we go to St. Anthony in Cornwall to take the dogs on their annual holiday. Our house guests Tony and Janet are excited, and so is Rob. Clare, Ashleigh and David will be joining us and we'll be arriving a few days ahead to give us time to relax and prepare.'

'Good planning. It's lovely staying in the house where we found Lucy all those years ago.'

'Do you remember when we found her, her owners had to bring the entire litter of pups on holiday as their mother whelped prematurely, just before their holiday? The havoc that her mother Grace created when she walked into one of the other holiday cottages, helping herself to two families' early Christmas dinner! She had a big appetite with all those puppies to feed!'

'Typical Labrador,' Simon responded. 'I remember how you sat with the litter of puppies every day, persuading me that we needed another dog, and how Lucy kept snuggling into your arms, always wriggling over to be close when you sat quietly.'

'Yes, she had that distinguishing birthmark on her abdomen, like a raspberry. That's how I always knew it was her.'

It wasn't long before the much awaited holiday arrived and we were back in the farmhouse where we had first laid eyes on Lucy. We booked a table at a favourite pub, The Trengilly Wartha, to celebrate the annual gathering, and Simon had ordered a local minibus to take us there so everyone could relax.

When Simon left the table after the main course to go to the loo and Ashleigh hurried after him, no one paid particular attention. Simon returned and asked me to quietly go to the bar with him, as Ashleigh sat down at the table.

'What's the matter?' I asked.

'If I tell you, it has to be kept a secret,' he said earnestly.

'If you don't tell me…'

'Ashleigh's been trying to get me alone all day. He nearly succeeded after a pint in the pub at lunchtime, but then Rob wanted to join us for the walk home through the woods. Ashleigh's just asked me for permission to marry Clare!'

'Oh, that's wonderful!' I said bursting with delight.

Simon continued, 'Being so close to bonfire night, rockets were going off on the hill beyond the car park behind Ashleigh. We both laughed about that afterwards.'

I was squealing now and squeezing Simon's arm, and a young barmaid wandered over to see if I was okay.

'You didn't look like that when you came in,' she observed. Simon tried to look serious but failed.

'I'm over the moon! Our daughter's boyfriend just asked my husband for permission to marry her,' I blurted out.

'Yes, but Clare doesn't know yet,' said Simon. 'Ashleigh's planning on asking Clare on a little romantic outing. Now let's go back to the table and act natural.' The barmaid looked ecstatic, on an otherwise normal winter's evening, and quietly told her two colleagues, swearing them to secrecy.

Three waitresses, including the barmaid, arrived with the pudding, each with a jug of custard to sneak a look at Clare and Ashleigh.

'I know I like custard,' said Clare surprised, 'but why so much?'

The three women and I exchanged a brief knowing look. Bracing myself and breathing deeply, I silently thanked the self-control I'd had to learn with my various disciplines over the years and made a supreme effort to appear normal. Throughout the remainder of the weekend, I never managed to find Ashleigh alone to say that I couldn't be happier.

I hardly slept that night; my heart hurt with all the joy and happiness. Having a daughter on the threshold of marriage to someone we'd always felt towards as a son was a new and overwhelming experience. Simon eventually dropped off to sleep, driven mad by my whispering.

The following morning I felt terrible, aching all over with contained excitement. Simon kept my feet on the ground, reprimanding me after I phoned my mother to share the news with her from a clifftop on his mobile phone. He stressed the importance of keeping Ashleigh's intentions a secret, so as not to steal Clare's magical moment.

After everyone had gone and we were once more left alone with the dogs, I spent time sitting on the rocks by the beach, enjoying the sea, the sky, the Cornish light and reflecting on my thoughts, while also resting and having early nights. Simon took the dogs on long walks along the coastal paths with their stunning scenery and enjoyed spotting some rare choughs.

Three long weeks later the phone rang. Simon answered it and was deliriously happy as Clare told him her joyous news, then he handed me the phone, interrupting my dancing on the stairs with excitement.

I listened as she enthused, 'Ma, we're in Paris. You'll have heard from Dad that Ashleigh's proposed to me and I've accepted.'

'I couldn't be happier for you.'

'Ashleigh booked us into a gorgeous hotel. He'd planned to propose in a particular spot by the River Seine en route to dinner but there was a massive film crew there when we arrived. I wondered why he was so put out we couldn't walk that way. Anyway, eventually he found another secluded spot…'

'Hello, it's Ashleigh.' Clare had handed the phone over so I could congratulate him. 'I'm so glad you're happy,' he said. 'You went so quiet in Cornwall I wondered if I'd done something to offend you.'

'Goodness, no! You never could; it was the exact opposite,' I babbled. 'I just found your secret so hard to keep and went into shut-off mode.'

Laughing now, Ashleigh said, 'I can only imagine how difficult keeping that secret must have been for you. Now we'll have to arrange for you to meet my parents.'

When I was off the phone, Simon swung me off my feet as we hugged, while Lucy and Charlie stood wagging their tails furiously. 'The funny thing with life and parenthood is that you never know what's around the corner. We'll have fun planning the wedding,' said Simon.

When we did meet Ashleigh's family, after initial pleasantries we got on right away, as Clare and Ashleigh knew we would, amidst chatter and laughter.

The following March I was showering as usual and suddenly felt a sickening lump in my left breast. Feeling faint, I slumped against the shower wall. Breathing deeply and grabbing a towel, I rushed for the back door, shouting for Simon at the bottom of the garden.

'What's the matter?' he called running up the garden. 'You look pale.'

'Look at this,' I said pointing to the lump.

'No, it can't be, but…' He turned ashen.

'I'll phone the doctor's surgery,' I said reaching for the phone.

'You can't have an appointment today unless it's an emergency,' replied the receptionist. After listening to me, she replied, 'Right, Mrs Gill, please come over as soon as you can.'

Next our friends Veronica and John arrived for a visit planned some time previously. Knowing my history they took one look at us both and instantly knew something was up. 'Try not to worry too much,' said Veronica reassuringly, and after a few moments chatting they made haste to leave, saying, 'We'll phone later, to see how you are.'

Simon drove us the few miles to the doctor's surgery. Terrified that the dreaded cancer had returned, I felt defeated, as if there were no more reserves of energy to draw on, and a part of me couldn't help but to morbidly think perhaps this was finally it.

'It's unusual,' said my GP examining me on the couch, 'but no more than a ruptured vein. You'll have nasty bruising later.' We all breathed a sigh of relief. 'While you're lying here I'd like to examine your abdomen, if you don't mind?' Pressing lightly, she said, 'It's incredible how your mass has shrunk. Ah, I can just feel it, together with some small nodules in your right groin region. There's a small hernia in your left groin.' Walking out of the surgery I felt immediate relief. There was no deferred response to the good news this time, which alone told me how much better I was physically, mentally and emotionally, because now I could suddenly process good news right in the moment, something that I hadn't been able to do for years.

Returning home shaken, I retreated to my healing room and sat down to pray and meditate, first giving thanks before asking what my body was trying to tell me. It was then that I became aware of something I'd been running away from. For some time people had been asking me to share my story by writing it. The clarity I received during that meditation crystallized itself into what felt to me like another challenge, but a welcome one. If I was alive, then I had to share my healing story with others. I had to get over my reluctance, including my fear of revisiting ghosts of the past. Confronted with such an obvious sign, I realized I couldn't run away from it any longer, and the idea was born. Daunted at the prospect, but determined that nothing was going to stop me, I began writing about my healing path, which I'd attempted many times previously but failed to persevere with.

Curiously enough, the predicted bruising after the ruptured vein never occurred. By April 2009 I'd made an appointment through my GP to have an ultrasound scan, as well as making an appointment for blood tests. It felt in some strange way as though I was coming full circle, back to where I'd begun eight years ago with my cancer diagnosis. At Simon's suggestion I had sought Rosy's advice after Professor Thomas ceased to be my oncologist, and she explained I had a choice to either see another oncologist or, as I seemed so well, to go through my local GP. That seed of an idea took hold. The prospect of visiting my GP was less daunting than travelling to a different hospital, visiting a new oncologist and facing the ordeal of repeating my history, and possibly ending up under the care of someone far less sympathetic to the holistic route. I decided not to find another oncologist but to be seen by my GP and visit my local hospital just to have any necessary scans.

I could no longer face CT scans and their after effects, which made me feel unwell for days, so had elected to have an ultrasound instead, which my body found easier to process. Whatever scans I had lately had always disturbed me, no matter what I did. They always made me nervous, disturbing my emotions. Through this ordeal I realized that being human involves confronting our complex emotions, and one thing I've discovered about myself is just what an emotional creature I am. So, I endeavoured to harness my emotions by using my mind to direct my thoughts, trying to balance my head and my heart, reassuring myself, as I'd been encouraged by Eli, that 'knowledge is power'. I had buried my head in the sand for too long not wanting to know the facts. The scan was long overdue and it was with renewed strength and determination that I requested my next hospital appointment.

'There's a letter for you,' said Simon handing it over.

Ripping it open, I said, 'It's from the hospital with my appointment.'

'Why are you crying?' asked Simon bemused.

'Because somehow it's at the hospital where I've previously been seen privately, under our health insurance scheme when you were employed. I just can't believe how lucky I am.'

'Do go to the hospital alone if you prefer, but you know I'll always come with you,' said Simon when my ultrasound appointment was due.

'Thank you. I thought I had wanted to go alone, but I'd rather you accompanied me.'

On the day of the ultrasound scan I defrosted the freezer to distract myself.

Charlie, doing his usual quality control check, stood firmly at my shoulder as I crouched. He seemed contented when I finished and he went to curl up in bed with Lucy for his nap, using her back as a pillow.

The previous day I'd attended a meditation and distant healing prayer group, which I had formed with a few friends some months after recovering from my mental breakdown. Based on the principles that I'd learned from Gee Sumerary, my spiritual mentor many years previously, we'd been meeting regularly, forging a deep bond that supported each of us differently as we gathered to pray for all those we knew, as well as causes close to our hearts around the world.

'Are you ready? It's time to go,' said Simon, as I was mulling over yesterday's prayerful intentions.

Walking out of the front door we heard the sound of geese in the sky, and looking up saw over a hundred Canada Geese flying in close formation low over the roof.

On the journey I braced myself for the gruelling process of going through my history again with someone at the hospital who didn't know me. Like all things in life, changes are inevitable and we have to adjust to them and accept them, however difficult.

Simon sat in the waiting room. My name was called and I walked through into the Imaging Department to be met by a nurse.

'Would you please change into this gown?' she asked, handing me the regulation hospital attire. I waited alone, feeling vulnerable and apprehensive while reflecting on the good relationship that I'd had with my former oncologist.

As I sat there a man in a gown came out of a side room looking disorientated and flushed, saying to his waiting wife, 'It's alright, I'm not pregnant!' Witnessing such courage brought a lump to my throat. My name was then called and a nurse led me to the examination bed in a small room where we started chatting.

Then the radiologist arrived and asked me all sorts of questions, becoming confused about me not having received any conventional treatment when looking at the images on his scanning equipment.

'Would you please change this scanning machine?' he asked the nurse. 'It doesn't appear to be working properly. I'll be back in ten minutes.' He turned hastily and walked from the room.

The nurse and I resumed our conversation. After listening to what I'd done to achieve such good results, she told me how few cancer patients walking through their hospital doors consider their diet, let alone spiritual support.

A different scanning machine was wheeled in, interrupting our chat, and the radiologist returned. He asked me what form of chemotherapy and radiotherapy treatment I'd used to get these results. Having already told him about my diet, Ayurvedic herbs, lifestyle changes and spiritual quest, I began to feel anxious. Then he asked the nurse to fetch my previous scans. Leaving the room she smiled at me, and returned with my file. He looked long and hard at them all and visibly blanched, finding it almost impossible to believe.

I'd seen such a reaction before and knew that, for a newcomer to my case, it was hard to understand; yet witnessing his response I became totally deflated and felt mounting tension. I misread his reactions and felt challenged. He was baffled viewing the evidence of the previously vast tumour on former scans and comparing them to recent ones, where the original tumour had transformed into something very much smaller. It must have been a surreal experience and it's no surprise that he couldn't make sense of the scans. I felt it was better to remain quiet as it had taken nine years of commitment to achieve these results and there was too much for me to explain. How could I?

In fact, there is no point in trying to convince anyone. I merely wish to share my experience and hope it may act as an inspiration to others.

I was finding it distressing and, with the scan over, climbed down from the bed with shaky legs as one of the nurses helped me put on a dressing gown. The radiologist had casually mentioned the words tumour and cancer, and this had spiralled me back to the early stages, triggering panic as I revisited my past torment. I couldn't wait to get home and rebalance myself by quietly meditating. This was the same issue I had confronted when commencing writing this book, but now I was struggling to retain my belief patterns and not get caught up in the drama of events and words. Meditating helped.

Some days later it was a relief when, after a couple of missed phone calls, my GP and I spoke. She'd received the hospital results and confirmed my mass had shrunk to 12.3 cm and was mostly fluid with two floating particles in it. My GP's positive comments did me inestimable good.

She said the report confirmed that the few lumps she'd felt in my right groin had disappeared, and that the hernia in my left groin was barely distinguishable. The good news flooded me with relief. Those results confirmed that the path I was taking was still working for me.

The following is an extract from the hospital report:

... there is an approx 12.3 cm mass within the pelvis adjacent to the uterine fundus which is predominately anechoic (with a few internal reflections). There is some focal wall nodularity. No ascites demonstrated.

... the appearances are suggestive of a cystic mass (most likely an ovarian neoplasm). No definite inguinal lymphadenopathy has been demonstrated. Further evaluation with CT abdomen/pelvis is advised.

Shortly after my hospital visit, Eli's son and his family invited us to join them at their home nearby to celebrate his birthday. Whilst his grandchildren were excitedly helping their mother put the finishing touches to his birthday cake, Eli and I sat talking quietly in the garden. Listening to my recent health scare over the ruptured vein in my breast, and how the shock had turned a line of hair across the centre of my head grey, he suggested giving me some healing while lunch was being prepared. Leading the way from the garden into the house, we walked into the sitting room where I lay on the sofa. Eli knelt beside me. His late father was a passionate church minister and I could feel that same passion coursing through Eli in his desire to help me. He gently placed his hands on my shoulders saying, 'Focus your breath now, feel the cold air coming into your nostrils and feel the warm breath going out of them. Just relax. Now, breathe in oxygen and healing and breathe out anxiety and toxins. Visualize everything melting and vanishing from your body.' He knew I understood how to place my focus on my ovarian cyst. 'Now breathe in again, long and deep, and take all that healing energy to help you. When you return home after the party, rest and let the healing continue as it boosts your immune system. All that worry, all that fear is very tiring and lowering to your entire nervous system, so you need to rest.'

Feeling renewed, I had thanked Eli both for listening to me and for the healing, to which he replied, 'It is something other than you and me that has opened up to the healing flow of energy.'

Some time later, when talking to Nick, who helps us with the garden, he asked about my recent hospital check. Listening intently he sagely said, 'Words carry such power. Everyone needs hope, don't they? Tell a person they have two weeks to live and what an impact those words have.'

'Yes,' I agreed, sensing there was more.

'I bet when hearing that statement at least fifty per cent of people around the world would believe it, give up and die. It's a bit like going on holiday.'

'Is it?' I asked puzzled.

'Yes. Imagine if I told you we're going on holiday in two weeks' time. You'd probably get a bit stressed up about the packing, travelling and everything.'

'Yes,' I replied, thinking how it takes me about two weeks to pack, adjusting to the idea of leaving home and then sifting through what I really need to take. I have to physically overcome the anxiety of leaving the house, saying farewell to the dogs, locking up and not forgetting anything I may need.

'Well,' he continued, 'think how differently you'd react if I said "Come on, go and get your suitcase packed now. I'm taking you on holiday today!" Think of the excitement.'

'Yes,' I replied, acknowledging his viewpoint, being aware of a surge of excited energy flowing through my entire being.

He continued, 'So imagine if a doctor said, "Come on, you're doing well. Let's see what we can do to keep you going," in the belief that you could overcome it with support.'

Prompted by my unsettling encounter with the radiologist, over the next few weeks I reflected on how I'd had to learn to redirect many of my feelings after experiencing challenges in different situations and arrived at the following conclusions.

Having come to the point of recognizing that certain behaviour in another is damaging to yourself, then it is time to think about forming a strategic plan of action. That can take place in a friendly but firm way. Know how to be detached and sit tight, keeping focused on personal motives and not getting caught up in arguments or attempts to justify your own position. It is important to hang onto any remaining peace of mind. Finding a balance in life to maintain personal boundaries, we need to know where we stop and others begin, to prevent too much unconscious merging of energies, sometimes exchanging detrimental vibrations.

When dealing with unacceptable behaviour from another, you can politely convey how you wish to proceed in the future, to protect yourself from being dominated when weakened. Set your intent and feel it powerfully, knowing that you are doing this purely for your own well-being. Carers also need to know their boundaries as, by their very nature, they are consumed by taking care of the sick person, using up vital energy, and they so often neglect themselves.

If a friend is not true then they will naturally go on and find another like-minded soul; yet if a friend is true then any disagreement will be overcome. A new understanding will be arrived at, one that then has the potential to lead on to a further blossoming of an entirely different level of friendship.

Drawing strength from these reflections I began to feel surer of myself and resolved to look beyond surface reactions and not let dealings with others shake my faith in what I was doing.

With the start of writing my book, I tracked down my former oncologist's secretary to ask for copies of her letters to my GP monitoring my progress. She was incredibly co-operative. Then with her help I contacted the relevant hospital to ask for my CT scan results. All this took months, but I had begun the process of revisiting my past.

Shortly after beginning the writing I ran into more health trouble. My abdomen felt as it had when first diagnosed with cancer. This was the same weekend we were visiting Ashleigh's parents, Belinda and Michael, at their holiday home on the coast in Salcombe. Unable to reach Rosy, in desperation I phoned Cathy-Mae, one of my yoga teachers. She empathised, reassured me and then explained how to differentiate between the past and the present, giving advice on how to continue gently with deep abiding awareness, respect and compassion for myself. Later Rosy echoed the same sentiment. That weekend away was so timely, and everyone understood my need for rests throughout our visit as we got to know one another. It was both relaxing and stimulating.

Home again and picking up the threads of writing, I was sitting at the computer with all the windows wide open when something extraordinary happened. Just as I was worrying about diving into my past and stirring up old memories, I suddenly heard the beating of small wings. A chaffinch flew in through the window behind me, low over my head and straight out of the window in front of me into the garden! Feeling ecstatic I vowed to keep going, no matter what. I delight in finding the occasional solitary feather in inexplicable places as an angelic sign, and I'd just had an entire bird full of feathers flying right over my head.

That summer we all began noticing how Lucy wasn't quite herself. She'd slowed right down and during a walk had stumbled over a stile before struggling through a field of corn stubble to the end of the walk.

David was alarmed one morning at breakfast when I walked into the kitchen saying, 'Lucy just stood rigid in front of me and didn't appear to recognize me. What's wrong with her?'

Simon walked in, having heard the distress in David's voice, and said, 'I think Lucy's just had a minor seizure. The same thing happened to your grandfather.'

As I stroked her, talking quietly, she responded to me by gently nudging my 'lump', and she seemed to have recovered from her episode, but over the following weeks she became increasingly slow. The vet confirmed how, for a Labrador of almost 15, she was remarkably healthy looking. Charlie always tried to snuggle up to Lucy, but sometimes she now preferred to lie on her own in the dog's bed in front of the grandfather clock. Sitting with her and stroking her head, I recalled how she'd given Jack a new lease of life shortly after her arrival, despite chewing his neck, and how she'd run amok in the flowerbeds full of my best ever tobacco plants, flattening many. As a puppy she accompanied me on flower arranging trips to David's prep school, where she helped by chewing a few stems, then flopped out asleep, making the crocodiles of boys passing by on their way to assembly smile.

As she matured she accompanied me, together with Jack, to the hospice I volunteered at. Both dogs helped the residents and day care patients in unique ways. When I was giving flower arranging demonstrations, Jack would circle the conservatory then select someone to lie next to, while enjoying a proffered biscuit at coffee break.

One day, bursting through the hospice entrance, Lucy dived onto the receptionist's desk, scattering orderly files and papers. The receptionist having her own dog merely smiled, hugging Lucy. Later that morning she disappeared from the conservatory and wandered off to a side room next to the mortuary. When I found her she had her head in the lap of an elderly gentleman who was balancing his lunch tray.

'I am sorry,' I said, 'I'll take her out.'

'Oh, please don't,' said the man's wife sitting tearfully opposite. 'We miss our dogs, don't we dear?' Her husband nodded, patting Lucy's head and not taking his eyes off her.

Lucy remained as I left the room, uncharacteristically docile.

Such memories recurred as Clare came home, sadly noticing the rapid deterioration in Lucy. The vet said she would do all she could to make Lucy comfortable and prescribed medications. During the next few days they rallied Lucy's energy sufficiently to enjoy one last walk out of the front door and part way up the drive. She returned home from that walk looking better than she had for a long time, as is often the case before the end.

The following morning I noticed her lying inert, alone in her bed. I encouraged her to get up and she made it outside onto the cobbled courtyard then slumped. She'd suffered an internal rupture that would prove fatal. We phoned the vet and were told to bring her straight over.

Lucy's remarkable spirit enabled her to attempt to jump into the back of the car as Simon sprang forward to lift her. Once we'd arrived the vet and nurse tended Lucy in the boot of our car to make it as easy as possible for her. Simon watched, wracked with grief, as I cradled Lucy in my arms. I told her how much I loved her and that Jack would be waiting. She'd only needed our permission to let go, and before the vet had inserted the needle, she was gone.

We took her home and folded her in her favourite bed, while Simon prepared her grave next to Jack's. We unwittingly kept Charlie away from her body, not realising how important it is that he should have seen her in order to understand.

Charlie took Lucy's death badly, having had a vulnerable start to life. He pined inconsolably; his nose dried and his coat lost its lustre. He'd identified himself in life as Lucy's companion and was lost without her.

After her burial, Charlie refused to go to the bottom of the garden as was usual. On the third day after her death, in the small hours, I woke suddenly and heard an eerie howl emitting from the bottom of the garden.

'That's strange,' said Simon the next morning, having slept soundly. 'For the first time since I buried Lucy, when taking Charlie round the garden first thing, he walked down to sniff her grave.'

Autumn soon arrived, accompanied by eagerness on my part to have another ultrasound scan. I had a renewed zeal for my health and well-being and had become increasingly focused on wishing to see my 'lump' shrink further. My GP kindly repeated the booking procedure three times, sending me forms to book my own appointment as I kept losing the papers.

Finally, we had a date, a time and a hospital. It was the hospital where I was first diagnosed, but this time my appointment was for a scan in the obstetrics unit. Sitting waiting with Simon beside me I dropped a magazine. A young pregnant woman sitting next to me bent down to retrieve it for me. I could almost read her thoughts: 'What a mature mother to be.'

Reappearing after the scan I exclaimed to Simon, 'It's still shrinking!' He was grinning, wondering what the expectant mother might make of that. My GP told us the good news in more precise terms when we visited her for a follow-up appointment, and Simon translated her measurements into something recognizable for me, that my 'lump' had shrunk from the size of a goose egg to the size of a small hen's egg.

In spite of those good results, I'd had even greater expectations and was hoping that somehow my 'lump' would have completely disappeared. It was almost Christmas time and, while quietly gift wrapping alone by the tree, tears rolled down my cheeks. I couldn't seem to shake off my dark mood. Suddenly I was jolted out of it as a reel of Sellotape rolled by itself from my healing room behind me and into the soles of my kneeling feet. Joanna's presence filled the room, and then I felt something different, a familiar nudge to my abdomen.

CHAPTER 17

Life Continues

When you are inspired by some purpose, some project,
all your thoughts break their bonds. Dormant forces,
faculties and talents become alive and you discover
yourself to be a greater person than you ever imagine
yourself to be.

This is one of my favourite yoga texts from Patanjali, the ancient Hindu sage
who first popularised yoga.

Writing this book has been unimaginably cathartic. Originally I wrote the
first version in a blur. It was difficult revisiting the past and it evoked all my
original pains and fears. My system flooded with cortisol from the stress,
so Claire, my yoga friend, taught me the seated yoga twist to squeeze and
heal my vital organs.

Nevertheless, I knew I had a story to share and would at times wake in
the night filled with a need to reach out to others similar to myself and
write down those buried memories bubbling to the surface. And so I started
again, but this time from a calmer, more reflective place. I began my day
earlier than usual to first pray and then meditate for one to two hours.
Afterwards I followed on with my morning's writing and had note pads and
pens scattered throughout the house.

Disciplining myself to write only in the morning, followed by a
short walk with the dogs, then lunch, a rest and self-healing became my

daily practice. Trying to find a clear way to articulate my journey from a grim cancer diagnosis to wellness was all-consuming. There have been a great many elements that have contributed to my current good health and I haven't wanted to leave anything out. However, I have learnt from experience not to put too much pressure on myself and to make sure to be more focused in my use of energy and time.

During the afternoons I would walk the dogs, see friends or work in the garden and focus on the simple everyday things of life. I discovered that it was important to take days out from writing and revisiting the 'ghosts of the past' in order to replenish my energies, which I was acutely aware of as they ebbed and flowed.

We were lucky enough to be approached by a major literary agent and had a very positive meeting, except that we were clearly told the book had to be rewritten if it was to be a success. It took a while to recover from this shock, but I was determined I had a story to tell so I started all over again.

Rewriting was an enriching and ultimately valuable process, though not without its growing pains, particularly being plagued by the question 'Can I do this?'.

This self-doubt is something I battled with at the start of my healing journey, when I was convinced it was everyone else's prayers, rather than my own efforts, that were having such a dramatic effect on my health. Eventually I was able to accept some of the responsibility for these achievements and recognise that I do have a role to play in creating and maintaining my own health. In the same way, I have had to work hard at instilling a sense of self-belief in my writing, to have faith that I could make this longed-for book a reality.

During this second time of rewriting I found hidden memories were easier to access and I was able to go deeper into the heart of my experience. In turn this has helped me make sense of certain periods during my recovery, particularly my mental breakdown. With each step along the way of revisiting the past, I've been able to see my journey as a whole.

I have spoken to many people about writing this book, not least the family members of those mentioned in the 'Death and Dying' chapter.

Each has offered to help me in my quest to convey the fullest sense of their loved ones' individual experiences, of those who have passed and of those remaining. I have the greatest of gratitude for this generosity of spirit of these dear souls.

Some time after completing the rewrite of this book, whilst on holiday on the west coast of Scotland, we received the good news that my literary agent was ready to send it to publishers to see who would be interested in taking it on. Sharing this good news with our daughter on the phone, I stood on the beach at Port Appin watching a playful seal riding the currents.

Months went by. My busy literary agent had many important clients to oversee. She was difficult to reach. Her personal assistant was always most helpful whenever I phoned, giving me my agent's feedback.

My prayers for my book to see the light of day continued in earnest. Eventually, after many months had passed, I heard from my agent that a film company had been interested in making a documentary but were lacking in funds. Publishers she had approached both in the US and UK had rejected the book. She gave me the choice that either she would publish it for me as an e-book, or I could self-publish.

Sitting at home in the garden I felt disappointment and disillusion wash through me. Simon returned from a bike ride and came to find me, asking what was up. I told him. 'You've taken it well,' he observed, looking into my eyes deeply. Words failed me; my ego had taken a knock.

After I had asked my agent some questions about her e-book offer, a year and a half passed without a reply. We never did receive her answers.

One morning something shifted inside me, having recently spoken at a training seminar in a London hospital on a module entitled 'Living with long-term conditions'. Seeing the impact my story had on the audience, especially the sceptics, motivated me to find a way for my story to be heard. There was no going back now as people kept asking me 'When will your book be out?'.

With eternal gratitude, as well as some disappointment, I wrote to my literary agent saying I wished to withdraw from our contract. Then I was physically ill with shock, having decided we would self-publish after all.

Three days after this decision, I began to feel as if a massive weight was lifting off my shoulders, realizing how the weight of 'not knowing' had unwittingly preyed on me. Scary though my decision was, the curious thing is I gradually began to feel stronger and more positive as each day passed, having taken back control of my work.

During 2009 on holiday in Islay, an island off the west coast of Scotland, we talked about forming a charity and donating the book profits to it to enable more people to follow my route to wellness.

I had been fortunate because, firstly, we had the financial means to fund my holistic approach, as most of the therapies that I took were not available on the NHS nor covered by medical insurance. Secondly, I was able to access one of the few experienced integrated medicine doctors in the country. The idea developed between us that the charity could make the biggest difference by promoting change in the medical profession so that more doctors could understand and support the route to recovery that I had undertaken. It has certainly made many scratch their heads when reviewing my case history and seeing the results for themselves. Although some would say my recovery is a one-off miracle, and most doctors would refer to 'spontaneous remission' or misdiagnosis, there is a small group of enlightened doctors who are not so surprised by my achievement. They understand my holistic or integrated medicine route to healing.

Thereafter, we decided the best use of the charity's funds would be to widen the education of young medical professionals. They could then offer support to their patients by using the best of conventional medicine, complementary medicine and self-help techniques on a personalized basis. This approach is sometimes referred to as integrated medicine, or integrative medicine as it is known in the United States. Focusing the charity's aim in this direction would see not only the direct benefit to the patients of these doctors but also the impact of their work within the medical profession from such young and inspired future leaders in their field. This has already occurred in the United States to some extent, where the movement has been going on for some years now, and there are some well-respected doctors who have survived the controversies, one of whom I was lucky enough to meet.

Dr Andrew Weil, a physician and respected IM pioneer, founded the Arizona Centre for Integrative Medicine at the University of Arizona in 1994. During a visit to the United Kingdom it was immensely gratifying to meet him and learn of his integrative medical background and the success of his current work. He wasn't at all surprised to hear about the results I'd achieved via my complementary route, a refreshing contrast to the doctor who'd been unable to comprehend my ultrasound scan result and insisted that the machine must have been broken.

Gilly's Gift was established as a charity in November 2009. It aims to support young doctors and nurses with a commitment to public practice and a passion for integrated medicine by funding training opportunities, both in the United Kingdom and overseas, in the form of courses and electives at hospitals practising integrated medicine. The charity's overall objective is the advancement of integrated medicine and its availability to the whole community within the United Kingdom. Funds have come from family, friends, proceeds from my recipe book and financial gifts from those believing in our aim. Profits from this book will also go towards the charity.

Seeing the change in Simon with the charity's progress has been a humbling experience for me. The intense work and initial frustrations have turned into a labour of love, ignited by being able for the first time to part fund a small number of dedicated young doctors and nurses to have electives overseas in places ranging from Switzerland to China. They have experienced practices that they could not see in the United Kingdom, and we were given the opportunity to meet them and hear about their training, a moving and uplifting experience for us both, when we attended presentations on their electives. It was both overwhelming and a privilege to witness first hand not only their enthusiasm but also that of their fellow students. This day made it clear to us that, in Simon's words, 'This is the "sweet spot" for our charity's limited funds.'

I am still living what started as a lifestyle change targeted at getting rid of my cancer and has now become an all-encompassing way of life. A big part of this journey has been about listening to what my body needs, and we can all learn to be more intuitive and responsive to what our body is trying to tell us if we slow down and pay attention.

These days my daily regime has broadened and become much more accepting of both foodstuffs and demands on my energy. Along the way I have reintroduced certain foods that I was missing. For example, I now find I can eat bread as a treat, without feeling unwell afterwards. The same goes for the occasional small plate of chips, packet of crisps or the odd chocolate. If I were to eat too much or too often, that could compromise my health and well-being, but my body is now able to process these small variations in my diet. So it's about being discerning and monitoring reactions.

My energy levels are now very good. In preparation for the winter we had a lorry load of logs delivered and I stacked them all in the shed, something that would have been an unimaginable feat during the early years following my diagnosis. When visiting my bereaved friend Eric in hospital in Holland, Simon and I cycled ten miles along the canals through the freshly cut meadows, enjoying spotting huge storks' nests on top of poles. I do still have to be careful, though. My good friends and family know that I'm an early riser, and thus early to bed, and accommodate this. I've learned to overcome my embarrassment over my need to retire early when entertaining. It's the same after lunch; my body and mind have become so accustomed to resting and self-healing at this time that I feel myself dropping off even if I do not have the opportunity to lie down. Clearly my body is still telling me what it needs.

When Clare and Ashleigh became engaged in 2008, I remember being concerned about being able to cope with the demands of having my daughter's wedding reception at home. I never forget what I've recovered from, and am so grateful and content to still be alive, that I am wary of being reckless and putting too much strain on my health. As the wedding approached I was full of joy, but aware of my tendency to overdo it, especially when excited about something. I made sure I had extra time for meditating, both early in the morning and again in the early evening, and took extra resting time as well as increasing my yoga practice. I took care to monitor and respond to my energy levels, and Claire, my acupuncturist, gave me treatments to support my system, as did my reflexologist and friend Fran. Just days before the wedding, the honeybees that arrived four years earlier and which live in a void in our roof space swarmed, turning the sky dark! That sight in our garden was breathtakingly wonderful and I took it to be a good omen for the marriage.

One of my longed-for dreams and goals, set at the onset of my healing journey, was to be alive to attend my daughter's wedding. Having the energy as the wedding approached permitted a greater level of enjoyment and excitement. On the day itself I never imagined I had the capacity to feel so purely joyous for such a prolonged period of time. I was ecstatic. My health no longer held me back and I was able to enjoy the full Mother of the Bride experience, from travelling to London for Clare's wedding dress fittings to sharing a magical day with extended family and friends.

Dogs are still very much part of our lives and we took on a puppy in the hope it would help Charlie over his grief for Lucy. She is a Labradoodle called Tina and bears quite a resemblance to a muppet! For the first six months Charlie did his utmost to ignore her. Then, as she grew, so did Charlie's interest in her. Charlie changed beyond recognition, becoming Top Dog, and looked on proudly as Tina followed and copied him. She is the most playful of dogs and frequently dragged Charlie along the ground by his collar, much to his delight. Once she did this while I was writing and, hearing a commotion, I glanced up to see Charlie lying blissfully on his back, his hind legs rapidly disappearing through the doorway.

During Tina's second year with us Charlie became unwell. Our dog groomer spotted a suspicious lump on his rear end. Immediately, we took him to the vet, who diagnosed a cancerous tumour. We made the hard decision to concentrate on his quality of life rather than letting the vet operate on him, with the associated risks and suffering. During our many visits, the vet offered information and support for our choice. We accepted his advice to put Charlie on a course of steroids and various medications, which without a shadow of a doubt both improved Charlie's quality of life and helped him see out the remainder of his days to the full. A year after diagnosis, when the time came for him to go, we had him put to sleep. This was the hardest decision I've ever made.

With Charlie's demise, a gaping hole was left in our lives, none more so than mine. The grief that followed overwhelmed me at times. Charlie had been my constant companion, a most loyal and beloved canine friend throughout most of my recovery. There were times when only he could comfort me. He always intuitively knew how to.

Charlie's farewell gift to me – as he was one of my greatest teachers in showing me how to live a fully and joyous life – was how to grieve, and grieve well. The emptiness and sadness that I felt following his death opened the gate to so many past deaths, including my late sister Joanna, whose death I discovered I had not completely grieved. When she died I had two young children and a husband working away from home for some of the time. In order to keep strong and keep going, I consciously, and perhaps misguidedly, held back the tears in the belief the children might suffer if I didn't.

Charlie showed me how to touch the place hidden within that had lain sealed for many years. His parting gift was showing me how to grieve to my agonizing, innermost depths of despair, for which I shall be eternally grateful.

One day, remembering Charlie and with Simon and Tina beside me walking through a favourite National Trust wood, where in the spring bluebells are like a carpet, I felt his presence all around me and I got the urge to do more outside. When discussing this with Simon and wondering how I might achieve this, Simon suggested, 'You know how much I enjoy being a volunteer with the National Trust and working outside. Why not meet my boss, Ruby the Ranger, and Rex her rescue dog, to see if she has any other voluntary vacancies that might be suitable for you?'

Soon I was discovering new ways of being and living that I could never have imagined, as I took on new tasks and learnt new skills. I always remember Charlie when working outside. Finding a fresh sense of inner achievement and of belonging to a team has added a new dimension to my life, one of tremendous fulfilment, in all weathers and throughout all seasons.

I now live a life I love. It is simpler, and I don't want to jeopardize it. Managing my life as best I can, I am grateful for my hard-won good health, and I continue with my yoga, dietary disciplines, walking in all weathers, Pilates, healing and meditation. From time to time I contact my GP for blood tests and an annual ultrasound scan at the local hospital; these appointments no longer fill me with fear.

Imagine, then, my surprise and delight when just before Christmas 2012, while waiting for my latest blood test and ultrasound scan results, my GP phoned to tell me that my CA125, the ovarian cancer tumour marker test, was in the normal range for the first time in over twelve and a half years. In addition she said that with my blood being normal, my 'lump' or cyst will dissolve and disappear from my body of its own accord over time.

Listening to the good news, my legs weakened. Thankfully I was sitting on a kitchen chair. Putting the phone down, long-awaited tears of relief followed.

AFTERWORD

by Professor Hilary Thomas

I had the privilege of witnessing Gillian's care from when she first had her abnormal scan in October 2000 until I gave up clinical practice in 2007. She was always a tonic – her unfailing positive attitude and the conviction and tenacity with which she adhered to her treatment were really inspiring. She remained well for much of this time, apart from some episodes which appeared to coincide with tumour necrosis – this was supported by improvements in her scans and tumour markers. Over this period her scans continued to improve and her tumour markers declined. But the best evidence of all was that her abdominal and pelvic masses continued to shrink on clinical examination and she remained very well.

Gillian is aware that my one disappointment is that she declined having her tumour biopsied. However, she felt strongly for her own reasons that this would risk exacerbating her condition and I was happy to respect her wishes. As a conventional oncologist it would have been very rewarding to demonstrate the efficacy of Carctol beyond doubt by proving the nature of her tumour. This is a treatment which, thanks to Gillian's progress, I wanted to encourage other patients to pursue. Disappointingly, many were unable to tolerate the alkaline diet and could not continue with the regimen. It is a tribute to Gillian's unremitting determination that she has adhered to her treatment and has been able to reap the benefits. I have no doubt that she is also an inspiration to others as a result.

ACKNOWLEDGEMENTS

It would not have been possible to survive without the love and support from family, friends, doctors, nurses and therapists, many of whom urged me to write this book. To each I extend deep gratitude.

My appreciation and love to Simon my husband, Clare our daughter and David our son for always being there.

My respect and gratitude to Dr Rosy Daniel, the holistic doctor who led my recovery programme, for her expertise, loving support and for writing the foreword to this book.

My gratitude goes to my oncologist, Professor Hilary Thomas, for her innovative support, keeping every option open to me and granting permission to use correspondence charting my progress.

I give deep gratitude to those that gave permission to mention their loved ones in the chapter 'Death and Dying', and in particular to Suzi Harvey for her contribution to the chapter.

To Veronica for keeping all my letters throughout my illness and reminding me of aspects I forgot.

Finally, I give thanks to all the others who have generously given their help and support.

ALSO BY THE AUTHOR

WHERE'S THE MEAT: *Acid-free vegetarian dishes*
Gillian Gill with illustrations by Clare Gill
£6.00 – available on Amazon
ISBN 978-0-9563121-0-5

A collection of recipes that helped Gillian's recovery from cancer.

> When I was told it would help my husband's health if
> he ate an acid-free vegetarian diet, I felt daunted and
> overwhelmed, having cooked meat and used dairy products
> all my cooking life! That was until *Where's the Meat?* found
> its way into our kitchen, and since then we haven't looked
> back.
>
> Amazon reader review